International Conferences Interfaces and Human Computer Interaction (IHCI2020); and Game and Entertainment Technologies (GET2020)

Held at MCCSIS 2020 (Held online due to COVID-19)

Lisbon, Portugal
21 - 25 July 2020

ISBN: 978-1-7138-2277-6

Printed from e-media with permission by:

Curran Associates, Inc.
57 Morehouse Lane
Red Hook, NY 12571

Some format issues inherent in the e-media version may also appear in this print version.

Printed with permission by Curran Associates, Inc. (2021)

For permission requests, please contact International Association for Development of the Information Society (IADIS) at the address below.

International Association for Development of the Information Society (IADIS)
Rua Sao Sebastiao Da Pedreira
No. 100, 30, 1050-209
Lisbon, Portugal

Phone: 351 21 3151373
Fax: 351 21 3151244

secretariat@iadis.org

Additional copies of this publication are available from:

Curran Associates, Inc.
57 Morehouse Lane
Red Hook, NY 12571 USA
Phone: 845-758-0400
Fax: 845-758-2633
Email: curran@proceedings.com
Web: www.proceedings.com

TABLE OF CONTENTS

DESIGN OF ROBOTIC PETS TO HELP THE ELDERLY WITH SOCIAL INTERACTIONS

Hsin-Yi Huang [1], Wen-Huei Chou [1], Mieko Ohsuga[2] and Tsuyoshi Inoue[2]
[1]*National Yunlin University of Science and Technology, 123 University Road, Section 3, Douliou, Yunlin 64002, Taiwan, R.O.C.*
[2]*Osaka Institute of Technology, 1-45 Chayamachi, Kita-ku, Osaka, 530-8568 Japan*

ABSTRACT

Aging is a global issue. The human body and mind are interlinked during this process. Specifically, an unhealthy mental state has an adverse effect on the body, and loneliness and inadequate social ties affect people's moods. After retirement, elderly people lead a different life. Real pets can help elderly people develop good social relationships, and their characteristics can improve people's social ties. However, elderly may have difficulties to raised real pets as the cause of pets' allergies, uncontrollability behaviors, and elderly's living conditions. Hence, as an alternative solution, many pet robots have been developed as a companion for the elderly and to provide emotional care for them. Even if some of them are used to accompany elderly people or assist them in their social activities, these applications are limited to indoor places and interactions between people and pet robots. Hence, there is a lack of interactions that can strengthen personal activities and promote interpersonal relationships. This study explored how elderly people should interact with robotic pets, and investigated the functional requirements for robotic pets. Through a combination of technological means and pet characteristics, the intent is to help the retired elderly people maintain and strengthen social ties and even develop new social relationships. Using a semi-structured interview approach, this study investigated the daily life of their life after retirement to explore the appropriate time at which interaction design can intervene, and explore the requirements for robotic pets. Furthermore, this study provided follow-up research ideas and design reference.

KEYWORDS

Social Ties, Elderly People, Robotic Pet, Pet, Interaction Design

1. INTRODUCTION

Aging is a global issue. According to the United Nations' World Population Prospects (2019 revision), elderly people aged 65 or above will account for more than 16% of the global population by 2050, far higher than that (9%) in 2019. Nearly every country in the world is facing the challenge of an aging population. An aging population calls for more putting effort into medical care and makes an impact on all social fields (e.g., labor and financial markets, demand for goods and services, housing, transportation, and family structure (United Nations, 2015).

In the process of aging, the elderly are faced with the degradation of physical functioning, as well as the emotional problems which need support. Physical health involves the interactions between body and mind, and social isolation and loneliness have a negative impact on the health and well-being of elderly people. Technological intervention is used to alleviate the loneliness and social isolation of the elderly. Social isolation and loneliness can adversely affect the mental and physical health of elderly people, but their basic social needs can be satisfied through technologies such as man-machine interfaces, assistant robots, and virtual social networks (WHO, 2015). Nowadays, many service organizations still emphasize on satisfying the physical and physical needs of elderly people, rather than providing services to improve their social ties. However, social participation signifies a major opportunity to improve the overall health of the elderly people and hence, social participation can be effectively linked with communities to produce social benefits (Douglas, Georgiou, & Westbrook, 2017).

Information technology can offer an effective solution to tackle the social isolation of the elderly people. Overall, technologies can help reduce their sense of social isolation through four mechanisms: 1) strengthen ties with the outside world, 2) gain social support, 3) engage in and take part in interesting activities joyfully to maintain self-confidence, 4) help them establish ties with family members, friends, former colleagues, and people with common interests or needs (Chen & Schulz, 2016). In addition, pets have characteristics that can help people communicate with each other. According to a study, more than 80% of owners think of their pets as their friends, and in particular, cats and dogs that account for the majority of the pets. They often talk to their pets, feel good when the pets are around, and engage in conversations with people interact with their pets (Mueller, Gee, & Bures, 2018). However, raising a pet has problems such as allergies, cleansing, and scratching and biting. Also, elderly people might not be able to raise pets due to physiological or living constraints. Although pets improve the mental health of the elderly, not all can afford to solve these problems and hence, an alternative solution is to develop robotic or virtual pets (e.g., Tamagotchi) instead (Lin, Faas, & Brady, 2017).

According to a related study, continuous social participation plays an important role in the process of positive aging; in particular, pets might play an important role. Robotic pets instead of real pets can not only solve the problems ensuing from the raising of real pets but also help the elderly maintain continuous social participation and establish social ties. Even after retirement, robotic pets enable the elderly to form new social relationships, maintain social ties, and increase social interactions through the behavior pattern of real pets. Therefore, this study discusses how robotic pets should help elderly people improve their social relations, as well as attend to the needs of the elderly. In summary, this study aims to:

1. Discuss the development status of robotic pets and the elderly's opinions on robotic pets;
2. Investigate the interaction design to satisfy the functional requirements of the elderly for robotic pets and social ties;
3. Provide the results of the needs analysis for reference by related designs and studies in the future.

2. LITERATURE REVIEW

2.1 Socially Assistive Robots

Socially assistive robots are a type of special robots, which are designed to interact with people and can play an important role in improving the physical and mental health of the elderly. Many studies have argued that the elderly hold a positive attitude toward social assistive robots, and they have a positive impact on the medical care of the elderly (e.g., improve moods, alleviate loneliness, and promote social interactions (Broekens, Heerink, & Rosendal, 2009). Social assistive robots cover diverse disciplines (e.g., robotics, engineering, medicine, communications, and psychology), and have a great potential for extensive application (Rabbitt, Kazdin, & Scassellati, 2015).

Robots offer a better social assistive solution than the ones based only on interfaces (e.g., software or smartphones). Fundamentally, people tend to interact in real social scenarios. Even if robots take on very simple creature-like appearance and attributes, goals and emotions on physical devices are superior to those of ordinary interfaces (Mataric, 2011). In the fields of behavioral science and neuroscience, more evidence reveals that people are more interested in interactions with physical entities (e.g., people, pets, and robots) than with screens. Although robots were originally invented to attain industrial automation and reduce manual labor, today's robots should be able to help people with their social interactions (Matarić, 2017).

2.2 Aided Therapy by Robotic Pets

AIBO, a robotic pet dog developed by SONY (Japan), has a smooth and rounded appearance and incorporates artificial intelligence and deep learning technologies. According to a Japanese study program, AIBO is used as a robot-aided therapy to intervene in the treatment of patients with early psychosis; before the interventional therapy. AIBO can effectively relieve the pathological symptoms of early psychosis and general psychosis, enhance the patients' social competence, reduce their loneliness, and increase their overall well-being. Through interaction with robotic pets, the elderly can improve their social communication, interaction, and participation. In the future, the elderly may rely on innovative technology such as robotic care, both mentally and physically which unlike ordinary animals, will not have a risk of infection or biting (Narita et al., 2016).

Along with AIBO, PARO, a seal-shaped robot with furry skin and cute seal baby appearance, is also a well-known robotic pet. PARO is currently a best-known robotic pet used as assistance during emotional therapy for the elderly, and can effectively pacify the patients in hospitals or sanatoria. So far, many studies have been conducted to investigate the applications of PARO in retirement homes. A study found that due to the seal shape, the elderly tried to bring PARO into the water to swim. Hence, this should be considered during designing the appearance of robotic pets. If robotic pets lack appropriate appearance design, people might misunderstand them and take care of them based on the user's previous experience (Yu et al., 2015). Although PARO has many advantages in helping with emotional therapy for the elderly, it is used in specific places (e.g., retirement homes or daily care centers) because it is large and heavy.

Robotic pets can be a great help in assisting the elderly in the future. At present, studies have been conducted to examine the emotional assistance and emotional engagement of pet-like assistive robots, and some positive results have been obtained. Therefore, this study aims to explore robotic pets that are portable and suitable for personal use for the elderly, so that the elderly can carry them conveniently and increase social interactions by using them as pets.

2.3 Interaction Design of Robotic Pets

Pets (particularly, pet dogs) can be the best design orientation for the development of robot behaviors because pets can establish effective social interactions with people. In the process of design, it is also necessary to identify and avoid pet characteristics that people do not like (Konok, Korcsok, Miklósi, & Gácsi, 2018). Moreover, fondling and contact are often ignored in human-machine interactions (Yohanan, 2012).

If robotic pets are designed for elderly people, it is important to understand that robotic pets are not used as a substitute to eliminate loneliness or be a companion for the elderly. Instead, robotic pets are used to satisfy their unfulfilled social needs or to strengthen social interactions with others. Metal robots do not appeal to them, whereas robotic pets with soft skin and a cute appearance are accepted, fondled and hugged by the elderly. The elderly will talk to robotic pets, and use them like teddy bears while sleeping, and robotic pets will react a little when they talk. Hence, a little comfortable, friendly and pleasant design can create more interesting and unexpected interactions (Lazar, Thompson, Piper, & Demiris, 2016).

Pokémon GO is the best-known example of enhancing social ties by a technological intervention. This game can create a sense of belonging, make the players talk to strangers, and strengthen people's social ties. It often triggers game-related conversations and also on unrelated topics (Vella et al., 2019). Pokémon GO allows gamers to experience new scenes and share their passion for the game, thus establishing new ties between people. Similarly, pets offer an opportunity for conversations between people who raise pets but are strangers.

3. RESEARCH ANALYSIS

To understand the functional requirements for robotic pets used by the elderly, this study adopted the interview method commonly used in social science research to gather the respondents' life experiences and views on things. The interview results can be used as a reference for designing robotic pets. The participants were elderly people of Japan aged 65 or above, who were leading a good independent life. A semi-structured deep interview was conducted for this study. Two Japanese respondents were interviewed for 37 and 44 minutes, respectively, to understand their opinion about owning robotic pet in Japan. We obtained approval from the Osaka Institute of Technology Ethics Review Committee (Approval No. 2019-44). To protect the privacy of the respondents, their real locations were kept anonymous, and the respondents' personal data were denoted by code.

The interview contents covered the respondents' daily life, experience in pet rising, and views on robotic pets. According to the daily life of the elderly, we can gather data about their social interaction status; way of life, views, and how robotic pets should help in their everyday life. According to their experience in pet raising, we can know their views on physical pets and how they interact with them. Finally, the respondents were asked about the mode of interaction and functional requirements concerning the design of robotic pets. Their answers could be used as a reference for the functional design of robotic pets in the future. The analysis of results also focused on the three parts.

Figure 1. Experiment photos

During the interview, in addition to the questions asked, photos of three scenarios indicative of Japanese culture were provided (i.e., living room, bedroom, and park), shows in figure1. Furthermore, different kinds of dolls were prepared, and their shapes were similar to the shapes of real animals, cartoon-style animals, and human shapes. Specifically, the dolls included the following: 1) series of verisimilar animal dolls produced by TOMICA (including AS-34 rabbit, AS-31 penguin, AS-26 wolf, and human, and AS-02 elephant); 2) Baby Animals series produced by Lego (including giraffe, elephant, panda, and white tiger); 3) decorative dolls produced by Sanrio (including Rilakkuma bear, white bear, penguin, fried shrimp, lizard, and snail). Unlike the dolls produced by TOMICA, the dolls produced by Sanrio were presented through a cartoon image. In total, 18 different shapes of dolls were provided to the respondents for scenario simulation during the interview that provided more data about their real life. During the interview, both audio-recording and video-recording devices were used. To protect the respondents, their faces were not recorded during the video-recording process and instead, only tables and process of doll selecting and scenario simulation were recorded. Two researchers; one researcher from the Faculty of Robotics and Design, and one assistant Taiwanese researcher interviewed each respondent.

Table 1. Respondent profile

Respondent No.	*Sex*	*Age*	*Place*	*Date*
A1	Female	81	Osaka Institute of Technology	November 2019
A2	Male	77	Osaka Institute of Technology	November 2019

3.1 Data Analysis

3.1.1 Daily Life of the Elderly

Part 1 focused on the respondents' current life patterns, places they visited frequently, and who they interacted within their daily life. The intent was to gather the following data: 1) their interactions with others, home alone status, and people they met; 2) people they frequently interacted with, reasons why they interacted with them frequently, and how they communicated with each other; 3) places they visited frequently, and activities held in such places. Based on these interview data, we can understand the living status of the elderly, and determine how robotic pets should be designed to help them in their daily life.

The respondent A1 liked to check the broadcasting time of TV programs by reading newspapers, but often forgot the broadcast time. Once, A1 attempted to pre-record TV programs but gave up because the operation settings were too complex. Hence, the products for the elderly should be designed to simplify operations and interfaces. Usually, A1 took a walk for some time in the park or baseball field, and watches children play. During this period, A1 did not talk to others. If meeting familiar people (e.g., parents of playing children) in the park, A1 just said simple greetings to them without engaging in deep communication. Apart from the supermarkets for shopping, A1 had no places or medium through which he/she interacted with others. At the most, A1 chatted with neighbors about the community's affairs or his/her past days. For A1, at this stage, reunions or travelling with his/her family was a very enjoyable event in daily life.

Respondent A2:

"In the morning, I send the children to schools, approximately a 2.5-kilometer journey, and then I take a walk together. I usually talk with my wife during breakfast. When I stay at home, I talk a lot all the time so life is not boring."

The respondent A2 was working as a volunteer for disaster prevention during his holidays, and could contact different people every day. Even at home, A2 was an active speaker, and often talked to other elderly people. For A2, the happiest moment in their everyday life was spending time with family members, especially with his/her grandson.

According to the answers of the two respondents', except in specific places (e.g., workplaces, parks and supermarkets), they did not initiate a conversation with others. According to the literature review, general pets can help strangers start a dialogue. Hence, robotic pets should be designed to offer more opportunities for in-depth dialogue between people and establish their social ties with others. During the interview, parks were mentioned repeatedly. Parks are worthwhile places that allowed the elderly to engage in social activities. In addition to daily leisure walks, parks can promote interpersonal communication, especially through pets. Therefore, the design of robotic pets should consider their mobility and portability. In addition to enhanced usability in parks, robotic pets should be designed to be portable to other daily living spaces.

3.1.2 Views on Raising Real Pets

This part aims to summarize the respondents' experience with raising a pet or interactions with other people's pets, as well as their current thoughts and motivations about raising a pet. The experience and thoughts can be used as a reference for the interaction design of robotic pets.

Respondents felt no repulsion towards raising real pets, and even wanted to raise dogs at this stage. Due to some constraints (e.g., care, schedule, allergy of family members, or wounds), they failed to raise real pets. Robotic pets can help elderly people who want to raise real pets. With robotic pets, the elderly doesn't have to worry about problems such as care or allergy of family members, and still make it possible for people to enjoy the benefits of owning real pets.

Respondent A1:

"I'm injured now I can't keep pets...I think AIBO is cute."

Respondent A2:

"I don't have pets right now. I have raised rabbits and chickens as a child. My children are allergic to animals, so I can't raise pets. Now I want to have a dog. But, as the Spring Festival is approaching, and I can't leave the dog in places such as a hospital."

The two respondents happened to have experience in raising a pet, and had motivations and ideas about it, but they were unable to do so due to physical and environmental constraints. Just like robotic pets serving to provide aided therapy, real pets can be therapeutic and provide companionship. However, the elderly fail to get such benefits for various reasons. Hence, it is of great importance to design good robotic pets to solve these problems.

3.1.3 Characteristics of Robotic Pets

In part 3, the respondents were asked to choose between animal or non-animal dolls, and different scenario photos for simulation, allowing them to choose the appearance for the robotic pets. The respondents were asked about their ideas for robotic pets. Based on the simulation of the portability scenario, we could understand how the respondents could make use of the robotic pets, their expectations on interactions with the pets, and their reaction to interactions with others through robotic pets and their feelings about it.

Among the animals chosen for scenario simulation, the respondents chose existent animals; specifically, one respondent chose the panda, and the other respondent chose the wolf with a resemblance of a dog. The respondents previously knew AIBO, a well-known Japanese robotic pet dog. The respondent A1 specifically mentioned that he/she preferred the doll to have big eyes like AIBO, and preferred the design of the eyes like that of the panda. The respondent A2 said that she preferred the most common dog appearance. Besides, the two respondents hoped that robotic pets could feel the owners' emotions. Of course, they hoped that robotic pets should follow the owners when they are talking, provide company at home, or engage in interactions, such as talking and smiling.

Respondent A1:

"I hope that robotic pets are designed to feel soft, but not ice-cold. "

Respondent A2:

"If I talk with robotic pets, I will be happy they answer me. But I don't want to touch them. I think it is not warm, because robots are made of metal. If I touch dogs or cats, it makes me feel warm."

The respondents shared the same view on the appearance of robotic pets, and hoped that the robotic pets felt soft and warm, not as ice-cold as metal. Besides, the respondents also hoped that robotic pets could act and interact with their owners. Taking that into consideration, the size of the robotic pet should be designed to be flexible. The respondent A2 feared that extremely a life-like fierce animal shapes would scare children during outdoor activities, so they preferred robotic pets to have the appearance of most common pets. To enable robotic pets to improve people's social ties, their appearance should be acceptable to most people. Regarding the functions of robotic pets, A2 said: "When I go to the park, people will be very excited to see the robotic pet and then I will have more opportunities to talk to others." Robotic pets can create opportunities to talk to more people; which is consistent with the argument in previous studies that ordinary pets can help people who are not familiar with build conversational relationships. It is of utmost importance to use robotic pets as a medium, to facilitate the elderly's interactions with others and acquire or maintain new social ties.

3.1.4 Other Functions of Robotic Pets

In addition to the aforementioned basic requirements regarding the appearance and behaviors of robotic pets, respondents also expressed their ideas on the functions of robotic pets. The available functions of technology-based robotic pets were not the same as those of real pets. Both A1 and A2 expected robotic pets to be their home assistants, who should act like smart speaker and have a systematic (although not real) talk (e.g., remind them of the current time, and inquire about the current weather and today's itinerary). Moreover, they were wanted safety measures to be installed in the robotic pets. The respondents hoped that robotic pets should be fitted with cameras to help look after their homes and a smart speaker, which can send SOS signals or information to their relatives or friends through text message in case of emergency. Based on the above interviews, we can understand that in daily life, the elderly need to interact more with others, acquire or maintain social ties, and receive home care.

3.2 Functional Design

According to the analysis of the interviews, this study argues that agile action and follow-the-owner behavior are the keys to the portability of robotic pets. To simplify the operation of robotic pets and facilitate their use by the elderly, this study recommends that their operation instructions should not be extremely complex, and there should not be too many switches or other functions on them. Figure 2 shows basic conceptual architecture and Figure 3 shows the conceptual draft based on the data of this study and interview, as well as interactional functions. The appearance is designed like a common dog, with big and round eyes. As A2 said, an extremely strange appearance will affect others' impressions. Other design details include furry skin and heat generation, which were required by both respondents. In addition, available robotic pets on the market do not yet accomplish supplying warmth. Moreover, the robotic pets are designed to have specific behavioral expressions (e.g., wag ears and tails after receiving messages, detecting the walking path, and following the owners), or react timely to external conditions (e.g., react joyfully when the owner is happy). Robotic pets can be designed to be more realistic. For example, robotic pets will bark at a fixed time, indicating that the owner needs to bring them out. Robotic pets help owner have social interactions. In addition to the basic appearance design, the motivation for carrying a robot pet to go out also needs to be enhanced.

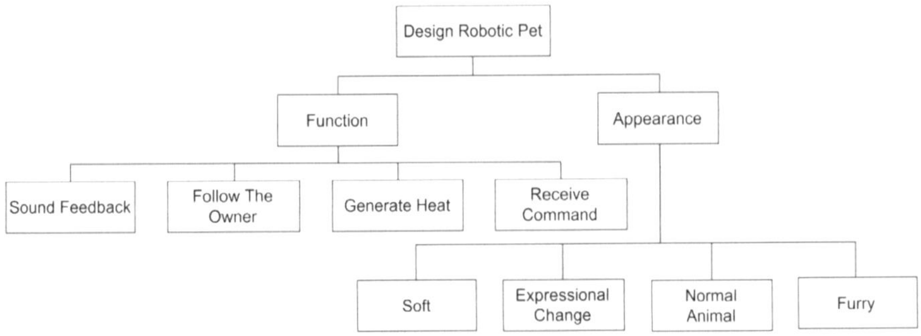

Figure 2. Basic Conceptual Architecture

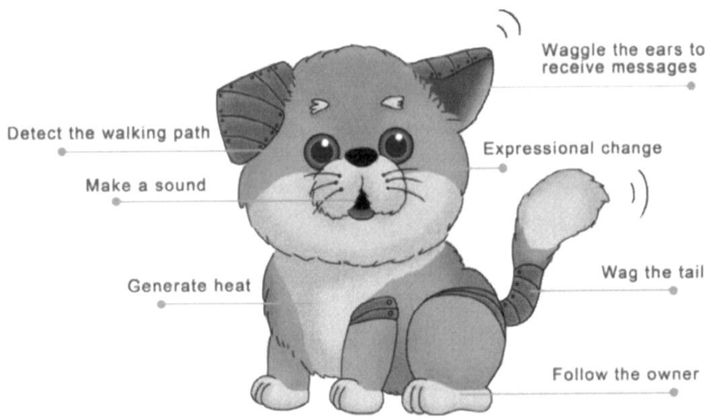

Figure 3. Conceptual draft

4. CONCLUSION

According to this study, the appearance of PARO and AIBO is suitable for respondents' needs. But the PARO is lack of warm and portable function; it is primarily used in retirement homes. However, the AIBO has a lot of functions, the operations are too complicated for the elderly. Even though, there are various products of robotic pets existed on the market, some robotic pets focus on psychological treatment and physical assistive in nursing home, the robotic pets which are designed for the elderly still have not satisfy their need for outdoors social interaction.

This study discussed the development status and application of robotic pets as well as assistant robots. At present, robots are used in many fields to solve specific problems. Home-based robots perform their functions in fixed places and are mainly used for psychological treatment or companionship at home. However, robotic pets can be used more widely. Similar to real pets, robotic pets can strengthen social ties between people, and help the elderly establish social relationships after retirement. Through the interviews, the following data were collected: 1) places the respondents visited frequently; 2) how the respondents interacted with others in these places; 3) their roles and behaviors in these places. The data are beneficial to understanding the behavioral pattern of the elderly and can be used as a reference for the highlights in the design of robotic pets. The interview also investigated the functional and designed requirements of the elderly for robotic pets. If robotic pets are used in actual scenarios by the elderly and designed for social interaction, the focus should be on their appearance and sense of touch. In the aspect of technological functions, the respondents emphasized their requirements for home safety and daily life. Such technological functions might not only be applied to robotic pets, but they can also be used as a reference for the development of other smart furniture.

The needs analysis will be used as a reference for the design and study in the related fields. In the future study, Taiwanese respondents will be interviewed, to deeply investigate the life experience of elderly people from different countries and cultural backgrounds, as well as their requirements for the interaction with robotic pets. The final intent is to obtain the views of more elderly people on the design of robotic pets. Japanese Respondent felt no repulsion for such virtual and technological products, but felt such products are novel and lovely and were eager to try. This was helpful for the test and can be of use for future designs. In contrast, the interview of Taiwanese respondents about robotic pets needs to provide more examples and descriptions, to keep them updated with the developments of robotic pet technology (e.g., AIBO), which are scarcely mentioned in Taiwan. In the future Taiwan-oriented study, this point should be given special attention.

REFERENCES

Broekens, J., Heerink, M., & Rosendal, H. (2009). Assistive social robots in elderly care: a review. *Gerontechnology, 8*(2), 94-103.

Chen, Y.-R. R., & Schulz, P. J. (2016). The effect of information communication technology interventions on reducing social isolation in the elderly: a systematic review. *Journal of medical Internet research, 18*(1), e18.

Donath, J. (2004). Artificial pets: Simple behaviors elicit complex attachments. In: The Encyclopedia of Animal Behavior, Greenwood Press.

Douglas, H., Georgiou, A., & Westbrook, J. (2017). Social participation as an indicator of successful aging: an overview of concepts and their associations with health. *Australian Health Review, 41*(4), 455-462.

Konok, V., Korcsok, B., Miklósi, Á., & Gácsi, M. (2018). Should we love robots?–The most liked qualities of companion dogs and how they can be implemented in social robots. *Computers in Human Behavior, 80*, 132-142.

Lazar, A., Thompson, H. J., Piper, A. M., & Demiris, G. (2016). *Rethinking the design of robotic pets for older adults.* Paper presented at the Proceedings of the 2016 ACM Conference on Designing Interactive Systems.

Lin, C., Faas, T., & Brady, E. (2017). *Exploring affection-oriented virtual pet game design strategies in VR attachment, motivations and expectations of users of pet games.* Paper presented at the 2017 Seventh International Conference on Affective Computing and Intelligent Interaction (ACII).

Mataric, M. (2011). Socially assistive robotics. *IEEE Robotics & Automation Magazine - IEEE ROBOT AUTOMAT, 18.*

Matarić, M. J. (2017). Socially assistive robotics: Human augmentation versus automation. *Science Robotics, 2*(4), eaam5410.

Mueller, M. K., Gee, N. R., & Bures, R. M. (2018). Human-animal interaction as a social determinant of health: descriptive findings from the health and retirement study. *BMC public health, 18*(1), 305.

Narita, S., Ohtani, N., Waga, C., Ohta, M., Ishigooka, J., & Iwahashi, K. (2016). A pet-type robot AIBO-assisted therapy as a day care program for chronic schizophrenia patients: a pilot study. *Australasian Medical Journal (Online), 9*(7), 244.

Patsoule, E., & Koutsabasis, P. (2014). Redesigning websites for older adults: a case study. Behaviour & Information Technology, 33(6), 561-573.

Rabbitt, S. M., Kazdin, A. E., & Scassellati, B. (2015). Integrating socially assistive robotics into mental healthcare interventions: Applications and recommendations for expanded use. *Clinical psychology review, 35*, 35-46.

United Nations (2015). *World Population Ageing Report.* Retrieved from https://www.un.org/en/development/desa/population/publications/pdf/ageing/WPA2015_Report.pdf

United Nations (2019). *World Population Prospects: the 2019 Revision.* Retrieved from https://population.un.org/wpp/

Vella, K., Johnson, D., Cheng, V. W. S., Davenport, T., Mitchell, J., Klarkowski, M., & Phillips, C. (2019). A sense of belonging: Pokemon GO and Social Connectedness. *Games and Culture, 14*(6), 583-603.

World Health Organization (2015). *World report on ageing and health.* World Health Organization.

Yohanan, S. J. (2012). *The haptic creature: Social human-robot interaction through affective touch.* University of British Columbia.

Yu, R., Hui, E., Lee, J., Poon, D., Ng, A., Sit, K. Shibata, T. (2015). Use of a therapeutic, socially assistive pet robot (PARO) in improving mood and stimulating social interaction and communication for people with dementia: Study protocol for a randomized controlled trial. *JMIR research protocols, 4*(2), e45.

FACTORS INFLUENCING READING PREFERENCE FOR OCCLUDED SINGLE COMPOSITION STRUCTURE CHARACTERS

Ching Chih Liao
Department of Commercial Design, Ming Chuan University
5 De Ming Rd., Gui Shan District, Taoyuan City 333, Taiwan

ABSTRACT

Past studies have discovered that that occlusion on the right (top-right, bottom-right) or on the bottom yields faster recognition time and higher reading accuracy for Chinese characters composed of two or three radicals, regardless of vertical or horizontal arrangement, or occluding one or two sides. In order to investigate whether occlusion of single composition structure characters, in the absence of accompanying parts, would yield similar recognition results, this pilot study was undertaken. Given the hypothesis that different positions of occlusion applied to numerals and Chinese characters would yield different reading preference results, this research selected nine each of Chinese characters and Arabic numerals, occluding each at the top, bottom, left, and right, comprising 72 samples. Coming from design and non-design education backgrounds, 160 participants were recruited to investigate how and why they would rank the modes of occlusion for preference. Using nonparametric tests to analyze the experimental results revealed a significant difference among the occlusion position for numbers and Chinese characters. Chinese characters occluded on the left were most preferred, those with right occlusion least. Numbers occluded on the bottom were most preferred, those with right occlusion least. The primary reason given for preference, for both Chinese characters and numbers, was ease of recognition and visual balance. The main reason for not preferring either occluded Chinese characters or numbers was that they were not easily recognized, seemed unbalanced and non-aesthetically pleasing. Regarding differing education background of the participants, there was significant difference for the Chinese characters occluded at the top and bottom, and non-significant difference for reading preference of occluded numerals.

KEYWORDS

Single Composition Structure Chinese Characters, Arabic Numerals, Reading Recognition (Recognition), Reading Preference, Balance

1. INTRODUCTION

The primary function of written words is to communicate and transmit messages, thus clear and complete words are most recognizable. However, in visual communication, words not only serve to transfer information, but are sometimes treated as processed reading images (Leeuwen, 2005) and even used to express emotions through different forms of arrangement (Malik, Aitken & Waalen, 2016). All of these serve to achieve certain results such as increasing attention and memory. Focusing discussion on recognition and preference regarding occluded words aims to provide relevant research data which is beneficial to designers. When this is applied to graphic design, product design, or 3-D package design, designers can quickly decide on the positions of occlusion, proportions of occlusion and modes of occlusion, flattening their learning curve and decreasing uncertainty.

Luijkx, Thillou, & Gosselin (2006) defined incomplete words as unknown and unseen words, meaning parts of letters have been cut or occluded. Simplifying Chinese character strokes is not a modern design expression, but something that can be traced back to Emperor Qianlong of Ching Dynasty who, on a trip to the region south of the Yangtze River, was strolling around Mid-lake Pavilion on West Lake at night. He was fascinated by the beautiful landscape and carved 虫、二 (worm, two) on the stele of the pavilion to commemorate the unbounded scene by eliminating the outline borders of two Chinese characters 風月 (scenery = wind, moon). In the European language world, application of occlusion to design is common. One designer occluded parts of letters in the activity theme on a poster to imply that by people's neglectfulness, valuable history may die with time. From the above description, we can learn that processed words can transmit artistic concepts, increase delight, and stir up emotional reactions. From a semiotics perspective, the unique letters on the stele are able to form a typographic landscape (Järlehed & Jaworski, 2015). Due to different font features such as serifs, proportions, construction, organization, cohesion, etc. compared to texts, fonts can generate more of a local culture connection, a semiotic resource (Pescatore Frisk & Pauwels, 2019). Placing incomplete words or punctuation on a poster can connect intended meaning of the theme of an activity with an even more powerful appeal.

In their study, Tseng, Chang & Wang (1965) noted that words possess a certain amount of information and redundancy. Thus, this exploration on how far characters can be simplified and still retain reading recognition is undertaken. In related studies, the author of this paper (Liao, 2018; Tsao & Liao, 2015) also discovered that when Chinese characters composed of two and three radicals are partially occluded at appropriate positions, it does not affect recognition. This corresponds to the viewpoints of recognition by components theory and object simplification (Biederman, 1981, 1987). Thus, we can conclude that application of occluded characters in practical design is a workable technique, but the prerequisite is that we must first understand the construction of character composition, preserve the recognizable and crucial starting strokes and radicals, and apply the appropriate proportions of occlusion. However, Chinese characters are very complicated. The key to recognition of occluded Chinese characters that are composed of two and three radicals is in their top-left starting strokes; therefore, right occlusion (including top-right and bottom-right occlusion) has the least effect on recognition. Yet, is this so for a character composed of a single radical? Thus, this pilot study undertakes to understand factors influencing participants' reading preference for occluded single radical characters as to follow-up on discussion of the effects of their occlusion on reading recognition results.

1.1 Composition Structures of Traditional Chinese Characters and European Text Fonts

Traditional Chinese characters are primarily composed of recognized components and radicals. From the perspective of Chinese character design, they can be divided into nine forms: 1. One character which cannot be disassembled, such as 米 (rice); 2. Composed of right and left parts, such as 林 (forest); 3. Composed of right part with top-bottom radicals and left as a whole, such as 結 (tie); 4. Composed of left part with top-bottom radicals and right as a whole, such as 部 (part); 5. Composed of top and bottom parts, such as 歪 (crooked); 6. Composed of top part with left-right radicals and bottom as a whole, such as 然 (just so); 7. Composed of bottom part with left-right radicals and top as a whole, such as 蔽 (cover); 8. Composed of top, middle, bottom parts, such as 葉 (leaf); 9. Composed of left, middle, right parts, such as 邀 (invite) (Chen, 1974; Wu & Chiu, 1995). Besides these compositions of recognized components and radicals, Chinese characters also involve strokes, 26 kinds of strokes in all, which are mainly composed of various horizontal and vertical strokes, wherein horizontal strokes account for the majority (Peng, 1982).

Words in European languages are primarily composed from among the 26 English letters. In typography, a font set in European languages mostly includes English letters and numerals, the design of which can be divided into six types (Zhu, 2009): Old Style, Sans Serif, Slab Serif, Script, Modern, and Decorative (also known as Baskerville). Sans serif fonts, because of having no extending feature at the end of strokes, are simple, clean, and modern, with Helvetica as a representative. Slab Serif fonts, wherein strokes contain slab angular serifs and transitions with back-in-time features, are good for headlines, as represented by Memphis. In general, Arabic numerals and English letters comprise vertical, horizontal, slash, and curve strokes. Aside from 4 and 5, all other numbers can be completed in one stroke. The complexity of stroke and directionality for Chinese characters is higher than for Arabic numerals, even those with single structure composition such as 天 (sky).

1.2 Aesthetic Features of Chinese Characters

The classical concept of beauty is that it is a coherent unity of parts composing a pleasing aesthetic whole based on proportion, harmony, symmetry, and similar perceptions (Zalta, 2004; Ranscombe, Hicks, Mullineux & Singh, 2012). Sun, Lian, Tang, & Xiao (2015) tried to measure the aesthetic perception of Chinese handwriting using artificial intelligence and proposed three aspects for these measures. First, alignment and stability: Whether the composition of strokes is a vertical composition structure, horizontal composition structure, or surrounding composition structure, it must attain structural balance. Second, white space ratio (WSR): This illustrates that Chinese character strokes stress density; that is to say, the WSR cannot be too dispersed or too crowded. Third, gap between strokes: The means of composition between radicals involves stroke directions and positions (Xu, Jiang, Lau, & Pan, 2007) and gap dimension also affects the determination of aesthetic perception. From the aforementioned, we can see a balanced and stable overall structure, tight composition between strokes and radicals, and degree of density will all affect the decision as to whether a Chinese character is aesthetically pleasing or not.

1.3 Preference

Within psychology, preference is used to indicate an individual's attitude toward a person or an object (Lichtenstein & Slovic, 2006), or to express an evaluative judgement of like or dislike for a person or an object (Scherer, 2005). Preference is not stable; the decision-making process can significantly alter preference (Brehm, 1956; Sharot, De Martino & Dolan, 2009). Moreover, emotional factors have an important influence on preference formation and maintenance (Zajonc & Markus, 1982). From the literature, we understand that geographic location, cultural background, religion, education, and upbringing can all affect one's preferences. Besides continuing to investigate recognition of processed and incomplete characters (Liao, 2019), the motivation behind this research is to more deeply explore whether or not partially occluded character structure, that leads to aesthetic features such as seeming imbalanced and not stable, would affect research participant's preferences.

1.4 Comparison of Recognition between Those with Different Education Backgrounds

The literature indicates that individuals with design background can sometimes demonstrate different degrees of recognition in the same circumstance. For example: Eisner (1994) mentioned that individuals with art education background can accept more diversified objects as they are also encouraged to innovate and trained to think more with their right brains (mainly responsible for visual space) (Chiang & Sun, 2014). Thus, individuals with design background prefer visual thinking. Hsu & Wang (2009, 2010) discovered that individuals with non-design education training prefer figurative images more than those with design background. Liao (2018) discovered that individuals with non-design education background are faster on occluded Chinese character response time.

Herewith, a primary purpose of this study is to discuss the preference reaction to occluded characters by individuals with different education backgrounds. One reason is that understanding the recognition difference among those with different education backgrounds allows designers to avoid being caught in subjective thinking. The second reason is that the results of this preference pilot study will be useful for deepening future reading recognition research and these results can also be beneficial in future design applications. Therefore, two hypotheses are proposed.

Hypothesis 1: When characters are occluded in different positions, the basic factor affecting preference for these occluded characters is that they should be recognizable.

Hypothesis 2: Reading preference results for different positions of occlusion is not the same for numerals and Chinese characters.

2. Method

2.1 Experimental Design

This study investigated two independent variables - type of text (Chinese characters and Arabic numerals) and occlusion position (top, bottom, left, right) - according to the dependent variable of participants' reading preference, using a nonparametric Friedman test to analyze the experimental results. Two sets of participants from design and non-design education backgrounds, 160 in all, were recruited to investigate their ranking order, and the reason for the ranking choices, of reading preference for four-occlusion positions applied to the selected texts. Each participant observed nine each of Chinese characters and numerals, for a total of 18, which were respectively each occluded in four different positions, comprising 72 samples.

2.2 Participants

From among students at two universities in Taiwan, 160 participants were recruited, consisting half from each of design and non-design backgrounds. The so-called design background comprises students from the departments of Graphic design, Industrial design and Digital media design, because they took basic design courses in the first year, including Design theory, Color Science and Basic design. There were 88 males and 72 females, with mean age of 25.3 years, standard deviation of 17.63 years.

2.3 Producing the Stimulus Materials

From the list of 4,000+ most common Chinese characters resulting from Wu's (1987) study, nine single composition Chinese characters, of the 1000 to 9649 frequency levels, were selected as stimuli, including 出 (exit), 不 (no), 大 (big), 了 (understand), 天 (sky), 回 (return), 心 (heart), 之 (a possessive participle), 上 (top). According to the literature, Mingti (明體) is one of the easier-to-recognize Chinese fonts (Shieh, Chen & Cuang, 1997; Cai, Chi & You, 2001; Dobres, Chahine, Reimer & Mehler, 2014); as practical design technique for occluded characters is usually applied to large and bold characters to make it stand out and increase attention, bold Mingti font was selected for producing the design samples.

In previous pilot study results, Tsao & Liao (2015) found that when a character is occluded on top, bottom, right, and left positions by 2/9 proportion on each, it is not only recognizable but has the most obvious occlusion effect. Accordingly, 2/9 occlusion was applied on all four sides of each character, generating four samples for each of all nine selected Chinese characters, comprising the 36 samples shown in the left-hand columns of Table 1.

As for occlusion design of Arabic numerals, because of the long, narrow appearance, with width considerably less than height, and the stroke of the numeral 1 being too simple that occlusion has no effect, it was skipped. Thus the numerals 0 and 2~9 were used, to which Arial Unicode MS 300pt English font (a sans serif font just as Helvetica is) was applied to design samples, displaying the features of simple, clean, and modern. Due to their long and narrow appearances, the exact same occlusion principles used for Chinese characters cannot be applied to Arabic numerals. Rather, numeral width was divided into five equal parts and height into six equal parts. Occlusions of 1/5 on the width and 1/6 on the height were pre-tested. Based on the pre-test results, the actual experiment proceeded with slightly adjustments to occlusion proportions for the design samples as shown in the right-hand columns of Table 1.

Samples of one character or one numeral occluded at top, bottom, left, and right were placed on the same screen. Each occlusion sample appeared in black font on a white background and in a 12x12 cm square on a black background. A sequence of 18 screens were displayed through a self-developed program. Each sample was designed with pull-down ranking choices and a space for participants to note their reason(s) for the most and least preferred.

Table 1. Samples of Single Composition Structure Characters and Different Occlusion Positions

Chinese Characters				Numerals			
Occluded Top	Occluded Bottom	Occluded Left	Occluded Right	Occluded Top	Occluded Bottom	Occluded Left	Occluded Right
出	出	出	出	0	0	0	0
不	不	不	不	2	2	2	2
大	大	大	大	3	3	3	3
了	了	了	了	4	4	4	4
天	天	天	天	5	5	5	5

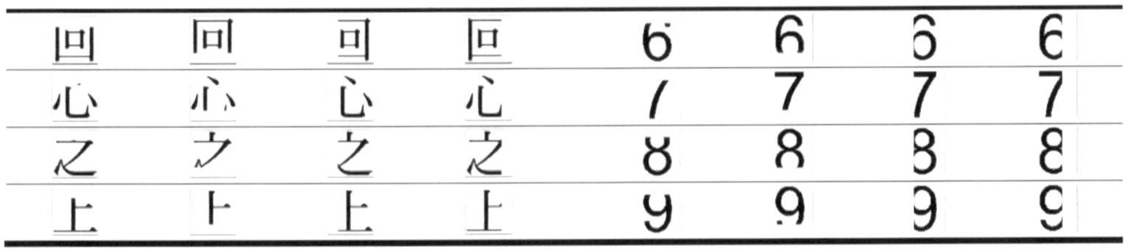

2.4 Experimental Procedures

Each of the 160 participants ranked each of the four occlusion positions on the same screen for all of the numerals and characters with 1 as the most preferred to 4 as the least preferred; moreover, participants wrote reason(s) for their order of preference. To avoid the learning effect on experimental results, the display order for numerals and characters was switched after each participant. The stimulus materials of the nine Chinese characters and nine numerals were randomly displayed. The test took approximately 20 minutes; each participant completed it independently and received a gift upon completion.

2.5 Results

The data was analyzed by nonparametric K-related-samples test. Results showed that $\chi^2(3)=126.07$ with $p<.001$ for Chinese character samples and indicated that all participants had at least one significantly different reading preference for one occlusion position among the four tested. Data was further analyzed by Two-Related-Samples Tests, revealing a rank of preference for occluded positions on Chinese characters as left, bottom, top, right, with left-side occlusion having highest preference and right-side occlusion as the least preferred.

Analysis of numeral samples showed that $\chi^2(3)=278.07$ with $p<.001$, which also indicated that all participants had at least one significantly different reading preference for one occlusion position among the four. Again, data was further analyzed by Two-Related-Samples Tests, showing a rank of preference for occluded positions on numerals as bottom, top, left, right, meaning bottom occlusion has highest preference and right-side occlusion was least preferred.

The results between two different education background groups for Chinese characters occluded on the top yielded $\chi^2(1)=5.872$ and $p=.01$, and for bottom-position occlusion $\chi^2(1)=13.69$ and $p=.001$. This indicates that individuals with different education backgrounds had significantly different reading preferences for certain characters being occluded in different positions. Participants with non-design background had a higher reading preference than those with design background for Chinese characters such as 出 (exit), 大 (big), 回 (return) being occluded on top; and individuals with design background had a higher reading preference than those with non-design background for Chinese characters 天 (sky), 上 (top) being occluded on bottom. There was no preference difference between the different education backgrounds for numerals occluded in different positions.

2.5.1 Preference Differences for Chinese Characters Being Occluded in Four Positions and Reasons

In order to further understand whether or not participants had significantly different preferences among the occlusion in four positions for the nine Chinese characters, analysis by nonparametric K-related-samples test was used. For Chinese characters, occlusion at top, bottom, left and right positions yielded the following results: $\chi^2(8)=742.76$, $p<.001$; $\chi^2(8)=523.22$, $p<.001$; $\chi^2(8)=490.18$, $p<.001$; $\chi^2(8)=460.29$, $p<.001$, respectively (Table 2). This indicates that at least one Chinese character among the nine differed significantly when occluded in each position.

As shown by the mean rank in Table 2, when Chinese characters were occluded on top, if the starting stroke was from the top and was a horizontal stroke such as 不, 了, 天, least preference was observed due to the occluded character not being recognized easily, according to reasons provided by the participants. On the other hand, if the starting stroke was not from the top, the reading preference was not easily affected and this position of occlusion had a higher preference, such as for 出, 上. When Chinese characters were occluded on bottom, if a primary stroke was a horizontal stroke and was on the lowest part of the character, such as for 上, this was the hardest to recognize and had low preference.

When Chinese characters were occluded on left, and the core of the stroke was toward the right, such as 了, this did not affect recognition and had a higher preference. But if the core of the strokes and features were preserved when occluded on the right, such as for 之, this did not affect recognition and had a higher preference. It is also worth mentioning that preference was low for right- or left-side occlusion of characters with bilateral symmetry such as 出 and 回, because of visual imbalance.

A list of reasons for preference and non-preference was collated from the participants' feedback. Examples of preference reasons that appeared most frequently included: easiest recognition, character appears very stable, recognize it at a glance, character can be recognized, no problem in recognition, and close to the complete character. Non-preference reasons were: hard to recognize, aesthetic sense is spoiled, mistaken for another character, uncomfortable to look at, and low level of stability.

Table 2. Comparison among Chinese Characters Being Occluded in Four Positions

	出	不	大	了	天	回	心	之	上
Occluded Top	**2.55**	**7.08**	**3.13**	**7.04**	**7.22**	4.41	4.68	6.02	**2.88**
Occluded Bottom	4.83	**2.58**	6.04	5.07	5.28	**3.02**	**3.78**	**6.94**	**7.47**
Occluded Left	6.83	5.19	**6.06**	**2.29**	3.48	**6.60**	6.04	3.46	5.05
Occluded Right	**7.09**	4.9	5.36	4.62	**2.89**	6.44	**6.23**	**2.55**	4.91

Note: The numbers in each column represent the mean ranks. The lower the mean rank, the higher the preference.

2.5.2 Preference Differences for Numerals Being Occluded in Four Positions and Reasons

Nonparametric K-related-samples test was used to analyze results; numerals occluded on top, bottom, left and right positions yielded the following results: $\chi^2(8)=742.76$, $p<.001$; $\chi^2(8)=520.42$, $p<.001$; $\chi^2(8)=334.63$, $p<.001$; $\chi^2(8)=305.38$, $p<.001$, respectively (Table 3). This indicates that at least one numeral among the nine differed significantly when occluded on the top position.

As shown by the mean rank in Table 3, when numerals were occluded on top, and the core stroke was a horizontal one from the top such as 7, this was least preferred and most difficult to recognize. On the other hand, if the starting stroke was not from the top, the reading preference for occlusion at the top was less affected and received higher preference, such as for 9 and 0. When numerals were occluded on bottom, and the core stroke was a horizontal one on the lowest part, such as for 2, the preference was low due to not being easily recognized. Otherwise, if a vertical stroke was involved and the numeral was occluded on the bottom, the reading preference was not affected much, such as for 6 and 7, thus yielding a higher preference.

When numerals were occluded on the left, and the core stroke and features were on the left, such as for 6 and 4, recognition was affected and preference was lower. But if the core stroke was on the right, such as for 7, the reading preference for occlusion on the left was not affected and preference was higher. When numerals such as 2 and 4 were occluded on the right, because the right-side feature was not occluded, higher preference was observed. Similar to Chinese characters, due to visual imbalance when bilaterally symmetric numerals such as 0 and 8 were occluded on the right or left, this was not preferred at all.

Reasons for preference that appeared the most in feedback from participants included: stylish, clear, numeral appears very stable, easy recognition, comfortable to look at, and close to a complete numeral. Non-preference reasons included: not aesthetically pleasing, aesthetics are spoiled, easy to be mistaken for another numeral, uncomfortable to look at, and balance is lost.

Comparing the preference descriptions between Chinese characters and numerals, the most frequently mentioned description for characters was reading recognition is easy, while for numerals the most frequent phrases were in regard to aesthetic sense and having stylish design features.

Table 3. Comparison among Numerals Being Occluded in Four Positions

	0	2	3	4	5	6	7	8	9
Occluded Top	**3.74**	4.35	**4.61**	**6.82**	**5.89**	4.74	**7.74**	4.52	**2.59**
Occluded Bottom	4.52	**8.05**	5.22	3.90	4.80	**3.71**	3.87	**4.31**	**6.63**
Occluded Left	5.48	3.44	5.08	6.00	5.38	**6.38**	**2.41**	5.52	5.32
Occluded Right	**6.58**	**3.23**	**5.71**	**3.21**	**4.23**	5.22	5.11	**5.97**	5.74

Note: The numbers in each column represent the mean ranks. The lower the mean rank, the higher the preference.

3. DISCUSSION AND CONCLUSION

Through preference rank analysis of single composition structure Chinese characters and Arabic numerals occluded in different positions, it is discovered that characters and numerals with bilateral symmetrical structures are both less preferred when the right or left part is occluded. According to the reasons given by study participants, aside from the main reason of not being easily recognized, the low preference arises from feelings about aesthetic sense. When this type of text is partially occluded either on the right or the left, balance is lost, thus it lacks the sense of being aesthetically pleasing. The Chinese character 天 is an exception; although it is bilaterally symmetric, when partially occluded either on the right or the left, it still preserves its structural wholeness and stroke density, thus recognition and balance are maintained and preference is unaffected. The numeral 9 only has a higher reading preference when occluded on top and low preference when other positions are occluded. It is deduced that top, left and right occlusion of this numeral affects its recognition and balance.

Thereunder, the primary reason for occluded character preference is shown to be recognition, followed by aesthetic sense of balance. The study results demonstrate that occlusion in different positions indeed affects preference and having design background or not only slightly affects reading preference for Chinese characters, with no preference difference for Arabic numerals. Moreover, the results of this study demonstrate that the effect of position of occlusion on reading preference and ease of recognition for single composition structure characters both differ from that of characters composed of two and three radicals. Future research will aim to further pursue the study of recognition for occluded single composition structure characters, to verify these results. Meanwhile, the outcomes of this study are sufficient to serve as an auxiliary reference and an application basis for design practices.

ACKNOWLEDGEMENT

This study was supported by Ministry of Science and Technology in Taiwan, under the grand numbers of MOST 108-2410-H-130 -010.

REFERENCES

Biederman, I., 1981. *On the semantics of a glance at a scene*. In Kubovy, M. & Pomerantz, J.R. (Eds.), Perceptual organization (pp.213-253). Hillsdale, NJ: Erlbaum.

Biederman, I., 1987. Recognition-by-Components: A Theory of Human Image Understanding. *Psychological Review*, 94(2), 115-147.

Brehm, J.W., 1956. Post-decision changes in desirability of choice alternatives. *Journal of Abnormal and Social Psychology*, 52, 384-389.

Chen, X.R., 1974. *Graphic design of English and Chinese characters*. Taipei, Taiwan: Dong-Woo Printing. (In Chinese)

Ching, S.B. & Sun, C.W., 2014. Impacts of learning background and different contextual sentences on shot interpretation in word-to-image transcoding process. *Journal of Design*, 19 (3), 41 - 62.

Eisner, E.W., 1994. *Cognition and curriculum reconsidered* (2nd ed), New York: Teachers College Press.

Hsu, C.C. & Wang, R.W.Y., 2009. The relationship between learning background and the preference to simplified graphics. *Research in Arts Education*, 17, 109 - 130.

Hsu, C.C. & Wang, R.W.Y., 2010. The relationship between shape features and degrees of graphic simplification. *Journal of Design*, 15(3), 87 – 105.

Järlehed, J. & Jaworski, A., 2015. Typographic landscaping: Creativity, ideology, movement. *Social Semiotics*, 25(2), 117–125.

Leeuwen, T.V. (2005). Typographic meaning, visual communication 4(2), 137–143.

Liao, C.C., 2018. Double-Sided Occluded Chinese Character Recognition Accuracy and Response Time for Design and Nondesign Educational Background. *SAGE Open*, 8(4), 2158244018810065.

Liao, C.C., 2019. Preference Impact of Diverse Modes of Occlusion on Single Composition Structure Chinese Characters and Arabic Numerals, *In Proceeding of International Conference on Advanced Research in Applied Science and Engineering*, Amsterdam, Netherlands. ISBN: 978-609-8239-71-3

Lichtenstein, S. & Slovic, P., 2006. *The construction of preference*. New York: Cambridge University Press.

Luijkx, A. et al, 2006. Aprolongation-based approach for recognizing cut characters. *Computer Vision and Graphics. Computational Imaging and Vision*, 32, 1125-1130.

Malik, S. et al, 2016. Communicating Emotion With Animated Text, *Visual Communication*, 8(4), 469–479.

Peng, R.X., 1982. A preliminary report on statistical analysis of the structure of Chinese characters. *Acta Psychologic Sinica*, 385-390.

Pescatore Frisk, R. & Pauwels, L., 2019. *The shared stories that written words tell when no one is reading: exploring modality in typographic landscapes as an ecosocial semiotic system*. visual communication, 1-34. doi:10.1177/1470357219860086

Ranscombe, C. et al, 2012. Visually decomposing vehicle images: Exploring the influence of different aesthetic features on consumer perception of brand. Design Studies, 33(4), 319-341. doi:10.1016/j.destud.2011.06.006

Scherer, K.R., 2005. What are emotions? And how can they be measured? *Social Science Information*, 44, 695-729.

Sharot, T. et al, 2009. How choice reveals and shapes expected hedonic outcome. *Journal of Neuroscience*, 29, 3760-3765.

Sun, R. et al, 2015. Aesthetic Visual Quality Evaluation of Chinese Handwritings. *Proceedings of the Twenty-Fourth International Joint Conference on Artificial Intelligence (IJCAI 2015)*, Buenos Aires, Argentina, pp. 2510-2516.

Tsao, Y.C. & Liao, C.C., 2015. Effect of structural composition and position of occlusion on the legibility of occluded Chinese characters. *Perceptual & Motor Skills*, 120(2), 560-575.

Tseng, S.C. et al, 1965. An informational analysis of the Chinese language: The reconstruction of the removed strokes of the ideograms in printed sentence-texts. *Acta Psychologic Sinica*, 281-290.

Wu, J.T., 1987. [*Exploring the phonetic and semantic features of Chinese words: Part 1. Frequency count of Chinese words, characters, and monosyllables*]. (Grant No. NSC-75-0301-H002-24) Taipei, Taiwan: National Science Council. [in Chinese]

Wu, M.S. & Chiu, I.T., 1995. *Graphic design of Chinese character formation*. Taipei, Taiwan: New Image. (In Chinese)

Xu, S. et al, 2007. An intelligent system for Chinese calligraphy. *In Proceedings of the 22nd National Conference on Artificial Intelligence, Vancouver,* British Columbia, Canada, vol. 2, pp.1578-1583.

Zajonc, R.B. & Markus, H., 1982. Affective and cognitive factors in preferences. *Journal of Consumer Research*, 9(2), 123-131.

Zalta, E.N. (ed.) 2004. *Stanford Encyclopedia of Philosophy*. Stanford, CA: The Metaphysics Research Lab.

Zhu, Q. M., 2009. *Graphic design (Typography)*. Publishing house: Longxi Books.

A SENSOR-LITE ANXIETY DETECTOR FOR FOREIGN LANGUAGE LEARNING

Daneih Ismail and Peter Hastings
DePaul University, USA

ABSTRACT

Foreign language learners face cognitive and emotional interference which reduces their learning acquisition. Foreign language anxiety (FLA) is one of the impediments to learning a new language. It hinders cognitive processes, interferes with attention, and reduces working memory capacity. Detecting foreign language anxiety is the first step toward reducing and eventually overcoming it. Here we present a novel design to detect foreign language anxiety in the context of an e-learning system using sensor-free and sensor-lite metrics. By adopting the Foreign Language Classroom Anxiety Scale (FLCAS) as a pre-test along with language difficulty self-report, system difficulty self-report, and score, we are predicting the current anxiety level of the learner when learning English as a second language using an e-learning system. We found that some components of the FLCAS can effectively predict FLA for listening and speaking exercises. Additionally, FLCAS plus the self-reports and the score are effective in detecting the learner's current anxiety level for all exercise types.

KEYWORDS

Foreign Language Anxiety, Emotion, Affect, Sensor-Free, Sensor-Lite

1. INTRODUCTION

Learning and emotions are strongly connected. Positive emotions such as engagement increase learning, while negative emotions such as anxiety obstruct learning. Foreign language anxiety (FLA) can appear in all learning environments such as classrooms and when using an e-learning system. Researchers are interested in understanding the reasons, impacts, and processes for overcoming anxiety.

Previous research has described the impacts of emotional state on learning and the effects of learning on emotional state (Bigdeli, 2010). Learners may feel not confident speaking a new language (Lu, Chang and Chen, 2007; Lai and Wen, 2012). Learners may feel anxious about reading, listening or writing a second language (Lin, Chao and Huang, 2015), which reduces their achievement (Shao, Yu and Ji, 2013; Huang and Huang, 2015) and impacts learner performance, production and retention (Rafada and Madini, 2017a).

Understanding fundamental aspects that produce anxiety within the context of foreign language learning could help to reduce it. (Horwitz, Horwitz and Cope, 1986) classified causes of FLA into three main categories: fear of negative evaluation, communication apprehension, and test anxiety. Other researchers have linked additional factors to FLA including task complexity (Chen and Lee, 2011; Levitt, 2015), native language proficiency (Gregersen, 2006; Liu, 2013), and lack of emotion intelligence (Shao, Yu and Ji, 2013).

Researchers are studying FLA because it affects learner performance (Liu, 2006; Bigdeli, 2010; Liu and Huang, 2011; Huang, 2018; Sparks *et al.*, 2018), reduces acquisition (Dewaele, Petrides and Furnham, 2008), and produces unwillingness to communicate in the foreign language (Liu, 2006; Liu and Jackson, 2008). FLA reduces motivation to learn (Liu and Huang, 2011), divides attention between emotion and cognition making performance less efficient (Kralova and Petrova, 2017), and moderates interest in learning a foreign language (Liu, 2006). According to the Yerkes-Dodson Law, moderate anxiety improves performance, but high levels of anxiety are disruptive. Furthermore, very low levels of anxiety are associated with a lack of desire to learn (Bigdeli, 2010; Levitt, 2015).

The Foreign Language Classroom Anxiety Scale (FLCAS) is a well-validated, reliable instrument which is widely used to measure foreign language anxiety within classroom contexts. It was initially designed by (Horwitz, Horwitz and Cope, 1986) for English speakers studying Spanish as a foreign language. It was used since 1986 to detect anxiety no matter what is the foreign language. FLCAS has been translated into many native languages to measure anxiety levels in various foreign language classes. The scale has 33 questions in three sections which correspond to the three categories or components of FLA. The first section has 11 questions dealing with communication apprehension, i.e., the respondent's feelings about listening and speaking a foreign language. The second section has 15 questions focused on test anxiety. For example, it asks learners about their emotions in a foreign language classroom: do they tremble in the class, do they fear to fail the class, or do they feel pressure in the class? The last section has 7 questions and about fear of negative evaluation. This part focuses on worries about peer or teacher judgments. The FLCAS has been used as a pre-test in some experiments (Chen and Lee, 2011; Alemi, Meghdari and Ghazisaedy, 2014; Lin, Chao and Huang, 2015; Ismail and Hastings, 2019) or as a standalone measure for examining different aspects that affect FLA (Shao, Yu and Ji, 2013; Rafada and Madini, 2017a). Some researchers have argued that self-report is unreliable because people may unintentionally lie to hide their emotions (American Psychiatric Association, 2013; Imani and Montazer, 2019), while within the context of e-learning systems, self-reports have been shown to be effective (Lopatovska and Arapakis, 2011; Imani and Montazer, 2019; Ismail and Hastings, 2019). There are several mechanisms for collecting self-reports related to anxiety such as Likert scales (Luo *et al.*, 2018), self-explanation texts (Lin, Chao and Huang, 2015), or sliders with emojis (Ismail and Hastings, 2019).

Various researchers have studied the relationship between FLCAS components and aspects of FLA. Some studied listening comprehension and found that anxiety impedes communication in a foreign language (Atasheneh and Izadi, 2012). (Mufidah, 2016) found that grammar comprises a large portion of the English proficiency test and more anxious students get worse scores in the grammar section of the test. Foreign language speaking anxiety is related to fear of unpleasant feedback (Rafada and Madini, 2017b) and lack of communication techniques (Balemir, 2009). With respect to vocabulary, (Chen, 2015) found that vocabulary anxiety can slightly predict foreign language achievement. At the same time, they mentioned that foreign language vocabulary is correlated with test anxiety and fear of negative evaluation. The previous study by (Ismail and Hastings, 2019) showed that using language difficulty self-report, system difficulty self-report, and the exercise score provides a significant moderate prediction for FLA.

Through this study, we want to discover how to detect FLA within an e-learning system using sensor-free and sensor-lite methods. Sensor-free means detecting anxiety using interaction patterns without using physical sensors. Sensor-lite methods use minimal sensors such as self-report (D'Mello and Graesser, 2014). Using level of anxiety self-report as the ground truth data of participants' emotional state, we posed the following research questions to determine if we could effectively identify anxiety without using explicit level of anxiety self-report, using instead their answers to components of the FLCAS:

1. Does communication apprehension predict the learner's anxiety level in listening exercises?
2. Does test anxiety predict the learner's anxiety level in grammar exercises?
3. Do fear of negative evaluation and communication apprehension predict the learner's anxiety level in speaking exercises?
4. Do test anxiety and fear of negative evaluation predict the learner's anxiety level in vocabulary exercises?
5. Can we predict the learner's anxiety level within an e-learning system using initial answers to the FLCAS plus language difficulty self-report, system difficulty self-report, and the score?

According to (Horwitz, Horwitz and Cope, 1986) foreign language anxiety could be related to three main reasons: communication apprehension, test anxiety and fear of negative evaluation. Communication apprehension is related to listening to native speakers and oral communication. Thus for question 1, we hypothesized that the communication apprehension questions on the FLCAS would effectively predict the anxiety level for listening exercises. Other questions on the FLCAS measure test anxiety. The grammar exercises of the system evaluate participants on their ability to use adverbs of quantity and prepositions, and generate indirect questions. For Question 2, our hypothesis was that the test anxiety component of the FLCAS would effectively predict the current anxiety level for grammar exercises. Speaking could be affected by both communication apprehension and fear of negative evaluation. Anxious individuals would have trouble communicating in a foreign language. Moreover, they are afraid of being judged by their peers, teachers or any native speaker. For Question 3, we hypothesized that fear of negative evaluation and communication apprehension would predict FLA in speaking exercises. Foreign language instruction often includes assessments that produce test anxiety and fear of negative evaluation. Learners may be concerned about the consequences of failing in the class, they may feel afraid that the teacher would correct their mistakes or their peers would laugh at them. For these reasons, for Question 4, we hypothesized that test anxiety and fear of negative evaluation can predict FLA in vocabulary exercises. Based on (Ismail and Hastings, 2019) and the previous research questions, we would like to address the anxiety level in an e-learning system regardless of the type of exercise. The eventual goal of this project is to develop means of mitigating anxiety when it occurs. Thus for Question 5, our hypothesis was that using the FLCAS, language difficulty self-report, system difficulty self-report, and the score of the exercise is effective to predict the anxiety level within an e-learning system.

We propose a novel design to detect FLA within the context of an e-learning system for English as a foreign language using sensor-free and sensor-lite measures. Our design uses FLCAS components (Horwitz, Horwitz and Cope, 1986) administered as a pre-test along with self-reports of language difficulty and system difficulty and the score on the current exercise (Ismail and Hastings, 2019).

2. METHOD

2.1 Participants

We recorded 30 participants who are non-native English speakers between the age of 18-54 years old. Their English proficiency language level was 17% beginner, 53% intermediate and 30% advanced. We conducted an observational study at software observation and usability lab. We paid $20 compensation for each participant.

2.2 Procedure

Each participant completed the FLCAS as a pre-test. Then they completed 27 exercises with the English E-learning System (EES). The exercises focused on listening, grammar, speaking, and vocabulary. After each exercise, the participants completed a brief self-report about their current level of anxiety as shown in Figure 1. The FLCAS and the self-report questions were presented in the participant's native language (Arabic, Chinese, Spanish, and Thai). The figure presents the English version of the self-report just for the purpose of this paper.

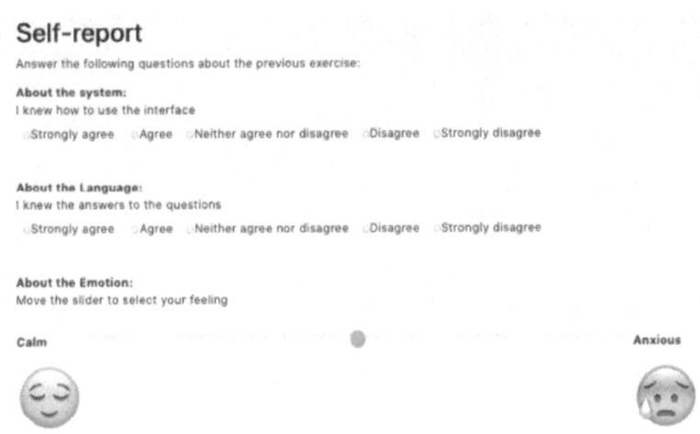

Figure 1. Level of anxiety self-report

2.3 Analyzing the Data

We did statistical analyses to understand the relationship between the FLCAS and the learner's current level of anxiety when using the e-learning system. We combined the FLCAS responses from the three main components: communication apprehension, fear of negative evaluation and test anxiety (Horwitz, Horwitz and Cope, 1986). We averaged the answers for each group (reversing scores where appropriate) and compared the results with the learner's current level of anxiety. Level of anxiety self-report, language difficulty, and system difficulty were coded from the participants' Likert scale responses. The score for each exercise for each participant was calculated as the percentage of correct answers. After that, we did regression, then we split the dataset into 80% trained and 20% tested data to check any overfitting.

3. RESULTS

3.1 FLA in Listening Exercises

To test our hypothesis that communication apprehension as measured by the FLCAS predicts anxiety level in a listening exercise, we did a linear regression with the average communication apprehension as the independent variable and level of anxiety self-report as the dependent variable. We used linear regression because we measure anxiety in a scale ratio from zero to hundred. The model provided a moderately good fit, R = 0.355. This predictor accounts for about 13% of the variation in anxiety, $R^2 = 12.6\%$, and $R^2(adj)=12.1\%$. The regression equation indicated that the model was a significant predictor of anxiety, $F(1, 179) = 25.647, p < 0.001$.

To evaluate the generalizability of the prediction we split the data into 80% training and 20% testing sets, and performed cross-validation by doing a Pearson correlation between the datasets and the dependent variable. We found a significant moderate positive correlation between the training dataset and the level of anxiety self-report, $p<0.001, r=0.370$. We found a significant moderate positive correlation between the test-set and the level of anxiety self-report, $p<0.013, r=0.395$.

3.2 FLA in Grammar Exercises

For our second research question, we hypothesized that average test anxiety would predict FLA in grammar exercises. To test the hypothesis, we did a linear regression with FLCAS test anxiety scores as the independent variable and level of anxiety self-report as the dependent variable. The model provided a good fit, $R = 0.423$. This predictor accounts for about 18% of the variation in the level of anxiety, $R^2 = 17.9\%$, and $R^2(adj)=17.3\%$. The regression equation indicated that the model was a significant predictor of anxiety, $F(1, 149) = 32.278, p < 0.001$.

To evaluate the generalization of this prediction we again did cross-validation using the 80/20 split mentioned above. We found a significant moderate positive correlation between the training data and the level of anxiety self-report $p<0.001, r=0.491$. However, we found no significant correlation between the test-set and the level of anxiety self-report $p<0.137, r=0.236$.

3.3 FLA in Speaking Exercises

For the third research question, we hypothesized that the average fear of negative evaluation and the average communication apprehension would predict FLA in speaking exercises. We did a multiple regression analysis with the average fear of negative evaluation and the average communication apprehension as the independent variables level of anxiety self-report as the dependent variable. The model provided a good fit, $R = .459$. These predictors account for about 21% of the variation in anxiety, $R^2 = 21.1\%$, and $R^2(adj)=20.3\%$. The regression equation indicated that the model was a significant predictor of anxiety, $F(2, 209) = 27.682, p < 0.001$.

On the 80/20 cross-validation split, we found a significant moderate positive correlation between the training set and the level of anxiety self-report, $p=0.001, r=0.466$. There was a significant moderate positive correlation between the test-set and the level of anxiety self-report, $p=0.008, r=0.436$.

3.4 FLA in Vocabulary Exercises

To predict the anxiety level when the learners do vocabulary exercises, we hypothesized that the average test anxiety and average fear of negative evaluation would be effective. We did a multiple regression analysis with the average test anxiety and the average fear of negative evaluation as the independent variables and the level of anxiety self-report as the dependent variable. The model provided a good fit, R = 0.502. This predictor accounts for about 25% of the variation in anxiety, $R^2 = 25.2\%$, and $R^2(adj)=22.6\%$. The regression equation indicated that the model was a significant predictor of anxiety, $F(2, 59) = 9.595, p < 0.001$.

To assess the generalization of the prediction, we again did a Pearson correlation between the training set, test-set and the level of anxiety self-report. We found a significant moderate positive correlation between the training set and the level of anxiety self-report $p=0.001$, $r=0.516$, but there was no significant correlation between the test-set and the level of anxiety self-report, $p=0.132$, $r=0.407$.

3.5 FLA in an E-learning System

To predict the anxiety level regardless of the type of exercise, we used the level of anxiety self-report as dependent variable and the FLCAS components as independent variable. We found that this predictor account for about 20% of the variation in anxiety. Thus for overall FLA within an e-learning system, we hypothesized that using FLCAS, language difficulty self-report, system difficulty self-report, and the exercise score would be effective predictors regardless of the type of exercise. We did multiple regression with those items as the independent variables and level of anxiety self-report as the dependent variable. The model provided a good fit, $R = 0.653$. These predictors account for about 43% of the variation in anxiety, $R^2 = 42.7\%$, and $R^2(adj)=42.2\%$. The regression equation, which indicated that the model was a significant predictor of anxiety $F(5, 599) = 88.404, p < 0.001$ is shown in Table 1. Average test anxiety was excluded because the tolerance was 0 which meant that the variance in predictor level of anxiety self-report was already contained in, or redundant with, the other predictors.

Table 1. FLCAS to predict FLA within an e-learning system

	Unstandardized Coefficients			
Term	B	Std. Error	t-value	p-value
Constant	-30.746	3.476	-8.844	<0.001
Fear of negative evaluation	7.853	1.102	7.125	<0.001
Communication apprehension	0.899	1.43	0.629	0.53
Language difficulty	11.331	1.01	11.223	<0.001
System difficulty	3.959	1.168	3.388	<0.001
Score	-0.453	0.232	-1.956	0.051

We split the dataset into trained and tested data. We did cross-validation to evaluate the prediction and prevent any overfitting. Then we did a Pearson correlation and found a significant moderate positive correlation between the trained data and the level of anxiety self-report, $p<0.001$, $r=0.66$. We found a significant moderate positive correlation between the test data and the level of anxiety self-report, $p=0.001$, $r=0.628$.

4. DISCUSSION

Through this study, we detected foreign language anxiety in the context of an e-learning system. We used the FLCAS as the main medium for predicting the learner's current level of anxiety. The FLCAS has been shown to be a reliable measure for foreign language in the *classroom* (Horwitz, Horwitz and Cope, 1986) but in this study we have demonstrated that it can be used to predict anxiety in an e-learning context as well.

For the first research question, we hypothesized that the average communication apprehension questions would give us a prediction about the learner's anxiety level in the listening exercise. Our hypothesis was supported, confirming (Horwitz, Horwitz and Cope, 1986; Atasheneh and Izadi, 2012) which indicated that listening is a factor of the communication apprehension. This provides an indication that regardless of the medium for learning --- in a classroom or through an e-learning system --- anxiety production would be the same.

Based on (Bodie and Villaume, 2003) people are less apprehensive when they communicate in an interpersonal situation and they become more anxious in public. This would explain the moderate correlation between the training and test data with the level of anxiety self-report. The listening exercise is within an e-learning system so the learner interacts with a computer without any connections with other people. The effect of communication apprehension is based on the habituation of previous listening exercises in class. Consequently, modeling FLA within a listening exercise can be effectively done using communication apprehension answers from the FLCAS. Using grammar in a foreign language is a complex task which frequently causes frustration for the learner in foreign language classroom (Mufidah, 2016). Research has identified grammar as the most difficult aspect of the English proficiency test (Mufidah, 2016). We hypothesized that average test anxiety from the FLCAS would predict the anxiety level in a grammar exercise. The analysis partially supported our hypotheses. The regression model was promising with moderate prediction. Nevertheless, the test data did not show a significant correlation with the level of anxiety self-report. We are using only one predictor which may require more variables to increase the prediction. Moreover, the questions in the test anxiety section are focused on worrying about the consequences of failure, forgetting known material, and getting more confused the more the learner studies. These items do not apply to the grammar exercises within the e-learning system because there is no effect of this study on failing, and there is no studying related to these exercises. There are two directions to take regarding predicting the FLA within a grammar exercise: either getting more data then check the prediction or add more predictors.

Foreign language speaking anxiety is a common topic discussed by researchers. Communication apprehension and fear of negative evaluation are the main speaking anxiety producers (Rafada and Madini, 2017b). Researchers found that a major source of FLA is the lack of automaticity (Balemir, 2009). Other aspect that affects speaking anxiety are communication and sociolinguistic competence (Balemir, 2009). Negative feedback from the teacher or the peer induces anxiety and prevents the learner from speaking in class (Rafada and Madini, 2017b). In our study, we hypothesized that fear of negative evaluation and communication apprehension is effective for predicting speaking anxiety in the context of an e-learning system. Our results supported the hypotheses and confirmed the previous research (Horwitz, Horwitz and Cope, 1986; Balemir, 2009; Rafada and Madini, 2017b) about the relationship of foreign language speaking anxiety, fear of negative evaluation and communication apprehension. We chose these two predictors because feeling worried about negative feedback would produce unwillingness to communicate which could prevent the learner from engaging in social activities (Rafada and Madini, 2017b).

(Chen, 2015) found that test anxiety and fear of negative evaluation is significantly correlated with vocabulary anxiety. To address the anxiety level in a vocabulary exercise, we hypothesized that average test anxiety and average fear of negative evaluation would be effective predictors. The results partially support the hypotheses. The training data showed a moderate positive correlation with the level of anxiety self-report while the test data did not show significance. We believe the results may be due to the small size of the dataset. There are only two vocabulary exercises and 30 participants so the total size of the dataset may not be sufficient. We need to investigate these predictors with more data to figure out if the amount of data is the problem or the predictors are not effective.

Our last research question was predicting the anxiety level in an e-learning system regardless of the type of exercise. Based on (McIntyre and Garder, 1994), when a participant is anxious in one situation, they are likely to be anxious in a similar context. (Ismail and Hastings, 2019) found that language difficulty self-report, system difficulty self-report, and the exercise score were effective for measuring anxiety in an e-learning system. Thus, we hypothesized that combination of FLCAS, language difficulty self-report, system difficulty self-report, and exercise score would be effective for predicting FLA. The hypothesis was supported because the training data and the test data were positively correlated with level of anxiety self-report.

We plan to use these indicators in the future to build an intelligent tutoring system for English as a second language that can predict anxiety level and work to remediate it. We propose to use animated pedagogical agent that provides emotional support to reduce FLA.

5. CONCLUSION AND FUTURE WORK

Foreign language anxiety hinders language learning. It produces a negative effect even after the stressor is gone. In this research, we studied indicators from different components of the FLCAS of learner anxiety level. Using multiple regression, we found that FLCAS components could provide a sensor-free predictor for foreign language anxiety within listening and speaking exercises. We found a sensor-lite predictor for FLA regardless of the type of exercise by including self-report of language difficulty, system difficulty, and the score of the exercise in addition to the FLCAS components. We suggest giving the FLCAS as a pre-test and using it to predict the anxiety level in the context of an e-learning system.

The main limitation of this work is that it does not include writing and reading exercises which are primary components in ESL teaching. But we believe that a sensor-lite method could predict FLA for these types of exercises as well. The dataset was rather small for some of the exercises which may have kept the test data from giving significant predictions.

For future work, we will build an intelligent tutoring system that detects FLA using sensor-free and sensor-lite anxiety indicators. This system will be able to recognize learner anxiety and change its behavior to overcome and eventually eliminate FLA.

ACKNOWLEDGEMENT

This project was partially supported by a grant from College of Computing and Digital Media at DePaul University. And thanking Media Semantics for providing us with a free license for the animated agent application which used in the e-learning system.

REFERENCES

Alemi, M., Meghdari, A. and Ghazisaedy, M. (2014). The Affect of Employing Humanoid Robots for Teaching English on Students' Anxiety and Attitude, *Proceedings of 2014 Second RSI/ISM International Conference on Robotics and Mechatronics*. Tehran, Iran, pp. 754–759.

American Psychiatric Association (2013). *Diagnostic and Statistical Manual of Mental Disorders (DSM-5)*, American Psychiatric Association Publishers, Washington, D.C., USA.

Atasheneh, N. and Izadi, A. (2012). The Role of Teachers in Reducing/Increasing Listening Comprehension Test Anxiety: A Case of Iranian EFL Learners, *English Language Teaching*, Vol. 5, No. 3, pp.178-187.

Balemir, S. H. (2009). The Sources of Foreign Language Speaking Anxiety and the Relationship Between Proficiency Level and Degree of Foreign Language Speaking Anxiety. *(Doctoral dissertation, Bilkent University)*.

Bigdeli, S. (2010). Affective Learning: The Anxiety Construct in Adult Learners, *Procedia-Social and Behavioral Sciences*, 9, pp. 674–678.

Bodie, G. D. and Villaume, W. A. (2003). Aspects of Receiving Information: The relationship Between Listening Preferences, Communication Apprehension, Receiver Apprehension, and Communicator Style, *International Journal of Listening*, Vol. 17, No. 1, pp. 47–67.

Chen, C.-M. and Lee, T.-H. (2011). Emotion Recognition and Communication for Reducing Second-language Speaking Anxiety in a Web-based One-to-one Synchronous Learning Environment, *British Journal of Educational Technology*, 42, pp. 417–440.

Chen, X. (2015). A Tentative Study of Vocabulary Learning Anxiety in College English Learning in China, *International Journal of English Linguistics*. Vol. 5, No. 1, p. 104.

D'Mello, S. and Graesser, A. C. (2014). Feeling, Thinking, and Computing with Affect-Aware Learning Technologies, *The Oxford handbook of Affective Computing*. pp. 419-434.

Dewaele, J.-M., Petrides, K. V. and Furnham, A. (2008). Effects of Trait Emotional Intelligence and Sociobiographical Variables on Communicative Anxiety and Foreign Language Anxiety Among Adult Multilinguals: A Review and Empirical Investigation, *Language Learning*, Vol. 58, No. 4, pp. 911–960.

Gregersen, T. (2006). The Despair of Disparity: The Connecttion Between Foreign Language Anxiety and the Recognition of Proficiency Differences in L2 Skills, *Lenguas Modernas*, No. 31, pp. 7–20.

Horwitz, E. K., Horwitz, M. B. and Cope, J. (1986). Foreign Language Classroom Anxiety, *The Modern Language Journal*, Vol. 70, No. 2, pp. 125-132.

Huang, H.-T. D. (2018). Modeling the Relationships Between Anxieties and Performance in Second/foreign Language Speaking Assessment, *Learning and Individual Differences.* Vol. 63, pp. 44–56.

Huang, Y. M., & Huang, Y. M. (2015). A Scaffolding Strategy to Develop Handheld Sensor-based Vocabulary Games for Improving Students Learning Motivation and Performance, *Educational Technology Research and Development.* Vol. 63, No. 5, pp. 691–708.

Imani, M. and Montazer, G. A. (2019). A Survey of Emotion Recognition Methods with Emphasis on E-Learning Environments, *Journal of Network and Computer Applications*, Vol. 147, p. 102423.

Ismail, D. and Hastings, P. (2019). Identifying Foreign Language Anxiety when Using an E-learning System, *Proceedings of 2019 Conference On Interfaces and Human Computer Interaction.* Porto, Portugal. pp.131-140.

Kralova, Z. and Petrova, G. (2017). Causes and Consequences of Foreign Language Anxiety, *XLinguae*, Vol. 10, No. 3, pp. 110–122.

Lai, A.-F. and Wen, S.-S. (2012). Evaluating an Online Role Playing Game for Promoting the Elementary School Students English Speaking Abilities, Proceedings of 8th International Conference on Information Science and Digital Content Technology. Jeju, Korea. Vol. 3, pp. 610-615.

Levitt, E. E. (2015). *The Psychology of Anxiety*. Routledge Publishers, London ; New York, USA.

Lin, H.-C. K., Chao, C.-J. and Huang, T.-C. (2015). From a Perspective on Foreign Language Learning Anxiety to Develop an Affective Tutoring System, *Educational Technology Research and Development.* Vol. 63, No. 5, pp. 727–747.

Liu, H. (2013). Effects of Foreign Language Anxiety and Perceived Competence on Learning Strategy Use, *International Journal of English Linguistics.* Vol. 3, No. 3, p 76.

Liu, M. (2006). Anxiety in EFL Classrooms: Causes and Consequences, *TESL Reporter,* Vol. 39, No. 1, pp. 13–32.

Liu, M. and Huang, W. (2011). An Exploration of Foreign Language Anxiety and English Learning Motivation, *Education Research International,* Vol. 2011.

Liu, M. and Jackson, J. (2008). An Exploration of Chinese EFL Learners' Unwillingness to Communicate and Foreign Language Anxiety, *The Modern Language Journal*. Vol. 92, No. 1, pp. 71–86.

Lopatovska, I. and Arapakis, I. (2011). Theories, Methods and Current Research on Emotions in Library and Information Science, Information Retrieval and Human--Computer Interaction, *Information Processing & Management.* Vol. 47,No. 4, pp. 575–592.

Lu, Y. T., Chang, C. W. and Chen, G. D. (2007). Using a Programmable Storytelling Robot to Motivate Learning Second Language, *Proceedings The 7th IEEE International Conference on Advanced Learning Technologies*, Niigata, Japan, pp. 841–844.

Luo, P. et al. (2018) State Anxiety Down-regulates Empathic Responses: Electrophysiological Evidence, *Frontiers in Human Neuroscience*. Vol. 12, p. 502.

McIntyre, P. D. and Garder, R. (1994) The Subtle Effects of Language Anxiety on Cognitive Processing in the Second Language, *Language Learning*. Vol. 44, No. 2, pp. 283–305.

Mufidah, N. (2016). The Effect of Gamification on English language Anxiety and Grammar Achievement. *(Doctoral dissertation, Widya Mandala Surabaya Catholic University).*

Rafada, S. and Madini, A. (2017a). Effective Solutions for Reducing Saudi Learners' Speaking Anxiety in EFL Classrooms. *Arab World English Journal (AWEJ)*, Vol. 8, No. 2, pp. 308–322.

Rafada, S. and Madini, A. (2017b). Major Causes of Saudi Learners' Speaking Anxiety in EFL Classrooms, *International Journal of English Language Education,* Vol. 5, No. 1, pp. 54–71.

Shao, K., Yu, W. and Ji, Z. (2013). An Exploration of Chinese EFL Students' Emotional Intelligence and Foreign Language Anxiety, *The Modern Language Journal*. Vol. 97, No. 4, pp. 917–929.

Sparks, R. L. et al. (2018). High School Spanish Students and Foreign Language Reading Anxiety: Déjà Vu All Over Again All Over Again, *The Modern Language Journal*. Vol. 102, No. 3, pp. 533–556.

DATA ANALYTICS WITH MLV-VIEWER

Carlos Manuel Oliveira Alves[1], Manuel Pérez Cota[2,*] and Miguel Ramón González Castro[2,*]
[1]*Instituto Politécnico de Castelo Branco, Av. D. Pedro Álvares Cabral 12, 6000-Castelo Branco, Portugal*
[2]*Universidade de Vigo, Rúa Torrecedeira 86; 36208 -Vigo, Spain*
[*]*Dr.*

ABSTRACT

Information visualization is defined as interactive visual representations supported by the computer, in order to increase cognition. The tools and methods applied can help to accelerate the understanding of a large volume of data, improving understanding, especially with multidimensional data sets. Visual analysis methods allow decision makers to combine flexibility, creativity and human knowledge with the enormous storage and processing resources of today's computers to gain insight into complex problems. If we add data mining to advanced visual interfaces, decision makers will be able to interact directly with data analysis, adapting to their tastes and needs. The MLV-Viewer is a decision support system, and its data analytics aspect will be described in this article.

KEYWORDS

Data Analytics in DSS, DSS, Big Data Visualization

1. INTRODUCTION

In the late 1960s, a new type of model-oriented information system emerged, Decision Support Systems (DSS) or also called Management Decision Systems (MDS) (Müller et al., 2016). Peter Keen and Charles Stabell, the pioneers of the DSS concept, point out that the concept has evolved from theoretical studies of organizational decision-making at the Carnegie Institute of Technology. However, the origin of the DSS goes back to the beginning of the 20th century, when the military objective was dominant. One of the oldest DSSs was the SAGE (semi-automatic terrestrial environment), designed to unify different images throughout the area and used in the Cold War. The SAGE was the largest computer ever built. According to another approach, the first DSS may have its origins in LEO I (Lyons Electronic Office) in 1951.

Data visualization is a dynamic way to react quickly to new developments using either virtual environments or network technology or new computer graphics algorithms. The user, that is, the decision maker, initially gets a total idea about a scenario before focusing on the details, but the observation in a graphical model of the data provides part of the information. It can also be said that visualization does not just mean seeing, but allows the user to see what is not seen naturally. Visualization is nothing more than a graphical representation of data with the main objective of providing the user with a qualitative and easy understanding of the content of information (which can be data, relationships, perceptions or processes) (Kumar & Belwal, 2018), transforming objects, numbers and concepts into a form that can be easily interpreted by the human eye. From a set of data, (Katrina E. Barkwell, 2018) says that the essential role of visualization is nothing more than visualizing data to tell stories, selecting, filtering and transforming that data and choosing the correct visualization type (such as bars, line or bubble charts).

The visualization techniques aim to simplify the data and that the representation of models provides relevant information from that same data, facilitating the production of ideas in a short time, especially if we have a large volume of data. That is why the integration of visualization techniques in dynamic and complex systems is highly recommended for data abstraction, allowing the user to quickly navigate through the wide range of data. However, data visualization requires interaction between the user and the system (Ellouzi, Ltifi, & Ayed, 2016).

The visualization of data in the DSS, despite increasing the requirements for modeling and use, also allows the extraction of relevant information and the interaction with them (Grignard, Drogoul, & Zucker, 2013). In this way, visual information combined with interaction techniques allows the user to obtain knowledge through visual representations, viewing, searching and analyzing a large volume of data quickly and clearly.

According to (Cota, Manuel Pérez; Castro & Domínguez, 2014), visual analysis is important for analysts and decision makers, reducing research by synthesizing large volumes of data as well as facilitating the task of exploration. It is also said that pattern recognition and inference of relationships between data is facilitated through visualizations using graphical interfaces, thereby amplifying cognitive factors and exposing the relationships between the various entities extracted from the data, producing useful information and minimizing the difficulty analysis. Visual analysis systems need to have the ability to identify patterns hidden in the data so that the decision maker can build knowledge from a large volume of data (Yan et al., 2012). Combining data mining algorithms with data visualization, we can reduce the information obtained but make the patterns more visible (Jorgensen et al., 2018), that is, the extraction of information about large volumes of data must use computational data mining methods.

To support knowledge discovery and decision making from large-scale data sets (Yan et al., 2012), new visual analysis systems need to be able to identify hidden patterns in the data which can be critical for further analysis.

In order to extract useful information from large volumes of data, computational data mining methods have the advantage over visualization, as they quickly capture data patterns (Jorgensen et al., 2018). By combining data mining algorithms with visualization, the information obtained can be reduced to make the patterns more visible.

Data mining is a key concept in Big Data Analytics consisting of the application of data science techniques to analyze and explore large volumes of data in order to find useful and significant patterns in that data as a way to facilitate the task of the decision maker, offering dashboards, graphs, or reports (Huru, Leordeanu, Apostol, & Cristea, 2018). For that, mathematical and statistical methods must be used to understand the data, simulate scenarios, validate hypotheses and make predictions, mainly to perform four types of analysis:

- descriptive analysis: transforms data into meaningful information for the purposes of interpretation, reporting, monitoring and visualization through statistical graphic tools, such as pie charts, bar charts and panels;
- predictive analysis: it is usually defined as an extrapolation of data based on the available data to ensure better decision making;
- prescriptive analysis: it is associated with descriptive and predictive analysis, offering options on how to obtain future benefits or mitigate a future risk, detailing the implications of each decision option;
- exploratory analysis: view unexpected or hidden relationships between data.

This prototype aims to build a universal DSS (MLV-Viewer, meaning Multi Level Visualization Viewer), multi-platform, free of cost and adaptable to the decision maker needs. In this article, the topic will be presented in the "I-Introduction" section, followed by a literature review on the topic "data mining" in the "II-Literature Review" section, in the section "III- New Approach: MLV-Viewer" the prototype will be described and, finally, in the section" IV- Conclusion and Future Work ", some conclusions and future works.

2. LITERATURE REVIEW

According to (Ellouzi et al., 2016) (Grignard et al., 2013) (Cota, Manuel Pérez; Castro & Domínguez, 2014) (Yan et al., 2012) (Jorgensen et al., 2018), DSS provide support for semi-structured and unstructured decision problems, usually interactive computer-based systems to help decision makers use various tools (such as communication, data, document, knowledge technologies and modeling) to assist in decision making in several areas, and the main components are: decision maker; data base; models and procedures; Software.

Decision makers demand better identification of metrics applied to data in order to be able to interpret these complex patterns more easily. For this reason, the area of data mining has been heavily invested, but there is still a gap between efforts to visualize these patterns and complex data recently extracted (Ashraf & Khan, 2015).

In the work carried out by (Groumpos, 2016), four visual analysis tools were developed to control which layers on a map the user displays to understand the impacts on black ice, these tools are: visual analysis tool, interpolation tool, animation tool and Analysis tool Decision Support.

The study presented by (Alves & Cota, 2018) states that the use of dynamic symbols (such as size, color, shape or outlines), instead of static symbols, according to the information they represent conveys additional semantics. AgMine (Imen, Chang, Yang and Golchubian, 2016) has an architecture focused on: pre-processing of data sets; visualization of data in general lines; visualization of data using spatial interpolation; data mining; analysis and interpolation of scenarios. InVEST (Reschka, Bagschik, Ulbrich, Nolte and Maurer, 2015) exports and adapts the data to create various interactive and abstract data visualizations, using web programming languages. The study (Wu et al., 2008) presents the top 10 algorithms for data mining for both forecasting and interpolation, namely the average, the weighted average, the linear regression, the expected maximum and the multiple imputation.

3. DATA ANALYTICS WITH MLV-VIEWER

The prototype developed, MLV-Viewer, and presented below, allows the user to dynamically and interactively select the data he/she wants to view and how to view it.

The developed prototype works in a web environment with a MySQL server as a database system (or any other database management system as long as it uses the SQL language), uses PHP and JavaScript as programming languages, uses canvasJs, Chart.js, JpGraph, HIGHCHARTS and three.js as graphic libraries (see Figure 1).

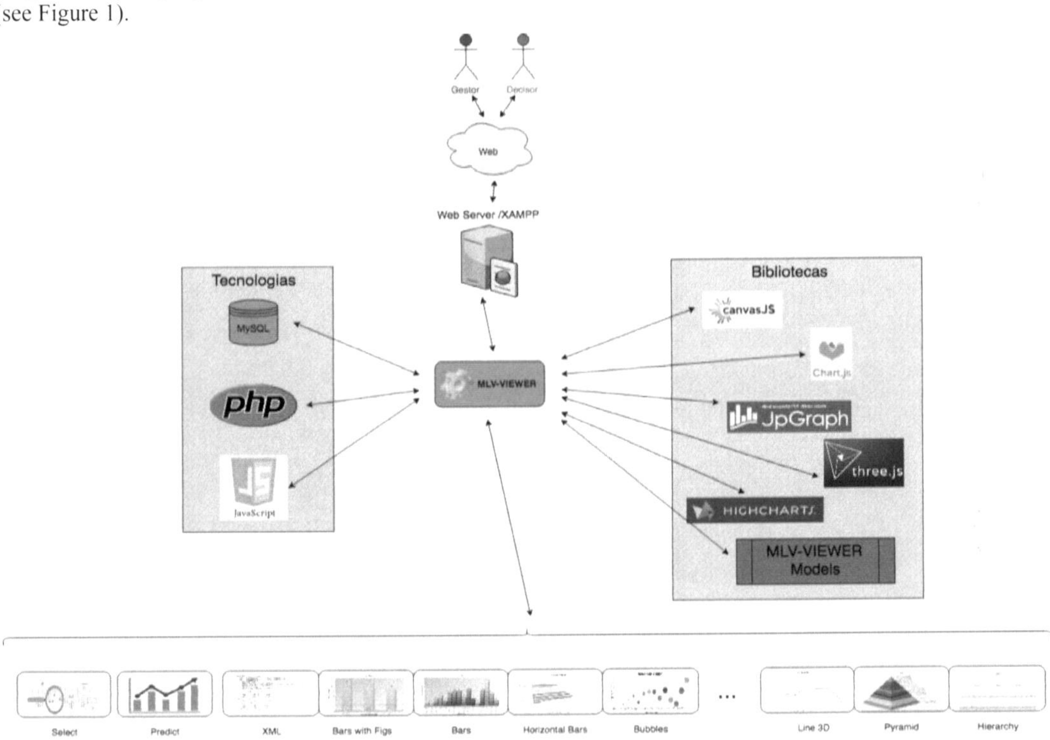

Figure 1. MLV-Viewer Architecture

If the data has not been previously imported into the MySQL database, then he can import both the logical structure (contained in an XML schema file) and the data (contained in an XML file). The MLV-Viewer also allows the export of data to XML and XSD. The user will be able to visualize these data in 1D 2D, 2D + 1, 3D and 3D + 1, 3D+2, 3D+3, 3D+4, as well as to analyze the data, and these are presented in 2D or 3D+1 format (see Figure 2).

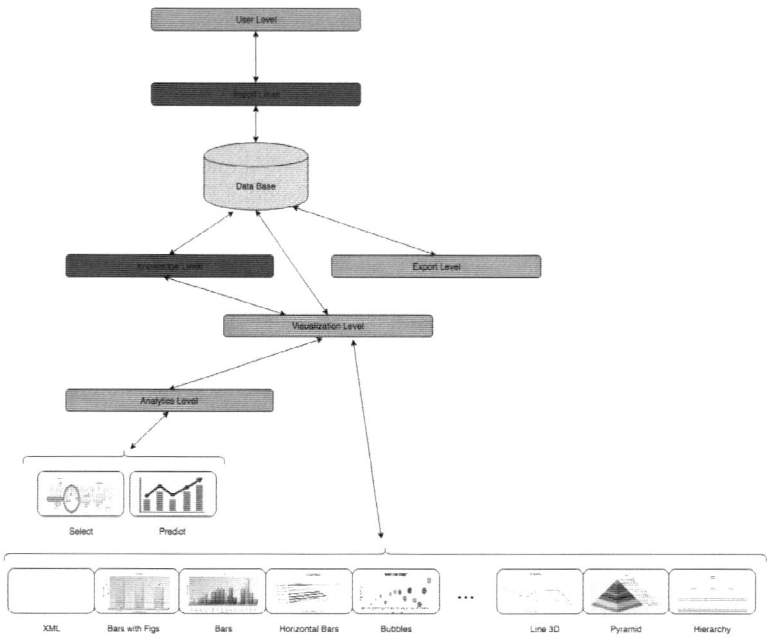

Figure 2. MLV-Viewer Ontology

The user has at his disposal a set of "smart" visualizations (due to the pairing between products / data) and also self-descriptive (when presenting the image associated with that data / product), see Figure 3.

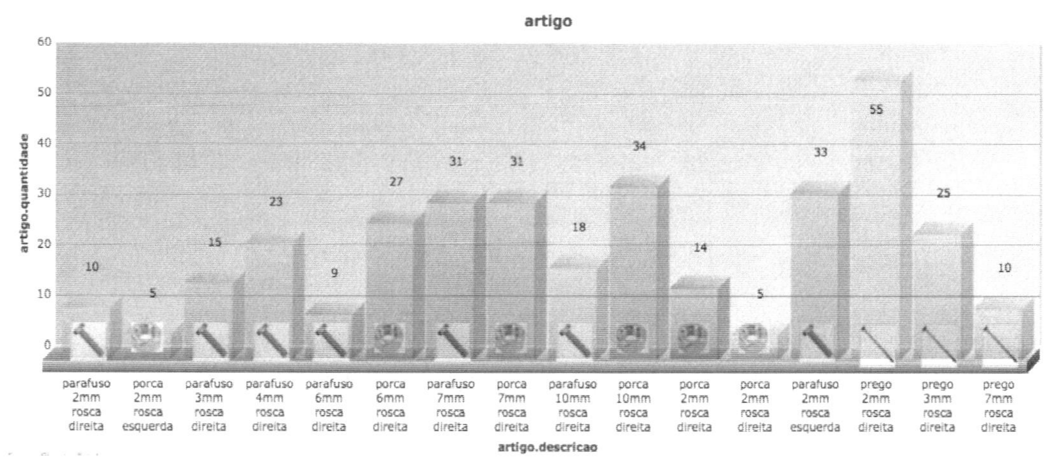

Figure 3. 2D image with bars

To describe the data mining of the MLV-Viewer, the data referring to the products "screw", "nut" and "nail" were chosen, this choice is due to the fact that they are products easily understood by all, but at the same time they can be as complex as you want.

In Figure 4, a 2D visualization, the products are presented in the form of stacked bars, and in this way it is easily noticeable to compare the existence in stock of the various products.

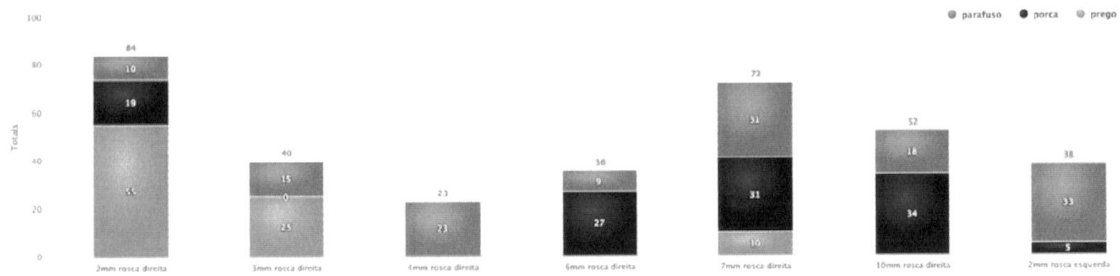

Figure 4. 2D data analysis with stacked bars

In Figure 5, it can be seen quickly and easily that for the products "screw", "nut" and "nail" there is a discrepancy in quantity in stock for the different measures ("2mm", "3mm", "4mm" , ...) displayed on the bars or through the lines that represent the minimum, average and maximum quantities for each of the different measures. It is also possible to view the total quantity for each of the products in the "cheese".

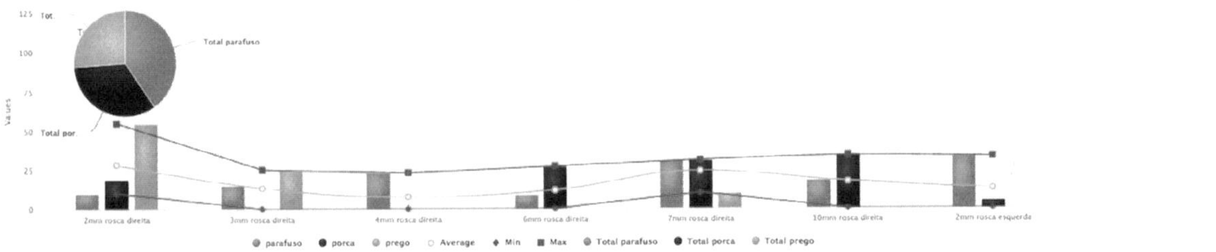

Figure 5. 2D data analysis with bars

Figure 6 is similar to Figure 5, but the bars have been replaced by dots, keeping all other information.

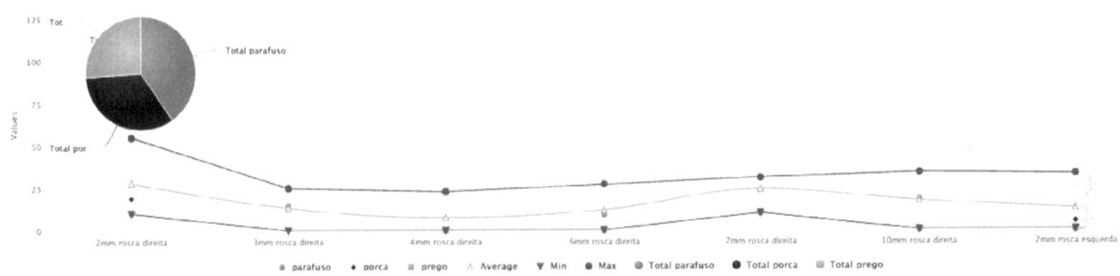

Figure 6. 2D data analysis with points

In Figure 7, a 2D + 1 visualization is achieved by varying the size of the stitch according to the quantity of the respective product.

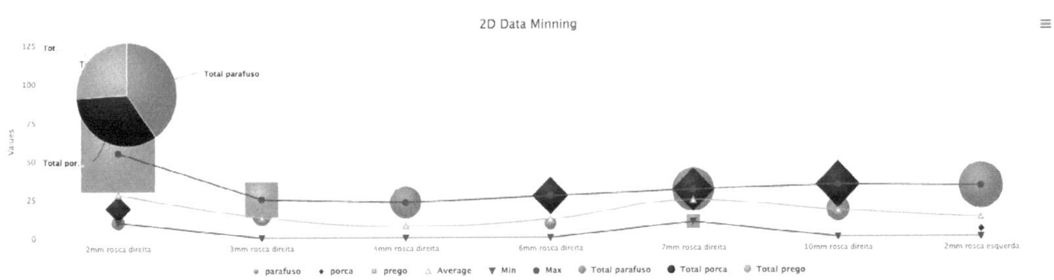

Figure 7. 2D+1 data analysis with radius points

A 3D view in which the user can rotate and zoom the view is very important when you want to do data mining, and if it is complemented with + 1D even more. In the following figure (Figure 8), the user can dynamically choose what to display on each axis (numeric or word) and choose another data / field as the fourth dimension that will be displayed as a point with dimension / radius according to the magnitude of that data / field. It is easy to see through this visualization that there is a very big difference between "left" and "right" thread products, as well as between the various measures (represented in the ZZ axis).

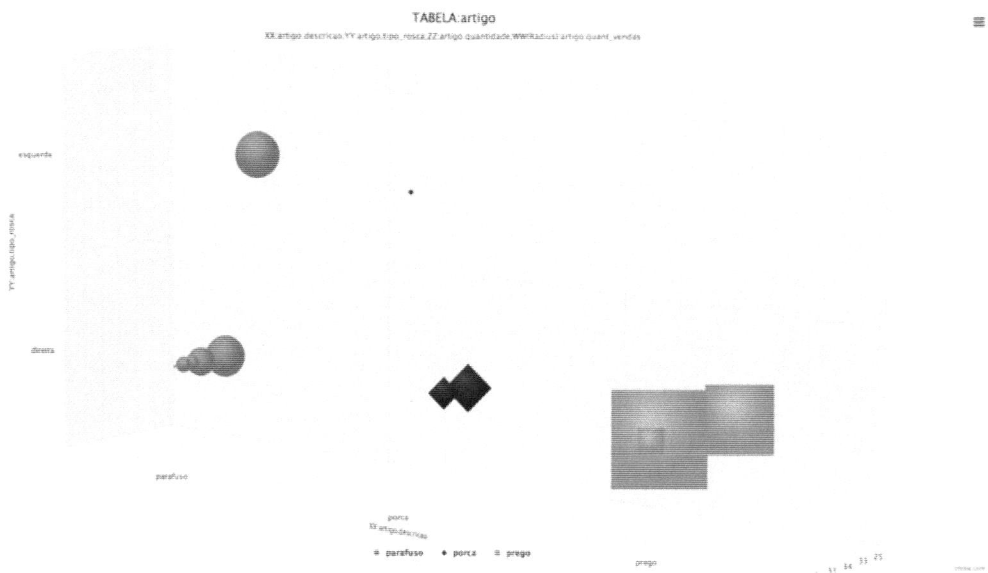

Figure 8. 3D+1 Data Mining "Radius Points"

At this stage of the implementation of this prototype, the objective was to allow the user, regardless of his competencies and privileges within the company, to view the data he selected most in a dynamic and easy way associated with meaningful visualizations.

4. CONCLUSION AND FUTURE WORK

It is important that a user can view what he wants, when he wants and how he wants. If these visualizations are associated, help for an easy interpretation of the data, even better. An incorrect choice of display type can prevent you from obtaining the desired information. The development of a software tool to support the design of the user interface of a DSS is not sufficient in itself and should, as far as possible, meet the specifics of each user. For example, while information may be displayed graphically, users may not be able to understand everything that is being displayed or they may be overwhelmed with too much data to be displayed on the monitor. A good system should help users to find meaningful information in a simple way, it should be friendly and customizable, and also suggest the best visualization to obtain that information.

Visualizing the information contained in the data by means of graphs or images is a technology in development that transforms traditional methods of observing and analyzing relational data tables so that people can discover relationships and structure in a more intuitive way. Thus, hidden information can be easily discovered. A good DSS visualization tool can be very important and advantageous in making decisions, supporting managers and leaders to make the right decision. As far as possible, DSS should be easy, simple, effective and customizable. Data visualization and, therefore, information play a fundamental role in decision making, supported by decision support systems, but we believe that the challenges are still in the beginning.

With the MLV-Viewer, it was intended to implement a dynamic and interactive system, in which the user can choose the best way to view the data. Converting simple data into meaningful information through data mining. MLV-Viewer has the following advantages: multiplatform; free; adaptable to the user; in real time; a system that allows importing and exporting data, various types of visualizations and with multiple dimensions, making analysis and forecasting of data; universal. As disadvantages can be pointed out: lacking the necessary tests, both of robustness and usability, among others; allow more user configurations.

As the future work it is intended that this prototype advises the user on a set of views that are more recommended or recommended for the industry in question. On the other hand, it is intended to implement more methods of data mining and to develop methods of extrapolation and data prediction.

REFERENCES

Ashraf, S., & Khan, S. A. (2015). Visualizations-based analysis of Telco data for business intelligence. *Proceedings of the IEEE International Conference on Software Engineering and Service Sciences, ICSESS, 2015-Novem*, 242–246. https://doi.org/10.1109/ICSESS.2015.7339046

Cota, Manuel Pérez; Castro, M. R. G., & Domínguez, J. Á. (2014). Importance of visualization usage in enterprise decision making environements. In 2014 9th Iberian Conference on Information Systems and Technologies (CISTI) (Ed.), *Importance of visualization usage in enterprise decision making environements*. Retrieved from 2014 9th Iberian Conference on Information Systems and Technologies (CISTI)

Ellouzi, H. ;, Ltifi, H. ;, & Ayed, M. Ben. (2016). New Multi-Agent architecture of visual Intelligent Decision Support Systems application in the medical field. *IEEE/ACS International Conference on Computer Systems and Applications, AICCSA (2016) 2016-July*. https://doi.org/10.1109/AICCSA.2015.7507135

Grignard, A., Drogoul, A., & Zucker, J. (2013). *A Model-View / Controller approach to support visualization and online data analysis of Agent-Based Simulations*. 233–236. 2013 IEEE RIVF International Conference on Computing & Communication Technologies - Research, Innovation, and Vision for the Future (RIVF).

Groumpos, P. P. (2016). *Conceptual Modeling and Decision Making Support Systems for Complex Dynamical Systems : A Critical Overview* (IEEE, ed.). IEEE.

Huru, D., Leordeanu, C., Apostol, E., & Cristea, V. (2018). BigClue: Towards a generic IoT cross-domain data processing platform. *Proceedings - 2018 IEEE 14th International Conference on Intelligent Computer Communication and Processing, ICCP 2018*, 427–434. https://doi.org/10.1109/ICCP.2018.8516597

Jorgensen, M., Spohn, J., Bunn, C., Dong, S., Li, X., & Kaeli, D. (2018). An interactive big data processing/visualization framework. In U. 2017 2017 IEEE MIT Undergraduate Research Technology Conference (Ed.), *2017 IEEE MIT Undergraduate Research Technology Conference, URTC 2017* (Vol. 2018-Jan, pp. 1–4). https://doi.org/10.1109/URTC.2017.8284188

Kumar, S. M., & Belwal, M. (2018). Performance dashboard: Cutting-edge business intelligence and data visualization. *Proceedings of the 2017 International Conference On Smart Technology for Smart Nation, SmartTechCon 2017*, 1201–1207. https://doi.org/10.1109/SmartTechCon.2017.8358558

Müller, H., Reihs, R., Posch, A. E., Kremer, A., Ulrich, D., & Zatloukal, K. (2016). *Data Driven GUI Design and Visualization for a NGS based Clinical Decision Support System*. 2–7. https://doi.org/10.1109/IV.2016.79

Wu, X., Kumar, V., Ross, Q. J., Ghosh, J., Yang, Q., Motoda, H., ... Steinberg, D. (2008). Top 10 algorithms in data mining. *Knowledge and Information Systems*, *14*(1), 1–37. https://doi.org/10.1007/s10115-007-0114-2

Yan, X., Qiao, M., Li, J., Simpson, T. W., Stump, G. M., & Zhang, X. (2012). A work-centered visual analytics model to support engineering design with interactive visualization and data-mining. *Proceedings of the Annual Hawaii International Conference on System Sciences*, 1845–1854. https://doi.org/10.1109/HICSS.2012.87

PLACE THE CONTROLLERS WHEREVER YOU WANT: USABILITY AND USER EXPERIENCE OF CUSTOMISABLE MUSICAL DEVICES

Matteo Fanchin[1], Patrik Pluchino[2] and Luciano Gamberini[2]
[1]*Department of General Psychology*
[2]*Department of General Psychology, Human Inspired Technology (HIT) Research Centre*
Via Venezia 8, Padova, 35131, Italy

ABSTRACT

The current study investigates how different types of multi-effects guitar devices can affect users' evaluations of usability and user experience. Participants were asked to interact with three different multi-effects devices while playing an electric guitar. Typically multi-effect pedalboards are used by musicians to modify an instrument sound. These tools allow us to distort notes or to change the duration of the produced sounds. The main difference between the three devices pertains to the placement of their controllers: *fixed-pedals* on the ground; *movable-pedals* on the ground; *movable* and *wireless pedals* that can be freely placed, at the discretion of the user (e.g., on the guitar, the user's body). The second and third devices were both prototypes designed and developed by the first author. Several usability dimensions (e.g., ease of use, enjoyment, etc.) were evaluated (i.e., ad hoc questionnaire). Besides the musical experience also the attitude towards novel technologies (i.e., personal innovativeness) was collected. Overall, the two prototypes appeared as easier to use and enjoyable compared to the *fixed-pedals* device. Furthermore, participants with high levels of personal innovativeness perceived the devices as more controllable. The opportunity of customizing the placement of the pedals positively affected the evaluations. The study outcomes lay the foundations for the implementation of new prototypes that could be tailored based on musicians' needs. The result will be an increment in usability and a more positive user experience.

KEYWORDS

Prototyping, Human-Computer Interaction, Usability, User Experience

1. INTRODUCTION

Nowadays, new technologies are changing not only the way we interact with musical instruments, and their hardware-related devices, but also the actual physical features of the instruments themselves (Saffer, 2008; Moggridge and Atkinson, 2007; Medeiros et al., 2014; Holland et al., 2013, 2016; Tanaka, 2019). Contemporary musical instruments are increasingly digitized and they become closely linked to computers (Cook, 2017). Effects units, music software, digital audio workstations, pre-amplifiers are only a few of the tools that musicians have to learn and deeply understand, in terms of their functioning, both in a solo performance or while they are playing in a band (Wessel and Wright, 2002; Paine, 2013). Furthermore, a recent paper highlighted the vision and challenges related to the Internet of Musical Things (i.e., IoMusT; Turchet et al., 2018). This domain considers, for instance, smart instruments, wireless and wired networks, and service for controlling parameters of Musical Things. The aim is enriching the overall experience of concerts (i.e., augmented and immersive), increasing audience involvement, improving e-learning of music, and the quality of music studio production (Turchet et al., 2018; Turchet, 2018). This new perspective goes in the direction of design (Morreale, De Angeli, and O'Modhrain, 2014) and developing products that could be easier to use, accepted, and more adaptable to the users' needs. In such circumstances, the musicians will consider these devices as tools that could enhance their performance skills, and as a consequence, their satisfaction within the performance. An additional result would be a higher intention to use. Fernandes and Holmes (Fernandes and Holmes, 2002) underlined how a musical device that does not match the above-mentioned requirements hinders the user's creative process by increasing cognitive demands. In contrast, user interfaces that are intuitive and clear, minimize interruptions to the spontaneity of performance or composition. According to Wanderley and Orio (2002), HCI methodology could be a suitable tool to evaluate the perceived usability and user experience of musical interfaces.

1.1 Usability and User Experience

When designing interactive systems, one of the main goals is that they should be usable for the users. The usability evaluation has to take into account the context of the application, the end-users, and the characteristics of the systems themselves (Sharp, Preece, and Rogers, 2019). Usability is a multidimensional construct that permits to investigate different aspects of the interaction with a tool (e.g., ease of use, safety, learnability). In literature, there are plenty of definitions but the most authoritative is the one provided by the International Organization for Standardization (ISO, 2009): "The effectiveness, efficiency and satisfaction with which specified users achieve specified goals in particular environments" (Boehm, Brown, and Lipow, 1976). In the present context, the effectiveness is considered as the accuracy and completeness with which users can achieve specific goals in particular environments. The efficiency refers to the resources invested concerning the accuracy and completeness of goals achieved. The comfort and acceptability of the working system might be affected also by its actual usage (Bevan, 2006). Higher usability increases perceived efficiency of a system (Sharp, Preece, and Rogers, 2019). Furthermore, usable systems positively affect the safety of the HCI interaction, decreasing the chance of errors, reducing the time of training, and the support needed by the users. The usability has also a relevant impact on the success of a product on the market: when two systems present the same functionality and similar prices the users will choose the one that better supports the interaction. While in the assessment of usability the primary focus is on the performance and fluid interaction, the user experience (UX) takes in consideration desirable (e.g., satisfaction, engagement, enjoyment) and undesirable (e.g., unpleasantness, frustration, boredom) aspects of the interaction (Sharp, Preece, and Rogers, 2019). The term "User Experience" was coined to describe what a person feels when interacting or imagining to interact with a prototype, a final product, a system, or a service. The International Organization of Standardization defined UX as: "a person's perceptions and responses that result from the use or anticipated use of a product, system or service" ISO (2009). As already mentioned, the previous experiences of use are part of the UX and they are relevant to consider when the designer aims to develop a new product or to improve a product that is already on the market. The various dimensions of UX can be evaluated during the entire lifecycle of a product (i.e. early prototypes, launch into the market, and product abandonment).

2. METHOD

2.1 Participants

Forty-two students from University of XX took part in the main study (F = 2, M = 40, mean age = 27.73, SD = 2.36). Twenty-one participants belonged to the category of experienced guitar players (i.e., nine years of active study of guitar and/or graduated at the conservatory). Besides, they were frequent users of multi-effects pedalboards. Twenty-one participants were considered beginners guitar players. Among all the participants, 21 usually use a pedalboard, 13 rarely, and 8 have never used it. A total of 11 participants have positioned the second prototype (wireless) on the ground, 13 on the guitar, and 18 chose mixed positions (i.e., ground, guitar, and/or body parts; see 3.2.3).

2.2 Experimental Design

Two factors were independently manipulated within the current study (3 X 2 mixed-design). The within-participants factor was the type of multi-effect device (three levels: *fixed-pedals* on the ground vs. *movable-pedals* on the ground vs. *movable* and *wireless pedals*; see Figures 1, 2, 3) utilized in the three musical sessions. The between-participants factor was the musical experience of participants (two levels: beginners vs. experts). The order of presentation of the multi-effect units was counterbalanced across participants. The between-participants factor was the musical experience of participants (two levels: beginners vs. experts). Following the literature, we defined the cut-off for considering an expert musician as an active study of an instrument for at least nine years or the attendance/graduation from a conservatory (Gaser and Schlaug, 2003; Hanna-Pladdy and MacKay, 2011), and the frequent use of multi-effect pedalboards.

Figure 1. Traditional Pedalboard (BOSS GT-10; i.e., *fixed-pedals* on the ground)

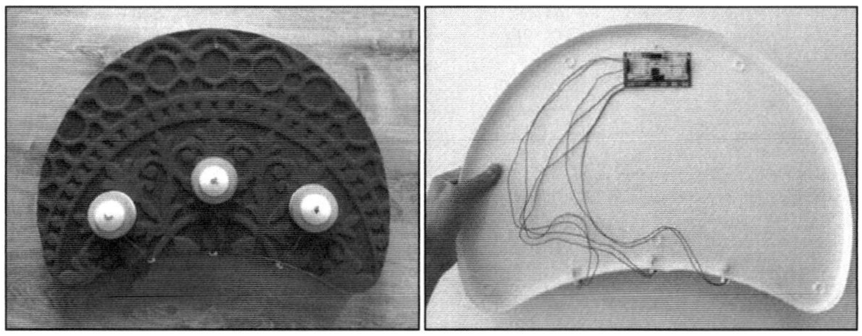

Figure 2. First Prototype (MakeyMakey based; i.e, *movable-pedals* on the ground)

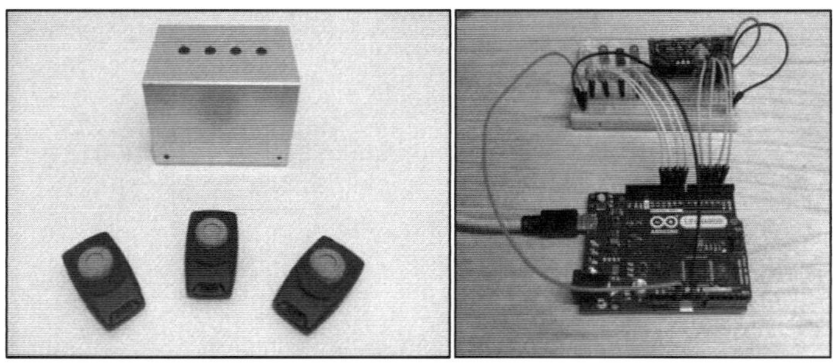

Figure 3. Second Prototype (Arduino Leonardo Based; i.e., *movable* and *wireless pedals*)

2.3 Experimental Equipment and Materials

The following equipment and materials were utilized in the study.

An MSI Notebook GE72 6QD was used to run the software Albleton 9 Live and to power the M-Audio Fast Track Pro Audio/MIDI interface. Participants wore a pair of Sony MDR-XB200 headphones to listen to the sounds output. A Samsung Notebook NP300E5C was employed to allow participants to fill out the questionnaires (using Google Modules).

BOSS GT-10 (i.e., *fixed-pedals* device). A traditional pedalboard already on the market (see Figure 1).

First prototype (i.e., *movable-pedals* device). A pedalboard realized utilizing the MakeyMakey board with wired but movable controllers (see Figure 2). Participants were allowed to customize the positions of the controllers on the external surface (i.e., red in Figure 2) of the device. The controllers were attached with Velcro on the chosen positions of the device surface.

Second prototype. A pedalboard realized utilizing the Arduino Leonardo microcontroller board (i.e., *movable* and *wireless pedals* device). The device comprises four parts: the central box containing the Arduino, three completely wireless controllers. The absence of wires allowed participants to freely choose where to place the three controllers. The controllers were attached with Velcro on the chosen positions.

Pre-Test questionnaire. This tool contained different items regarding general information (e.g. demographic, musical experience) and three items that evaluated the Personal Innovativeness of users. The gathered data allowed us to divide the participants' sample into two groups: beginners and expert musicians. Instead, the Personal Innovativeness dimension was considered to subsequently investigate if the judgments given to the items presented in the post-test questionnaires were influenced by participants' attitude towards the novel information technology (Agarwal and Prasad, 1998).

Post-test questionnaire. The second tool was administered to collect information about the participants' perceived usability and user experience of the various multi-effect devices. The same questionnaire was filled out three times during the experiment, namely after each session (Boehm, Brown, and Lipow, 1976). The presentation of the items was randomized.

2.4 Procedure

Upon arrival, at one of the laboratories of the Department XX of the University of XX, participants were welcomed and asked to read carefully a document containing general information about the study. Then, they were administered with an informed consent. Afterward, participants filled out the Pre-Test questionnaire. Based on a literature review (Barbosa et al., 2011), participants performed three sessions of practice to familiarize with the controllers of each multi-effect device respectively before each of the three performance sessions (i.e., one for each pedalboard; see Figure 4 for details). They were asked to play a song at leisure with the guitar and to interact at least once with each of the three controllers available on the multi-effects devices. Note that the *fixed-pedals* device presents six controllers but only four could be used. Concerning the two prototypes, participants had an additional temporal interval that allowed the decision of where to place the controllers. For the whole duration of the experiment, the researcher remained inside the experimental room, although out of participants' sight. A complete experiment lasted about one hour.

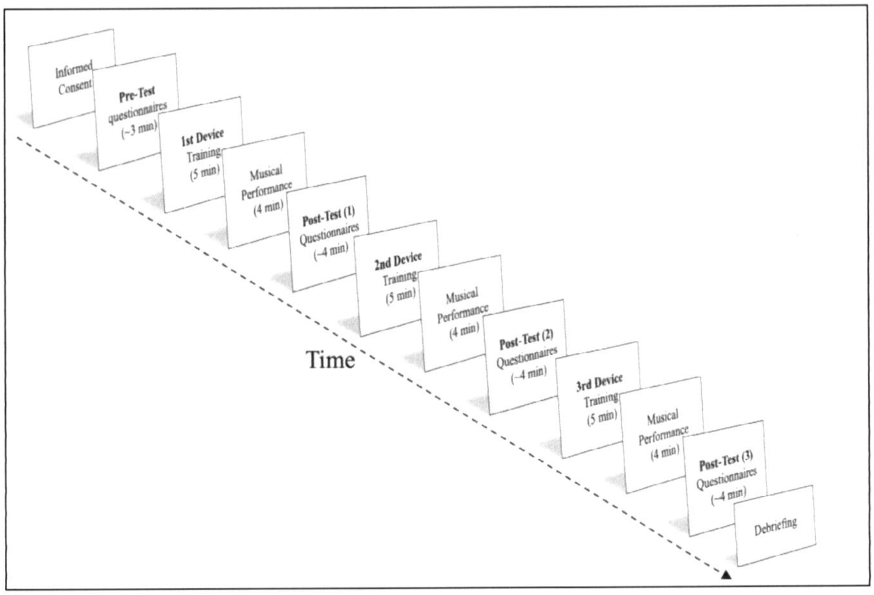

Figure 4. Experimental Procedure

3. DATA ANALYSIS AND RESULTS

All the statistical analyses were performed utilizing the R Studio software (Core Team, 2019). Non-parametric tests were used in so far as the considered dependent variables were ordinals (i.e. Likert scale scores).

3.1 Pre-Test (Personal Innovativeness and Expertise Level)

A series of Mann-Whitney *U* tests was performed to analyze potential differences in the participants' attitude towards information technology due to their musical experience. No main effects due to the musical experience emerged ($p > .05$). The beginners and experts showed similar mean scores to the personal innovativeness construct.

3.2 Post-Test

3.2.1 Usability and UX Items and Device

A series of Friedman tests was performed in order to analyze potential differences due to the three different multi/effect devices. An effect emerged considering each of the following dimensions: Perceived Ease of Use (PEOU; $X^2(2) = 12.24, p < .01$), Perceived External Control (PEC; $X^2(2) = 18.85, p < .001$), Enjoyment (ENJ; $X^2(2) = 30.75, p < .001$), Sound Output Quality (SOUT; $X^2(2) = 20.28, p < .001$), Interface Output Quality (IOUT; $X^2(2) = 12.25, p < .001$), Lights Out-put Quality (LOUT; $X^2(2) = 9.72, p < .001$), and Intent of Use (INT; $X^2(2) = 36.20, p < .001$). Pairwise comparisons using Wilcoxon tests were performed to compare the median scores given to the different devices (see Tab. 1, 2). The *p*–values were adjusted using the Bonferroni correction.

Table 1. *p*-values (Usability and UX items) as a function of the device

Constructs	1 Vs 2	1 Vs 3	2 Vs 3
PEOU	$p < .05$*	$p < .001$***	$p > .05$
PEC	$p < .05$*	$p < .01$**	$p > .05$
ENJ	$p < .001$***	$p < .01$**	$p > .05$
SOUT	$p < .05$*	$p < .05$*	$p > .05$
IOUT	$p > .05$	$p < .05$*	$p > .05$
LOUT	$p < .001$***	$p > .05$	$p < .01$**
INT	$p < .01$**	$p < .001$***	$p > .05$

Table 2. Median scores (Usability and UX items) as a function of the device

Constructs	Traditional	Prototype 1	Prototype 2
PEOU	*Mdn* = 4.75	*Mdn* = 5.50	*Mdn* = 6
PEC	*Mdn* = 5.33	*Mdn* = 5.83	*Mdn* = 6
ENJ	*Mdn* = 5	*Mdn* = 5.50	*Mdn* = 6.33
SOUT	*Mdn* = 4.33	*Mdn* = 5.66	*Mdn* = 5.66
IOUT	*Mdn* = 4.50	*Mdn* = 5.16	*Mdn* = 5.50
LOUT	*Mdn* = 4.66	*Mdn* = 5.33	*Mdn* = 4.66
INT	*Mdn* = 3	*Mdn* = 4.66	*Mdn* = 5.33

3.2.2 Usability and UX Items and Expertise Level

A series of Mann-Whitney *U* tests was carried out to evaluate the perceived usability and UX items (PEOU, PEC, ENJ, SOUT, IOUT, LOUT, INT) as a function of the expertise level. A difference emerged considering respectively the Perceived Enjoyment ($W = 2502.5, p < .05$) and the Sound Output Quality ($W = 2614, p < .01$). These *p*–values were adjusted for multiple comparisons utilizing the BH method (Benjamini & Hochberg, 1995).

3.2.3 Usability and UX Items, Devices and Placement

A series of Friedman tests was conducted to evaluate the perceived usability and the user experience as a function of the placement of the controllers. Three groups of participants were identified in terms of where they placed the *movable* and *wireless pedals* (i.e., on the ground, on the guitar, or in a mixed position).

Significant differences emerged only in the group of *mixed positions* (i.e., *movable* and *wireless pedals*) compared to the first prototype (i.e., *movable pedals*) and the traditional pedalboard (i.e., *fixed-pedals*). In particular, the differences were shown with the PEOU (X^2 (2) = 9.48, $p < .01$; see Figure 5), ENJ ($X^2(2)$ = 18, $p < .001$; see Figure 6), SOUT ($X^2(2)$ = 18.5, $p < .001$; see Figure 7) and INT ($X^2(2)$ = 23.85, $p < .001$, see Figure 8) dimensions. The subsequent Wilcoxon tests showed that the PEOU scores were higher for the second prototype compared to the traditional device ($p < .05$). The ENJ scores were higher for both the first ($p < .01$) and the second prototype ($p < .001$) in comparison to the traditional device. Higher scores in terms of SOUT were assigned to both the first ($p < .001$) and the second prototype ($p < .05$) compared to the ones of the traditional device. Finally, considering the INT dimension, higher scores were associated with both the first ($p < .05$) and the second prototype ($p < .05$) compared to the ones of the traditional device.

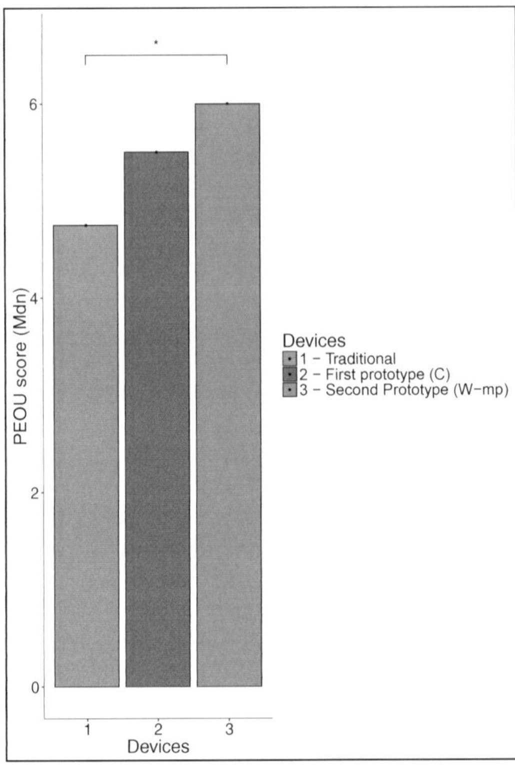

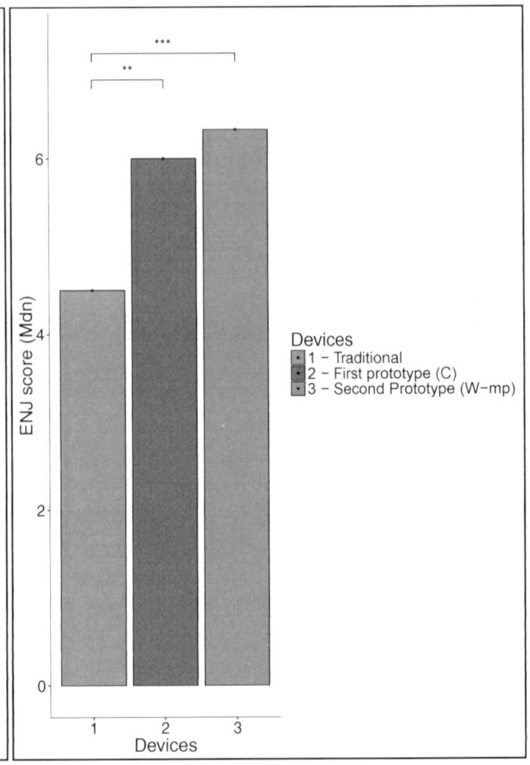

Figure 5 and 6. 5 (left) Median scores of Perceived Ease of Use as a function of devices in the mixed position group. C = customized; W-mp = Wireless mixed-position. 6 (right) Median scores of Perceived Enjoyment as a function of devices in the mixed position group. C = customized; W-mp = Wireless mixed-position

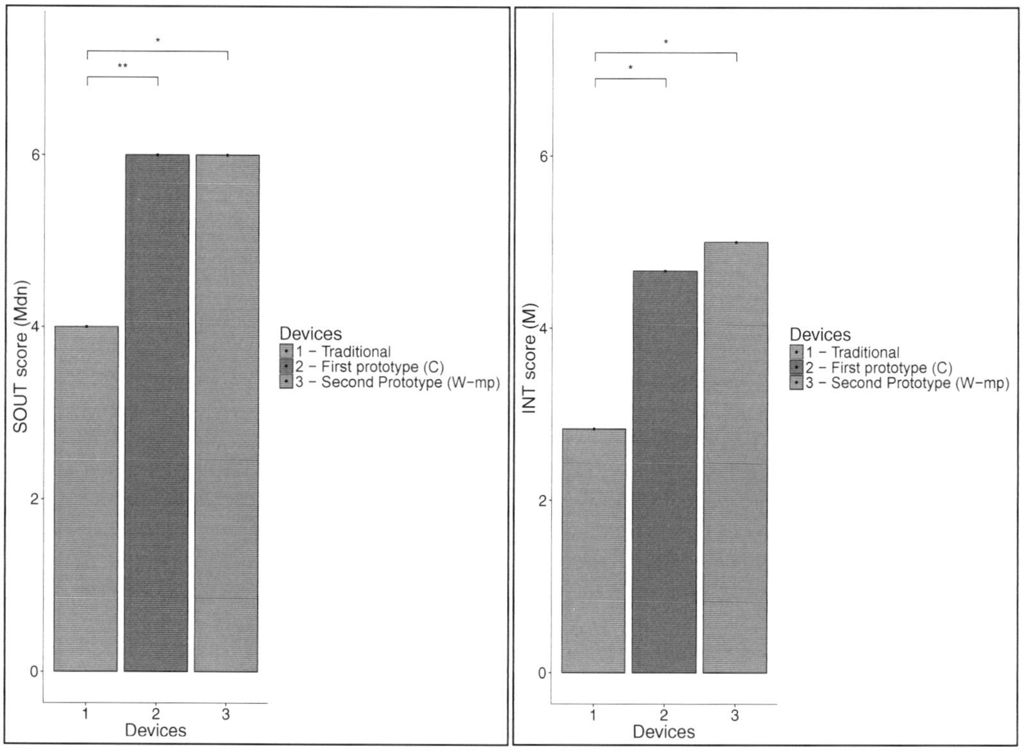

Figure 7 and 8. 7 (left) Median scores of Sound Output Quality as a function of devices in the mixed position group. C = customized; W-mp = Wireless mixed-position. 8 (right) Median scores of Intent to Use as a function of devices in the mixed position group. C = customized; W-mp = Wireless mixed-position

3.2.4 Usability and UX items and Personal Innovativeness

To investigate whether the attitude towards information technology could affect the usability and UX, a median split method was utilized to obtain two different groups of participants: high vs. low level of personal innovativeness (i.e., $Mdn = 4$). A series of Wilcoxon tests was performed and a significant effect emerged considering only with the Perceived Of External Control construct ($W = 2341$, $p < .001$).

4. CONCLUSION

The present study aimed to investigate how the features of three different multi-effects pedalboards for guitar affected their evaluation in terms of usability and UX. Furthermore, also the influence of musical experience (i.e. beginners vs. experts) and Personal Innovativeness were considered. Concerning to the usability and user experience as a function of the device, overall higher scores were assigned to the first (i.e., *movable pedals*) and the second prototype (i.e., *movable* and *wireless pedals*) compared to the traditional pedalboard (i.e., *fixed-pedals*). Findings showed that both prototypes appeared as more ease of use, more controllable, and enjoyable compared to the traditional device. Considering the quality of visual feedback a difference emerged. The second prototype received a better evaluation compared to the first one. This could be due to the presence, in the second prototype, of led lights with different colors (i.e., dedicated to each sound-effect). This feature helped the musician to promptly and effectively recognize which effect he/she had currently selected. Furthermore, an effect emerged considering the expertise level of participants. Both beginners and experts evaluated the prototypes as more enjoyable compared to the traditional device (i.e., *fixed-pedals*). The expertise level highlighted another interesting outcome. The beginner's group only evaluated the Sound Output Quality (SOUT) better while considering the second prototype (i.e., *movable* and *wireless pedals*) in comparison with the traditional pedalboard. An explanation can be that the experts are familiar with the small distortions in the

sounds that characterize an analogic pedalboard (i.e., the traditional one) in contrast to the clean sound that is produced by digital pedalboards (i.e., first and second prototypes). Thus, experts seemed to be able to recognize that the variation in sound quality was due to a different physical architecture of the pedalboard (i.e., analogic vs. digital) and not to the quality of the sound output itself. Considering the second prototype as the most advanced one, due to its customizable architecture, the authors deeply investigate the effect of the placement of the wireless pedals (i.e., on the ground, on the guitar, or in mixed positions, namely on the guitar, ground and/or musician's body). The emerged differences supported the assumption that the opportunity to explore a novel mixed and free pedals placement positively affected the perceived usability and UX. Besides, the attitude towards information technology was affecting usability and user experience. Indeed, a difference emerged comparing the usability and UX dimensions as a function of the two Personal Innovativeness groups (High vs. Low). A higher predisposition to information technology resulted in higher scores on the Perceived of External Control (PEC) construct. This result suggests that people who consider themselves to be more attracted by novel technologies perceived the presented prototypes more controllable. This research study underlined that there are no limitations to where a musician can place the controllers of multi-effect devices. For instance, participants of mixed-positions found new ways of interaction as a result of the freedom in the placement of the controllers (e.g., behind the neck of the guitar, between the knees and under the armpits). These were not foreseen before the study. Furthermore, the possibility of a high level of personalization led to more positive evaluation, in terms of usability and completely new interaction experience with musical devices, compared to a situation in which the multi-effect devices cannot be customized (i.e., traditional pedalboard with
fixed-pedals). In general, making devices more usable for novices is crucial to reduce the traditional barriers that may hamper the initial phases of learning how to play a musical instrument (McPherson, Morreale, and Harrison, 2019). However, some limitations of the study have to be pointed out. It should be crucial to increase the numerosity of the sample in the investigation of the wireless prototype especially regarding the positions chosen by participants for the pedals placement. A second limitation pertains to the sample composition (gender), herein the females involved were only two in the face of forty males, which limits the generalizability of the results. Finally, a potential development should be the further customization of the prototypes adding new pedals of different sizes and/or that provide different functions.

ACKNOWLEDGEMENT

The study was supported by a grant from MIUR (Dipartimenti di Eccellenza DM 11/05/2017 n. 262) to the Department of General Psychology.

REFERENCES

Arduino Leonardo, https: //www.arduino.cc/en/Main/ArduinoBoardLeonardo

BOSS GT-10, https://www.boss.info/us/products/gt-10/

Agarwal, R. and Prasad, J., 1998. A conceptual and operational definition of personal innovativeness in the domain of information technology. *Information systems research*, *9*(2), pp.204-215.

Barbosa, J., Calegario, F., Magalhães, F., Teichrieb, V., Ramalho, G. and Cabral, G., 2011, January. Towards an evaluation methodology for digital music instruments considering performer's view: a case study. In *Proceedings of 13th Brazilian Symposium on Computer Music*.

Benjamini, Y. and Hochberg, Y., 1995. Controlling the false discovery rate: a practical and powerful approach to multiple testing. *Journal of the Royal statistical society: series B (Methodological)*, *57*(1), pp.289-300.

Bevan, N., 2006. International standards for HCI. In *Encyclopedia of human computer interaction* (pp. 362-372). IGI Global.

Boehm, B.W., Brown, J.R. and Lipow, M., 1976, October. Quantitative evaluation of software quality. In *Proceedings of the 2nd international conference on Software engineering* (pp. 592-605). IEEE Computer Society Press.

Cook, P., 2017. 2001: Principles for Designing Computer Music Controllers. In *A NIME Reader* (pp. 1-13). Springer, Cham.

Faulkner, L., 2003. Beyond the five-user assumption: Benefits of increased sample sizes in usability testing. *Behavior Research Methods, Instruments, & Computers*, *35*(3), pp.379-383.

Fernandes, G. and Holmes, C., 2002, April. Applying HCI to music-related hardware. In *CHI'02 Extended Abstracts on Human Factors in Computing Systems* (pp. 870-871).

ISO, International Organization for Standardization, http://www.iso.org

Gaser, C. and Schlaug, G., 2003. Brain structures differ between musicians and non-musicians. *Journal of Neuroscience*, *23*(27), pp.9240-9245.

Hanna-Pladdy, B. and MacKay, A., 2011. The relation between instrumental musical activity and cognitive aging. *Neuropsychology*, *25*(3), p.378.

Holland, S., Wilkie, K., Mulholland, P. and Seago, A., 2013. Music interaction: understanding music and human-computer interaction. In *Music and human-computer interaction* (pp. 1-28). Springer, London.

Holland, S., McPherson, A.P., Mackay, W.E., Wanderley, M.M., Gurevich, M.D., Mudd, T.W., O'Modhrain, S., Wilkie, K.L., Malloch, J.W., Garcia, J. and Johnston, A., 2016, May. Music and HCI. In *Proceedings of the 2016 CHI Conference Extended Abstracts on Human Factors in Computing Systems*(pp. 3339-3346).

MakeyMakey, http://www.makeymakey.com.

McPherson, A., Morreale, F. and Harrison, J., 2019. Musical instruments for novices: Comparing NIME, HCI and crowdfunding approaches. In *New Directions in Music and Human-Computer Interaction* (pp. 179-212). Springer, Cham.

Medeiros, R., Calegario, F., Cabral, G. and Ramalho, G., 2014, June. Challenges in designing new interfaces for musical expression. In *International Conference of Design, User Experience, and Usability* (pp. 643-652). Springer, Cham.

Moggridge, B. and Atkinson, B., 2007. *Designing interactions* (Vol. 17). Cambridge, MA: MIT press.

Morreale, F., De Angeli, A. and O'Modhrain, S., 2014, June. Musical Interface Design: An Experience-Oriented Framework. In *NIME* (pp. 467-472).

Paine, G., 2013. New musical instrument design considerations. *IEEE MultiMedia*, *20*(4), pp.76-84.

Saffer, D., 2008. *Designing gestural interfaces: touchscreens and interactive devices.* " O'Reilly Media, Inc.".

Sharp, H., Preece, J. and Rogers, Y., 2019. Interaction Design-beyond human-computer interaction 5th, 636. isbn: 978-1-119-54725-9.

Tanaka, A., 2019. Embodied Musical Interaction. In *New Directions in Music and Human-Computer Interaction* (pp. 135-154). Springer, Cham.

Turchet, L., Fischione, C., Essl, G., Keller, D. and Barthet, M., 2018. Internet of musical things: Vision and challenges. *IEEE Access*, *6*, pp.61994-62017.

Turchet, L., 2018. Some reflections on the relation between augmented and smart musical instruments. In *Proceedings of the Audio Mostly 2018 on Sound in Immersion and Emotion*(pp. 1-7).

Wanderley, M.M. and Orio, N., 2002. Evaluation of input devices for musical expression: Borrowing tools from hci. *Computer Music Journal*, *26*(3), pp.62-76.

Wessel, D. and Wright, M., 2002. Problems and prospects for intimate musical control of computers. *Computer music journal*, *26*(3), pp.11-22.

A USER-CENTERED DESIGN OF A MAJOR AND MINOR INTRON ANNOTATION DATABASE (MMIAD)

Ruby ElKharboutly[1], Kyle Gorman[1], William Eccles[1] and Sahar Al Seesi[2]
[1]*Quinnipiac University, CT, USA*
[2]*Southern Connecticut State University, CT, USA*

ABSTRACT

Biologists and bioinformaticians heavily rely on data portals and repositories accessible through web application. While they mostly agree that the data is valuable, they find the interfaces hard to use and non-intuitive. In this paper we present a user-centered design of a database for classification and annotation for major and minor introns in various species. Our design is based on surveying and interviewing minor intron researchers and comparing the features of existing databases. In addition to its ease of use, the proposed database, Major and Minor Intron Annotation Database (MMIAD) offers high flexibility in querying and downloading subsets of information that interest the user in multiple commonly used file formats.

KEYWORDS

Bioinformatics, Introns, User-Centered Development

1. INTRODUCTION

Biologists and bioinformaticians heavily rely on web-based systems to retrieve data. Their efforts suffer due to poor usability of system interfaces (Javahery, Seffah, & Radhakrishnan, 2004; Holtzblatt, Wendell, & Wood, 2004). Such systems are usually developed from a programmer perspective to provide specific functionality giving little to no consideration to usability (Pavelin, Cham, de Matos, Brooksbank, & Cameron, 2012). These applications fail to meet users' needs and expectations requiring significant effort and time. One example is UCSC Table Browser (D, et al., 2004). The user interface for this tool is overly crowded and hard to read. It uses outdated UI controls and is built using CGI. Many of the input controls are non-initiative and require extra effort to understand. Finally, the Help tool is accessible through extra navigation which make it difficult to use.

This paper illustrates how software engineering and usability practices are used to elicit the requirements and develop the design of **M**inor and **M**ajor **I**ntron **A**nnotation **D**atabase (MMAID) by following a User-Centered Development (UCD) approach (Mao, Vredenburg, Smith, & Carey, 2005). Most bioinformatics tools ignore usability requirements and are hardly comparable to software designed for other domains (Rose, 51-60; Pavelin, Cham, de Matos, Brooksbank, & Cameron, 2012; Javahery, Seffah, & Radhakrishnan, 2004). There has been considerable effort that addresses the usability needs of biologists and bioinformaticians. Bolcini et. al. (Bolchini, Finkelstein, Perrone, & Nagl, 2009) discuss usability issues in a number of web-based search engines. They suggest recommendations for improvement for these websites. Javahery et. al. (Javahery, Seffah, & Radhakrishnan, 2004) describe their work in applying UCD while developing an integrated web-based interface to a popular bioinformatics portal such that access to web resources is optimized. Pavelin (Pavelin, Cham, de Matos, Brooksbank, & Cameron, 2012) worked on evaluating a number of projects and adopted a UCD approach to produce designs that satisfy usability requirements. de Matos et al. present a case study on how they applied UCD when creating a website that provides enzyme-related data.

As a result of the applying a UCD approach, we are proposing MMAID, user-centered, intuitive, task-based, and most importantly easy to update database that annotates major and minor introns in different species. MMIAD will support multiple genome and transcriptome versions for each species in the database. It will offer high flexibility in querying and downloading subsets of information that interest the user in multiple commonly used file formats.

2. BACKGROUND AND RELATED WORK

Most expressed genes go through the process of intron splicing. The cell machinery responsible for splicing identifies the introns by specific patterns at their boundaries (splice junctions). There are two sets of proteins that perform this job: the major spliceosome responsible for splicing the majority of introns (U2 or major introns) and the minor spliceosome responsible for splicing the rest of the introns (U12 or minor introns). (Sharp & Burge, 1997). There is a lot of interesting biological research that focuses on understanding the differences between these two splicing machineries and their effect on different biological phenomena (Baumgartner, et al., 2018; Madan, et al., 2015), and this research depends on existing annotations for minor introns. All the research that addresses minor introns uses the annotations from two databases that were developed in 2006, SpliceRack (Sheth, et al., 2006) and U12DB (Alioto, 2006). Both databases were created based on the genome and transcriptome versions at their time of creation and were not updated. As a result, numerous preprocessing steps are needed when using this outdated data. In this work, we aim to develop a new user-friendly and easily maintainable database that annotates introns and classifies them into major and minor introns.

The foundation work for classifying introns as either major or minor was laid out by Sheth et. al (Sheth, et al., 2006) using position weight matrices (PWM). They built a resource where the PWMs and annotated introns can be queried and downloaded for five species. Alioto et. al. (Alioto, 2006) built on this work and created a web-based repository that contains U12 introns for 24 species. Their repository included more query features and additional information, One of the main problems with both resources is that they were never updated with new intron coordinates, intron sequences, or gene IDs and links. Both resources were published in 2006, and the genome and transcriptome annotations of different species have been updated multiple times since then.

Very recently, Othlof et. al. (Olthof, Hyatt , & Kanadia, 2019) created the minor intron database (MIDB), with updated intron and gene information for human and mouse using PWMs. In addition to including annotations for only two species, the search feature of MIDB is restricted to searching by gene name or Ensembl ID. Moyer et al (Moyer, Larue, Hershberger, Roy, & Padgett, 2020) created The Intron Annotation and Orthology Database (IAOD). They use PWMs coupled with a support vector machine to classify the introns. Their database includes 24 species and they offer a wide range of search capabilities.

3. METHODS

Although most bioinformatics tools are built to run on Linux systems and are accessible through the command line, due to their high computational complexity, the end users of these tools are biologists with very limited experience in using Linux and command line. On the other hand, some of the available databases, like U12DB and SpliceRack, do not allow bioinformaticians to interface with them through APIs. That calls for incorporating UCD in the development process of these tools and databases. An evaluation of the existing U12 databases, was performed to identify missing features and usability short comings. We also collected requirements from target users through interviews and a survey. Our target users included eleven biologists and bioinformatics researchers.

3.1 Survey Design

The survey was designed such that it evaluates the effectiveness of commonly used U12 database, U12DB, in functionally providing data to the users as well as the usability aspects of the website. Usability aspects included ease of use and clarity. The survey was distributed via email to participants. The following is a list of questions included in the survey.

1. What is your field of study?
2. What is your main purpose in using the U12DB site?
3. Was the information easy to find? (y/n)
4. Was the information clearly presented? (y/n)
5. Were you able to find what you were looking for? (y/n)

6. When using the U12BD site or similar websites, what would you say is the most important feature you look for?
7. Which of these output formats would you make use of?
    - Intron Gff
    - Intron Fasta
    - Donor
    - GTF
    - BED
    - User Defined Tabular File Format
    - Other
8. What other features would you add to the website?

3.2 Interview Questions

We performed in-depth interviews with two bioinformatics scientists and one biologist to further understand the user requirements and usability challenges. We asked the interviewees to inspect each aspect of the U12DB UI such as query text and query options, tabular output, single intron output, and help options. We also asked the interviewees if the purpose of each feature is clear, whether it is intuitive and if it is correctly placed in the UI. Moreover, we solicited users' suggestions for changes in the UI and/or functionality.

3.3 Similar Websites Comparison

We performed a detailed comparison between the U12 database, and two other databases, namely MIDB and IAOD, that were very recently published. Despite the fact that SpliceRack is a valuable resource for intron splice junction PWMs, we found it to be less comprehensive in terms of features and usability; therefore, it was excluded from the comparison. The details of the comparison are presented in section 3.3.

4. RESULTS

4.1 Survey Results

The survey was emailed to around thirty biologists and bioinformaticians. Only eight responses where received from one biologist and seven bioinformaticians.

A summary of the resulted of questions 3-6 is presented in Table 1, and the statistics for question 7 responses are presented in Figure 1.

Table 1. Results of Questions 3,4 and 5

Question	Yes	No
Was the information easy to find?	75%	25%
Was the information clearly presented?	75%	25%
Where you able to find what you are looking for?	12.5%	87.5%

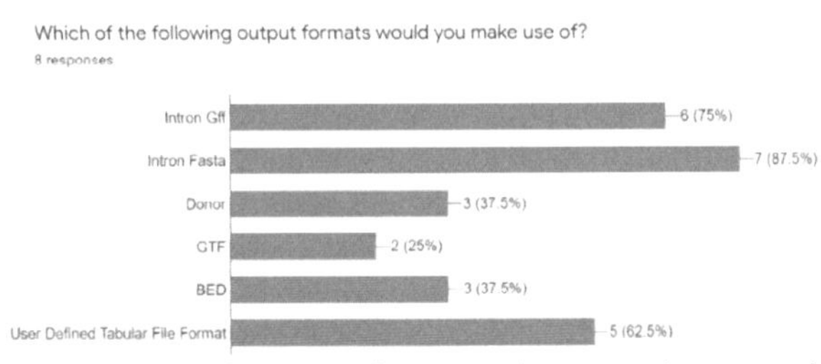

Figure 1. Responses to Survey Question 7

In summary, about a quarter of the population found the website interface confusing and the information presented unclear. A significant number of participants found it hard to access specific website features due to problems in navigation and confusing help menu. All participants agreed that the U12DB is lacking in the following two aspects:

- Updated intron information according to the latest genome and transcriptome versions
- Easier extraction of the sequence of the gene harboring the U12 intron

4.2 Interviews Results

The in-depth interviews were very useful in identifying missing features and usability challenges. The following features were found missing from the U12DB website:

- Allow the user to query by genome locus and query for all the introns in a certain chromosome.
- Allow the user to search by sequence
- Include the score, location and subtype of the intron in the output page
- Export results to comma separated format
- Allow the user to obtain the search results via email
- Make the interface more user friendly and the query criteria organized in a better way
- Generate output with user defined fields
- Change the color scheme to less flashy colors
- Include the complete set of U2 introns
- Enable the user to predict U12 introns for genomes other than the ones in the database
- Offer a more user-friendly website help feature

4.3 Comparison Results

We compared U12DB, MIDB, IAOD, and our proposed MMIAD databases in terms of the species included in each database, the different criteria by which the user can query the database, the data included in the output and the supported output formats. We also included in the comparison other features such as search response time, interface methods, and the prediction algorithms. Table 2 details the results of this comparison.

The comparison shows that among the three databases, IAOD has the most flexible query options and the most informative output. U12DB has the advantage of making the database accessible through a SQLDump. This gives the users the ability to download the data and query it by embedding SQL queries in their code. Each of the three databases have a number of downloadable file formats, but both MIDB and IAOD have this feature available only for the whole dataset; meaning that the user cannot download a subset of the data based on a search query. The search feature results are embedded in an HTML page. U12DB does not create downloadable files for search results, but it displays the results in the browser as unformatted text that can be saved to a file.

In addition to the comparison between the three databases, Table 2 also has a column that describes our proposed MMIAD features. These features were selected based on this comparison and the results of the conducted survey and interviews. One of the major advantages of MMIAD over the existing databases is that the user will be able to choose the genome and transcriptome versions. MMIAD will include annotations for different genome and transcriptome versions for each species. None of the other databases offer this feature except for IAOD, which supports only two human genome versions and only one version for the rest of the species. This is crucial because it eliminates the need to convert coordinates or gene IDs if the user is using a different genome or transcriptome version in their research. MMIAD will contain both major and minor introns. Therefore, the user does not need to download the major introns from another source, if needed in their research.

Additionally, MMIAD will provide the user the ability to download a complete transcriptome GTF, needed by most gene expression analysis tools, with extra annotation, showing which exons border minor introns. Another important feature is allowing the users to download the results of their search in multiple commonly used output file formats, such as FASTA, BED, and GTF. In addition to its web interface, MMIAD will also be accessible through REST APIs to enable bioinformaticians to easily integrate MMIAD queries into their analysis pipelines. For web interface users, MMIAD will send a notification email to the user including a link to view and/or download the requested results, which is a useful feature for time intensive queries that usually results in the website timing out in the existing databases. Other features of MMIAD that are related to the user interface are reflected in the web interface figures in Section 3.4.

Table 2. Comparing the features of the four U12 intron

Feature		U12DB	MIDB	IAOD	MMIAD
Major introns included		A small subset*	No	Yes	Yes
Species		20	2	24	NA**
Genome versions		No	No	Only for human	Yes
Transcriptome versions		No	No	No	
Query criteria	Species	Yes	Yes	Yes	Yes
	Ensembl Gene ID	Yes	Yes	Yes	Yes
	Gene name	Yes	Yes	Yes	Yes
	Ensembl Transcript ID	No	No	Yes	Yes
	Intron Type	Yes	No	Yes	Yes
	Intron cluster	Yes	No	No	No
	Intron subtype	Yes	No	Yes	Yes
	Frame	Yes	No	Yes	Yes
	Intron length	No	No	Yes	Yes
	Coordinate range	No	No	Yes	Yes
	Strand	Yes	No	Yes	Yes
	Sequence	No	No	Yes	Yes
Prediction algorithm		PWM	PWM	PWM and SVM	PWM and probabilistic grammars
Interface		Web interface & mySQL dump	Web interface	Web interface	Web interface with email notification & REST APIs
Downloadable formats		Intron GFF Intron FASTA Donor FASTA Acceptor FASTA Branch point FASTA	Intron xlsx file Gene xlsx file Intron FASTA Intron BED Donor exon BED Acceptor exon BED Transcript BED	U12 FASTA U2 FASTA U2 BED U12 BED	Intron BED Intron FASTA Donor exon FASTA Acceptor exon FASTA
Notes		Not downloadable but can be saved from browser	Dataset can be downloaded as a whole. Search results are not downloadable	Dataset can be downloaded as a whole. Search results are not downloadable	All output files can be obtained for data resulting from search results
Output fields	Species	Yes	Yes	Yes	Yes
	Common species name	No	No	Yes	Yes
	Genome version	No	Yes	Yes	Yes
	Ensembl version	No	No	No	Yes
	Gene name	Yes	Yes	Yes	Yes
	Gene description	Yes	Yes	No	No
	Synonyms	No	Yes	No	No
	NCBI gene ID	No	Yes	No	Yes
	NCBI gene link	No	Yes	No	Yes
	Ensembl gene ID	Yes	Yes	Yes	Yes
	Ensembl gene link	Yes	Yes	Yes	Yes
	UCSC link - gene coordinates	Yes	No	No	Yes
	Gene type	No	Yes	No	No
	Gene disease associations	No	Yes	No	No
	Gene Hman Protein Atlas link	No	Yes	No	No
	Gene Allen Brain Atlas link	No	Yes	No	No
	Gene sequence	Yes	Yes	No	Yes
	Strand	Yes (in gff)	Yes	Yes	Yes
	Gene coordinates	Yes	Yes	No	Yes
	Gene length	No	Yes	No	Yes
	Ensembl canonical trascript ID	No	Yes	No	No
	Ensembl transcript(s) ID(s)	Yes	Yes	Yes	Yes
	Ensembl transcript(s) links	No	Yes	Yes	Yes
	Internal intron ID	Yes - links to intron page	No	Yes - links to orthologus introns	No
	Intron cluster ID	Yes - links to orthologus introns	No	No	No
	intron coordinates	Yes	Yes	Yes	Yes
	UCSC link - intron coordinates	Yes	Yes	No	Yes
	Intron length	No	Yes	Yes	Yes
	Intron sequence	Yes	Yes	Yes	Yes
	Branch point sequence	Yes	Yes	Yes	Yes
	Donor splice site sequence	Yes	Yes	Yes	Yes
	Acceptor splice cite sequence	Yes	Yes	Yes	Yes
	Scores	Yes	Yes	Yes***	Yes
	Rank (exon number)	No	Yes	Yes	Yes
	Intron type (U2/U12)	Yes	Only U12 included	Yes	Yes
	Intron subtype - dinucleotides	Yes	Yes	Yes	Yes
	Frame	Yes	No	Yes	No

One of the main motivations behind this project is to create an updated and easily maintainable database, to address the problem of U12DB and SpliceRack being outdated. To ensure maintainability, we include in the design of MMIAD an administrator interface through which an automated process of classifying introns into U2 and U12 and adding a new dataset to the database can be performed. The input to this feature will be a genome FASTA file and a transcriptome GTF file. This feature will make it easy to update our database every time a new genome or transcriptome version is published. This feature will also be available to users through REST APIs allowing the users to classify introns in a genome of their interest (not in our database) into major and minor introns.

---

* Only U2 introns that are orthologous to U12 introns in other species are included. ** MMIAD has not been populated with intron data yet.***IAOD has one score for the whole introns. No scores given for individual features.

The three systems have been evaluated in terms of usability guidelines such as intuitive design, ease of learning, efficiency of use, memorability, and error frequency. The three websites have an intuitive design that resembles common repository search tools. U12DB search resembles running an SQL query. The labels such as "alt-spliced" and "type switch" match database fields and are difficult or remember. The help page for this website is located in a different page and requires extra navigation to access. The site takes a long time to respond depending on the search criteria.

MIDB was found intuitive and more user friendly as it provides very limited functionality. The search options are limited to species and search by gene name or Ensemble id. The presented search output for a single intron required significant scrolling and used internal system ids to identify minor introns which is non-initiative for the user. IAOD is the latest database, published in 2020. It has the best usability features compared to older database.

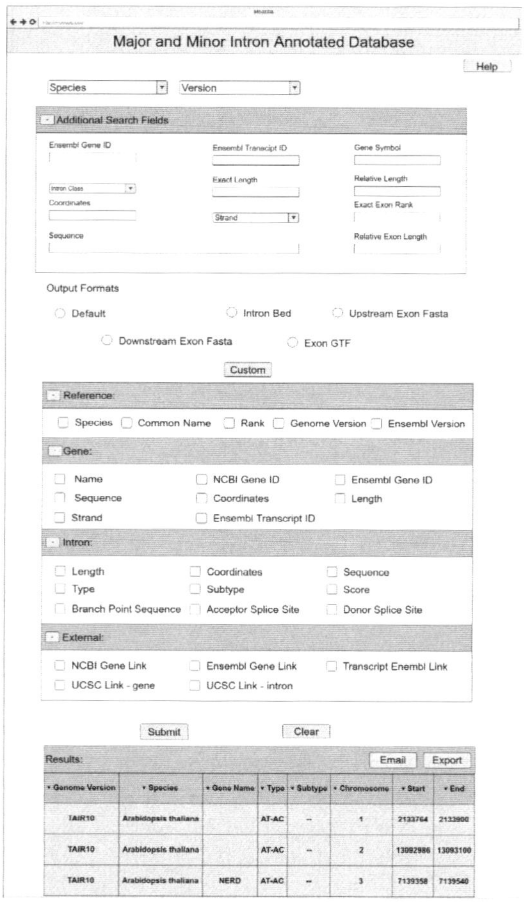

Figure 2. The MMAID homepage through which the user can query the database

4.4 Website User Interface Design

Each page of our website was designed with simplicity, clarity, and an intuitive design that is functional as well as user-friendly. We adapt a task-based approach that allows the user to go step-by-step as in the bioanalytical process. The user is provided with the most basic query options in the main search and can optionally choose to expand the search criteria and expose other options. Figure 2 is the landing page. This page provides the main search capability to the user. A simple search by species and genome version is provided. The user is given the option to expand the search criteria by selecting "+ Add Additional Fields".

The user will also be able to specify the output format of the data. If the user selects the "custom" button under output format, it will display the available output formats. Initially, each of the drop-down menus will be closed and the user will be able to open each in a step-by-step approach. The "Submit" button will run the search and the "Clear" button will clear the page and restore it to the default page. Through the "Email" button, the user can request to receive a notification email when the search is completed. This is useful for time consuming searches, like searching across all species. The "Export" button will bring the user to a popup page that will allow them to export the results to their desired file format. The "Results" table will be visible once the "Submit" button has been selected. By selecting one of the resulting introns, the user will be brought to the "Intron Information" page for that intron which will have all the available information on the intron. Figure 3 shows the intron information page. The user can choose which sections can be displayed on this page, for a more intuitive and cleaner interface

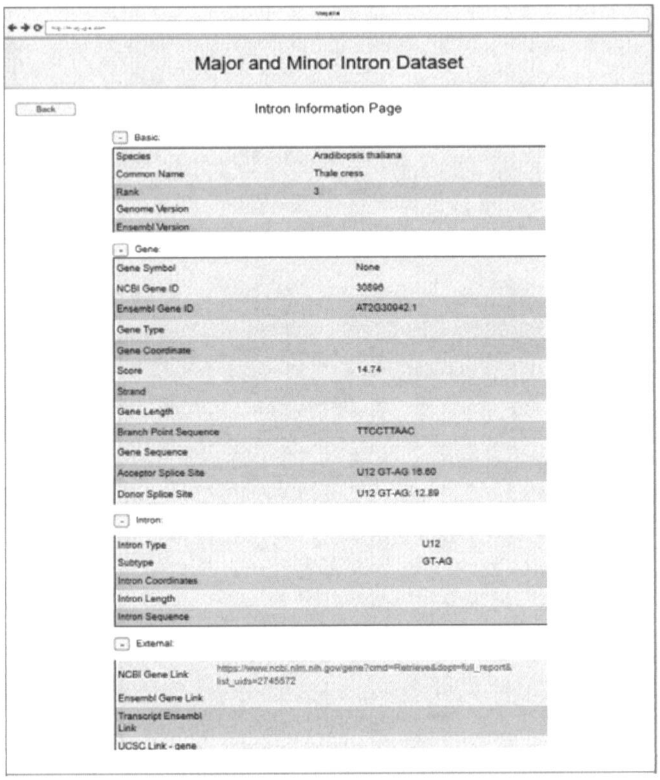

Figure 3. Intron information page

5. CONCLUSION AND FUTURE WORK

MMIAD was designed based on a user-centered software development methodology. Our proposed design is simple, intuitive, and user-friendly. MMIAD offers a task-based interface that guides the user in their selection in a step by step process. MMIAD features, output data, and output file formats were selected based on user input acquired from U12DB users through surveys and interviews. We also performed a detailed comparison between the features of U12DB and the two newly created U12 databases, MIDB and IAOD, and incorporated the results of this comparison in our design process. In addition to its ease of use, the resulting product offers high flexibility in querying and downloading subsets of information that interest the user in multiple commonly used file formats. A very important design feature of MMIAD is its administration interface that allows running the prediction algorithm and adding new datasets to the database. We included this feature to ensure maintainability of the database, solving a major drawback of U12DB and SpliceRack.

At this point, we are working on developing a probabilistic grammar inference model to be used in classifying major and minor introns. Our initial analysis shows promising results and we plan to experiment with using our grammatical solution independently or coupling it with the commonly used PWM approach. Once we have our prediction method finalized, we will use it to generate results for different species and populate the database with the resulting data. Part of our future plans is to create Galaxy (Afgan, et al., 2018) wrappers to make MMIAD accessible through the Galaxy portal.

REFERENCES

Afgan, E., Baker, D., Batut, B., van den Beek, M., Bouvier, D., Čech, M., . . . Blankenberg, D. (2018). The Galaxy platform for accessible, reproducible and collaborative biomedical analyses. *Nucleic Acids Research, 46*(W1), W537–W544.

Alioto, T. S. (2006). U12DB: a database of orthologous U12-type spliceosomal introns. *Nucleic Acids Research*, 35.

Baumgartner, M., Lemoine, C., Al Seesi, S., Karunakaran, D., Sturrock, N., Banday, A., . . . Kanadia, R. (2015). Minor splicing snRNAs are enriched in the developing mouse CNS and are crucial for survival of differentiating retinal neurons. *Dev Neurobiol , 75*, 895 – 907.

Baumgartner, M., Olthof, A., Aquino, G., Lemoine, C., Drake, K., Karunakaran, D., . . . Kanadia, R. (2018). Minor spliceosome inactivation causes microcephaly, owing to cell cycle defects and death of self-amplifying radial glial cells. *Development , 145*(17), dev166322.

Bolchini, D., Finkelstein, A., Perrone, V., & Nagl, S. (2009). Better bioinformatics through usability analysis. *Bioinformatics, 25*(3), 406-412.

D, K., AS, H., TS, F., KM, R., CW, S., D, H., & WJ, K. (2004). The UCSC Table Browser data retrieval tool. *Nucleic Acids Res., 1*(32 (Database issues)), 493-6.

Holtzblatt, K., Wendell, J. B., & Wood, S. (2004). *Rapid contextual design: A how-to guide to key techniques for user-centered design.* San Francisco, CA: Elsevier.

Javahery, H., Seffah, A., & Radhakrishnan, T. (2004). Beyond power: making bioinformatics tools user centered. *Comms ACM, 47*, 59-62.

Madan, V., Kanojia, D., Li, J., Okamoto, R., Sato-Otsubo, A., Kohlmann, A., . . . Koeffler, H. (2015). Aberrant splicing of U12-type introns is the hallmark of ZRSR2 mutant myelodysplastic syndrome. *Nat Commun, 6*, 1-14.

Mao, J., Vredenburg, K., Smith, P., & Carey, T. (2005). The state of user-centered design practice. *Commun. ACM, 48*(3), 105-109.

Moyer, D. C., Larue, G. E., Hershberger, C. E., Roy, S. W., & Padgett, R. A. (2020). Comprehensive database and evolutionary dynamics of U12-type introns. *Nucleic Acids Research, gkaa464*.

Nielson, J. (1983). *Usability engineering.* New York: Morgan Kaufmann.

Niemelä, E., & Frilander, M. (2014). Regulation of gene expression through inefficient splicing of U12-type introns. *RNA Biol, 11*, 1325–1329.

Norman, D. A. (2002). *The psychology of everyday, 2nd edition.* New York: Basic Books.

Olthof, A. M., Hyatt , K. C., & Kanadia, R. N. (2019). Minor Intron Splicing Revisited: Identification of New Minor Intron Containing Genes and Tissue-Dependent Retention and Alternative Splicing of Minor Introns. *BMC Genomics, 20*(1).

Pavelin, K., Cham, J. A., de Matos, P., Brooksbank, C., & Cameron, G. (2012). Bioinformatics Meets User-Centred Design: A Perspective. PLOS Computational. *Biology, 8*, 7.

Rose, A. F. (51-60). Using qualitative studies to improve the usability of an EMR. *Biomed. Inform, 38*, 51-60.

Sharp, A. P., & Burge, C. B. (1997). Classification of Introns: U2-Type or U12-Type. *Cell, 91*, 875–879.

Sheth, N., Roca, X., Hastings, M., Roeder, T., AR, K., & R., S. (2006). Comprehensive Splice-Site Analysis Using Comparative Genomics. *Nucleic Acids Research, 34*(14), 3955–3967.

Turunen, J., Niemela, E. H., & Verma, B. (2013). The significant other: splicing by the minor spliceosome. *WIREs RNA, 4*, 61–76.

ASSESSMENT OF THE USABILITY OF LATVIA'S OPEN DATA PORTAL OR HOW CLOSE ARE WE TO GAINING BENEFITS FROM OPEN DATA

Anastasija Nikiforova
Faculty of Computing, University of Latvia, Rainis Boulevard 19, Riga, LV-1586, Latvia

ABSTRACT

Nowadays, more and more countries are launching their own open data portals, seeking to provide their citizens with open data in a form that is useful and suitable for the original purpose of the open data, and Latvia is not an exception. Despite the fact that the Latvian open data portal was launched only in 2017, it is considered to be a fast-tracker. However, despite the overall high evaluations, critical voices, and many discussions about whether the Latvia's open data portal is of sufficient quality to be appeared. Therefore, while previous studies deal with quality of open data, this study focuses on the analysis of the Latvian open data portal and aims to find the key challenges that may have a negative impact on user experience. The paper assesses the current situation and recommends corrective actions, highlighting the aspects to be considered when developing and improving open data portals.

KEYWORDS

Open Data, Open Data Government, Open Data Portal, Portal Quality, Usability

1. INTRODUCTION

Nowadays, open data and in particular open government data (OGD) are the topics underpinning the recent governance, policy and process innovations around the world. However, open data itself does not play an important role since value is generated by the use of data (Faini et al., 2016). According to (Janssen et al., 2012), one of the primary objectives in the case of OGD is to accompany publicized data by an infrastructure - open data portal - capable of processing data in an easy-to-use manner to reduce the user threshold, thus maximising their re-use to a wide audience (Attard et al., 2015). As a result, more and more governments are establishing open data portals where different types of data are published by different data providers and Latvia is not an exception. However, despite many countries develop and launch their own OGD portals, they received a great deal of criticism from both, society, by which is meant users who may not have IT knowledge, and technical experts. Latvia is not an exception and one of the most important reasons to initiate a study were the critical voices appeared in Latvia, even though according to different international assessments, Latvia's Open Data Portal is considered as qualitative. Many discussions about (1) *whether our Open Data Portal is of adequate quality?* and (2) *what are the main challenges to be addressed*? took place, and this study addresses these issues. This was also discussed at the 13th annual conference of the Latvian Open Technology Association "Data Driven Nation", in which the author was an invited speaker.

Since the Latvian open data portal is relatively new, it is not included in other studies, while other portals of our neighbours (Lithuania, Estonia, Finland) have been investigated. Therefore, this study is unique to Latvia and has a high national value. However, in order to bring added value at the international level, this paper provides brief comparison with other open data portals, highlighting the aspects to be taken into account when developing and improving open data portals.

To sum up, the aim of this paper is to explore Latvia's Open Data portal, by evaluating it from different perspectives. As for the methods used, the number of existing methods was studied, selecting (Máchová et al., 2018) usability evaluation framework, supplying it with the author's requirements that the portal must satisfy which were formulated on the basis of experience with the portal.

The paper addresses the following issues: a brief overview of the related studies (Section 2), an overview of Latvia's open data portal (Section 3), an analysis of Latvia's open data portal, highlighting its main challenges (Section 4) and conclusions (Section 5).

2. RELATED WORKS

The relevance and popularity of [open] data portals and OGD topics are also reflected in the number of studies. According to leading libraries collecting researches, namely, *ACM Digital Library*, *Science Direct*, *Springer Link*, *Web of Science*, *IEEE Xplore Digital Library*, the total number of studies on open data portals and OGD published in recent years is less than 29% of the studies dedicated to open data (Figure 1). For *Google Scholar*, the number of open data studies exceeds the number of open data portal and OGD studies nearly 15 times - the ratio to total number of open data studies is ~6.25%.

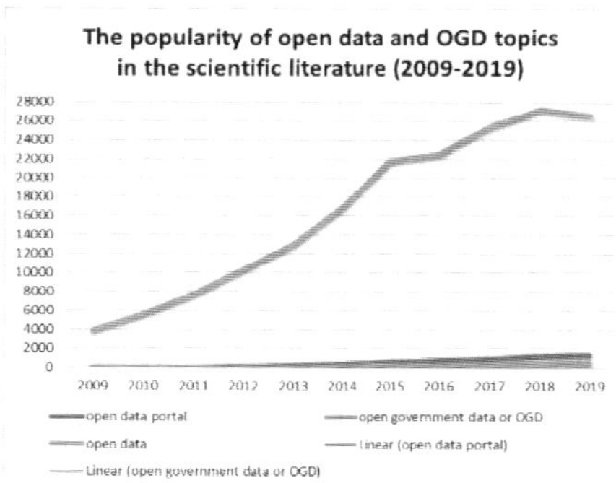

Figure 1. The popularity of open data and OGD topics

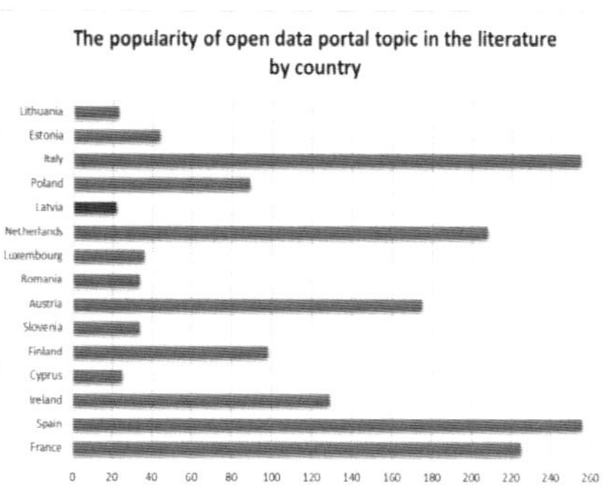

Figure 2. The popularity of open data and OGD topics

According to Figure 2, which shows how many studies were conducted by country on an open data portal, only a few studies were devoted to Latvia in the way of open data portals. Compared to the leading countries, the topic of Latvia's open data portal is covered nearly 12 times rarely (1.33% of all studies, while for the leading countries this ratio exceeds 15%). In most cases, the Latvian open data portal was mentioned in only one or a few sentences. Closest to the presented study – the analysis of the open data portal, was carried out in 2014 (Bojars et al., 2014), however, it was dedicated to another portal that no longer exists. For the most popular countries covered in scientific literature, they are Spain, France, Italy, Netherlands, Austria, Ireland and Finland, among which only Italy has a lower score of the state of the open data portal (according to *European Data Portal*). Therefore, it can be assumed that the popularity of this topic in scientific literature may sometimes (but not necessarily) be linked to the state of the open data portals, as the number of studies demonstrates the public's (at least the scientific part of society) interest in the subject.

For more specific studies, a number of benchmarks and indexes were recently introduced assessing the state of OGD - the *Global Open Data Index*, *EU Open Data maturity* indicators, *Open Data Barometer*, etc.

The *Global Open Data Index* follows the state of the OGD, that is, which countries publish the data in the right way and in timely manner. Currently, 94 countries are included in the index of 15 key datasets per country, and only 11% of the data set entries were open according to their open definition. Since data are currently available only for 2016 (because the evaluation process is quite complex), their finding may be considered outdated. This is also the case for Latvia, since many improvements in the state of open data [related to the launch of the national open data portal] took place.

Another example is the *Open Data Barometer*, which aims to provide a snapshot of OGD practices. The *Open Data Barometer* is focused on open data readiness, implementation, and emerging impacts. The most urgent, the 4th edition assessed these aspects for a sample of 30 countries. However, this assessment may also be considered to be outdated as the data provided reflect the state of OGDs in 2017. Moreover, since 113 countries were covered in 2016, it can be assumed that even for 2017 there was only a partial report.

The *European Data Portal* carries out an evaluation of national open data portals, assessing 4 key aspects, namely *policy*, *portal*, *impact* and *quality*. This assessment appears to be one of the most up-to-date assessments covering set of open data portals, as they have published results for 2019. According to their analysis, impact is currently the weakest aspect of OGDs, following by quality (partially addressed in (Nikiforova, 2020a)) and portal. As for the portal category, they focus on evaluation of portal functions that allow both versed and less versed users to access open data through the national portal and features that encourage interaction between publishers and re-users.

According to (Attard et al., 2015) and literature review performed by the author (partly covered in (Nikiforova, 2020b)), many studies cover their own national OGD initiatives, where for most studies, a lack of a common methodology that would allow comparisons between studies is observed.

Since the OGD may be used to create a new public service, one of the tasks to be performed is to get an overview of the available OGD datasets. Therefore, this study analyses not only a portal but also its datasets. For the approach to be used in this study, as a result of the analysis of existing studies, the preference was given to the (Máchová et al., 2018) methodology. This study proposes to evaluate open data portal using 3 key aspects - open data specification, open dataset feedback, open dataset request, divided into 14 sub-aspects (see subsection 4.2). This methodology was found to be appropriate for a number of reasons: (a) it is relatively new (less than 2 years old), (b) cited, meaning that it is accepted by the public/ researchers, (c) complies with the principles used by other researchers as the methodology is similar with (Attard et al., 2015), (Zuiderwijk et al., 2015), (d) easy to replicate; (e) considers a user perspective. It is also should be mentioned that despite the potential impact of the open data portals web interface on portal usability, this paper does not address it, leaving it for other studies.

3. LATVIA'S OPEN DATA PORTAL: GENERAL REPORT

Latvia's open data portal (*data.gov.lv*) was launched in 2017. At the time of its launch it collected only 33 datasets from 13 data publishers, however, in June 2020 the total number of datasets exceeds 395 from 74 data publishers, which is the highest among neighbours from the Baltic states.

As regards its development, Latvia is one of 79 countries participating in the *Open Government Partnership*. According to *Open Data Maturity report 2019* (Blank, 2019), that measures the maturity of open data across Europe, Latvia belongs to fast-trackers (among beginners, followers, fast-trackers, trend-setters) and has the highest level of maturity of open data compared to the Baltic States and Scandinavian countries. Furthermore, in recent years, the open data maturity of Latvia's open data [portal] has been steadily improving (Nikiforova, 2019). The maturity of Latvia's open data portal is assessed as the 11th among 32. In terms of general evolution, Latvia demonstrates the most impressive results, improving its position from the first appearance in this rating by getting from position 30 to 11 (Table 1).

Table 1. Maturity of portals

#	*Country/ year*	*2019*	*2018*	*2017*	*2016*
1	**France**	**1** ↑+4	**5** ↑+3	**8 ↓-5**	**3**
2	**Spain**	**2** ↑+6	**8 ↓-3**	**5 ↓-1**	**4**
3	**Ireland**	**3**	**3**	**3** ↑+7	**10**
...	...	...	...	...	...
11	**Latvia**	**11**↑+8	**19**↑+2	**21**↑+9	30
...	...	...	...	...	...

↓-n – decrease in rank by n positions compared to the previous year
↑+n – improve in rank by n positions compared to the previous year
ranking – below EU28+ average

Moreover, Latvia is one of 4 countries (Ireland, Latvia, Italy, Malta) which improves its positions from year to year (for more details see (Nikiforova, 2020b)).

4. ANALYSIS OF LATVIA'S OPEN DATA PORTAL

The analysis of Latvia's open data portal was carried out in 3 stages: (1) a questionnaire of Latvian citizens; (2) the methodology applied to the portal by 35 users with IT background; (3) additional aspects not covered in the applied methodology (or not detailed enough), that were defined by the author of this paper as the user of this portal based on observations, analysed by inspecting every data set (out of 395).

4.1 Survey on the Latvian Open Data Portal

As critical voices appear in Latvia more and more frequently, the first step in the analysis of the *Latvia's Open Data Portal* was a questionnaire. 105 voluntary participants were involved representing three groups: (a) users with IT background, (b) without IT background, divided into two additional groups: undergraduate and graduated. A list of simple questions was asked, in which the most important in the scope of this paper, are (1) *whether the participant knows that Latvia has its own national open data portal*?, if "*yes*" (2) *how he/ she assesses it* (2.1.) *from a "usability" perspective*, (2.2.) *from the quality of the data published in it*.

The results demonstrate that only 53% of respondents are aware of the existence of Latvia's open data portal and 13.5% suppose that this exists, however, are not sure. However, 74.3% of those, who know about the existence of the portal, have not used it, 18% used it only once, and only 7.7% use it in a daily manner. An interesting point is that the number of non-IT experts who are aware of the existence of Latvia's open data portal is higher than the number of users with IT background by 13%. However, this trend is not valid in the case of its use, as only 7.7% of non-IT users use this portal regularly, while for IT-users this ratio is 12%.

As for the assessment, which is a subjective opinion of each respondent, the overall usability of the open data portal was assessed by 6.3 points out of 10, while the quality of published data – 6.2 out of 10. The assessment received from IT users was lower by 1 point in the case of usability and 0.5 point in the case of quality. These results demonstrate that despite the high results according to international assessment systems, Latvian users are not satisfied with this portal in the highest way. This proves the importance of this study in determining aspects assessed by users as not high enough.

As for the next stage of the study, only users with IT background participated in it, that corresponds to the experiment design of (Máchová et al., 2018).

4.2 Results of the Application of the Methodology

As in (Máchová et al., 2018), a three-level Likert scale (fulfilled - 3, partially fulfilled - 2, and unfulfilled - 1), that belongs to the acceptability tasks, was used to measure the usability of open data portal. Latvia's open data portal was assessed by 35 participants selected on the voluntary basis using in-group (between subject) observational method to reduce the potential subjectivity of the results, which cannot be achieved if the total number of participants is less than 30. Table 2 summarises the results of the analysis, where a total score can vary from 14 to 42 points. Latvia was scored with 31.5 out of 42 (62.5%) while leading countries got between 35.6 and 38.2 points (Nikiforova, 2020b).

Table 2. Assessment of Latvia's open data portal

Category	*Aspect*	*Points (1 to 3 points)*
Open dataset specification	a) Description of dataset	**2,07**
	b) Publisher of dataset	**2,74**
	c) Thematic categories and tags	**2,36**
	d) Release date and up to date	**2,9**
	e) Machine-readable formats	**2,1**
	f) Open data licence	**3**
	g) Visualization and statistics	**1,26**
Open dataset feedback	a) Documentation and tutorials	**1,98**
	b) Forum and contact form	**2,02**
	c) User rating and comments	**1,76**
	d) Social media and sharing	**2,52**
Open dataset request	a) Request form	**2,83**
	b) List of requests	**1,88**
	c) Involvement in the process	**2,05**

1 point – not fulfilled, 2 points – partially fulfilled, 3 points - fulfilled
n – weak/ low result (under 2 points out of 3) requiring improvements

Let's briefly discuss the main results and challenges identified. For the first category, namely "**open data set specification**", while the portal provides an opportunity to describe the data set to be published, data publishers often do not provide any or sufficiently detailed descriptions, and in many cases only the name of data set is recopied as a description. As regards the "*publisher of dataset*", this information is mandatory for the publication of open data in Latvia's open data portal, therefore, this requirement is always fulfilled. Aspects such as "*machine-readable format*" and "*open data licence*" are one of those that ensured Latvian open data portal with such a high position in international ratings as all datasets meet these requirements. For the licence, all data sets correspond to CC0 1.0. This is also in line with (Máchová et al., 2018), where all the assessed portals were found to meet this requirement because open data license is today the key part of each portal. However, only a few years ago it was a major challenge for the open data portals, and, even now, in 2020, there are portals that either do not provide information regarding license, or use multiple licenses, where some of them assign limitations on data sets to be used, for instance, Germany, Greece, Hungary, Czech Republic (see (Nikiforova, 2020b)). As for "*thematic categories and tags*", despite 14 different categories exist, by the beginning of June 2020 there were 102 datasets not belonging to any category. It is not related to poor portal design, but the publisher did not specify a category that should be assigned to the specific data set. For instance, one of the data sets not belonging to any category, namely "*Distribution of scientific articles by genders and scientific disciplines in Web of Science 2015-2019*" could be linked to the "*Education*" category etc. However, as a result, this makes it impossible to find datasets that are not assigned to any categories if a user studies datasets by category. In such a case, the two recommended solutions: (a) make the choice of categories mandatory for data publishers; (b) include the category "*other*" or "*uncategorized*", as in the case of Bulgaria. Of course, one of the best options would be involving a mechanism that assigns datasets by extracting or using keywords, however this solution will require more resources from data portal holders. As for *visualisation and statistics*, by which are meant visualization and analytical capabilities to obtain information about a dataset, such as charts or visualizations in maps, this is partly fulfilled – sometimes the possibility *visualizing data* is provided. As a result, the Latvian open data portal gains 16.7 out of 21 points for the "**open dataset specification**" while an average for 40+ countries is 16.4 (see (Nikiforova, 2020b)).

For the second category, "**open dataset feedback**", which includes documentation and tutorials, forums and contact form etc., the Latvian open data portal scored 7.52 out of 12 points (an average for 40+ countries is 7.68). Despite the fact that one of the frequently discussed challenges for open data portals and OGDs is that users receive very little feedback from the service providers (Smith et al., 2018), the Latvian open data portal provides an opportunity to contact the holder or publisher of each dataset. However, despite this option, it is not known whether users receive/ get feedback. This may be a research question for future studies. For the contact forms, a positive aspect is that contacting data publisher can be performed without logging or registering as expected. As for documentation and tutorials, a number of documents are provided, however, this aspect was not assessed by 3 points, as their quality and level of detail may not be sufficient for the normal user. The "*user rating and comments*" opportunity is not provided; however, it is possible to use "*social media and sharing*" opportunity. This aspect is perfectly realised by Cyprus, Ireland and Finland that can be considered as an example.

Regarding the "*Request form*", "*List of requests*", "*Involvement in the process*", the Latvia's Open Data Portal was assessed by 4.31 point out of 9, while an average result is 5.16. This opportunity enables all stakeholders to request a new data set that could be of high interest to the public, but other stakeholders may vote in favour of this specific data set. This aspect allows to compare Latvia's Open Data Portal with Spain which portal is considered as one of the best portals, where this opportunity is provided as well, however, this showcase is even better since the number of possible values for the status of requests are provided such as *assigned, published, not feasibly, under study, or partially published* instead of *published* and *not published* as it is for Latvia. At the same time, Latvia's portal holders point out that this voting tool is of informative nature, so they have right to decide on the opening of these datasets by themselves that can be easily explained in several ways: (a) it is difficult to ensure the openness of all the data, in which the society may be interested in, because of challenges such as seeking an appropriate publisher, contacting him, preparing data sets etc., (b) users do not necessarily understand what the open data are, since a few requests were related to data that cannot be exploited as open data. Here the Ireland's portal should be mentioned, which supposes that the request can be commented, and as a result, the portal's employees explain to the users whether (and why) the request cannot be satisfied.

Based on these results, it can be concluded that the "**open dataset specification**" for Latvia's open data portal is the best category, which gained a higher number of points (even better than an average for 40+ countries), however, the "**open dataset feedback**" got the worst. This result is also consistent with *Open Data Maturity* in Europe, according to which the impact of Latvia's portal is the worst. At the same time for OGD feedback is one of the crucial aspects of the impact criteria.

As for more specific aspects, "*visualization and statistics*", "*user rating and comments*" and "*list of requests*", appear to be the weakest points assessed by participants between "not fulfilled" and "partially fulfilled". These aspects must be improved as soon as possible, not only because of the low result but also because of the importance of these aspects. Moreover, it is also seen that these aspects are closely related to aspects that affect user experience, resulting in the impact of the open data initiative. It would also be recommended to address all aspects that have been assessed by less than 2.8 out of 3 points, however, these aspects are those which are already implemented in a relatively high way and are not such important until now. Nevertheless, they will be studied in the near future, with a detailed analysis and conclusion on how they could be improved. Some of them are also addressed in the next subsection.

Compared to another study carried out by the author of this study and her students, where 42 portals were evaluated, using the same methodology, it can be concluded that the Latvia's open data portal takes 16th position (Nikiforova, 2020b). It demonstrates the competitiveness of the Latvia's open data portal at international level, but at the same time proves that there is room for improvements.

Although the methodology used is considered relatively objective and covers key aspects to be evaluated, further aspects need to be explored. These aspects were defined by the author as the user of this portal based on observations about using this.

4.3 An Evaluation of the Portal from the Perspective of Experienced User

This part of the study is based on the analysis of every data set currently available on Latvia's open data portal. Thus, 395 datasets were analysed from a variety of aspects including: (a) whether datasets are regularly updated; (b) whether the description of the parameters is provided (and what is its form); (c) whether API is supported; (d) whether a preview option is available.

One of the most crucial aspects for open data and OGDs, which affects users' intention to reuse data and increase their value, however, is rarely ensured, is a **frequency of updates** (Janssen et al., 2012), (Saxena, 2017), (Smith et al., 2018). Since there is a major challenge in most cases to understand when the data are up to date, this aspect was analysed taking into account the frequency of updates promised by the data publisher and the actual frequency of updates. First, data on the frequency of updates provided by data publishers were analysed. 13 different values for frequency of updates were identified, namely "*daily*", "*weekly (once)*", "*monthly (once)*", "*constantly*", "*constantly updated*", "*quarterly*", "*annually (twice)*", "*annually (once)*", "*triennial*", "*irregular*", "*unknown*", "*never*", "*other*". "*Annually (once)*" value appears to be the most popular value since it is valid for 27.3% of datasets, following by *irregular, monthly, daily, annually (twice), never*. Then, it was decided to examine whether the frequency of updates of the data was in line with real life. To perform this task, three parameters describing each dataset were analysed, namely "*created*", "*last updated*" and "*frequency [of updates]*" (defined by the data publisher). The results prove the necessity for such an analysis demonstrating that the value of "*frequency*" does not correspond to actual updates, since only 45.8% of data sets are updated as frequently as promised, 25.4% do not follow the promised frequency of updates, and for 28.8% data sets it is difficult to say at the moment since the value of "*frequency*" is greater than the difference between the publishing and the current dates. In addition, (a) the use of different names designating the same object or its property was observed for two values, namely "*constantly*" and "*constantly updated*" - it is recommended to involve a list of allowable values or to develop and introduce a vocabulary that would reduce this issue, (b) values such as "*unknown*" and "*other*" should not be allowed at all since they do not provide supposed information.

Another aspect that needs attention was a **description of parameters** aimed at clarifying, what the name of each parameter means. It was found that only 20% of datasets are supplied with a description of parameters, where the textual description appears to be less popular, since 54.4% of the data sets are supplemented with the description of the parameters that is available as a separate file.

Another aspect related to the representation of data is whether the Application Programming Interface (**API**) is available. It is well known that data sharing in the form of machine-readable APIs is more useful for its further use (Sanderson et al., 2019) and is one of the most critical success factors for open data initiatives (Zuiderwijk et al., 2015). This is one of the most significant challenges for open data (McBride et al., 2018), and, in the context of Latvia, this is also valid, since only 43.04% of datasets (170 out of 395) are supplemented with API feature.

In addition, despite the fact that it is good practice to provide users with information on the number of applications (and preferably nature) based on open data that have been re-used – **use-cases**, which are able to attract more people to the portal and its data ((Zuiderwijk et al., 2015)), these data are not provided. One of such examples is demonstrated by our neighbours, the Lithuanian open data portal, which provides 9 use-cases of open data, and Poland (with 27 applications) providing them with both, links on the result and description. Of course, these two countries do not limit this list, since according to (Nikiforova, 2020b), the majority of countries provide this feature (71.43% of 42 analysed open data portals). In some cases, such as France, Luxembourg or Portugal, the national portal has even a "*use case upload*" feature, and 18 portals offer a mapping between the use cases and the datasets that the use cases are based on. One of such examples is Ireland. As for Latvia's portal, as a result of contacting representative organisations, it was found that such an information on hackathons is collected for internal use and a total of 29 applications were developed during two hackathons in 2018 and 2019. Most of them covers topics such as tourism, calculation queues to the hospitals or kindergarten, finding parking, finding the best place of life. Most of the developed services address topics that are crucial for Latvia and tries deciding sensitive problems that demonstrate the potential of open data and opportunities to improve citizens' lives. Therefore, it is strongly recommended to publish this information on the portal to demonstrate the positive effects of the use of open data, thereby increasing public participation. At the very early stage it would be recommended to follow at least Sweden example, where the list of "*good examples*" is provided with external list on the developed services.

However, although the abovementioned mainly concerns challenges, the current state of Latvia's open data portal is relatively high, that is proved by (Blank, 2019). Therefore, at least a few positive aspects should be mentioned in order to demonstrate why Latvia's open data portal holds sufficiently high positions in various ratings, despite a list of the challenges mentioned above that has not yet been solved. Among the positive aspects, some of which were already mentioned, there are: (a) the number of datasets and data publishers are provided and frequently updated; (b) two languages, namely Latvian and English, are supported; (c) the majority of datasets are downloadable and have at least basic set of [meta]data on it; (d) search and filter by category, data format, tags, data publisher; (e) a social media facility that can help create a social distribution channel for open data; (f) a request form (appears to be a problem to a list of countries) and (g) a contact facility with data publisher; (h) guidelines and news. However, aspects (e)-(g) have not been checked on whether they are working as intended, thus, it is difficult to draw any conclusions on their quality, and here only the fact of their presence is highlighted.

5. CONCLUSION

Nowadays, list of possible benefits and advantages motivate governments around the world to implement the OGD initiative, where the open data portal is one of the most important success factors. However, challenges and barriers raise major concerns about how to achieve successful implementation and results. If the quality of the open data portal is not high enough, potential data publishers may decide not to publish their data since they do not see a positive impact and their efforts will outweigh the positive effects they may have, but data users will not trust the data and will not find this portal usable and fit for their purposes. This study is of high importance, as (a) critical voices on the OGD and the open data portal appear in Latvia, (b) a literature review demonstrates that there are no studies focused on the OGD initiative, and, in particular, open data portal of Latvia. This is a gap that is covered by this paper, since the current situation is being assessed, and corrective actions are being recommended, which will hopefully move towards the effective implementation of the open data portal in Latvia.

The proposed study seeks to address the various researchers' calls by dividing the analysis into three parts: (a) a survey which studies the knowledge of the Latvian society, (b) the application of (Máchová et al., 2018) framework to the Latvia's open data portal, (c) an analysis of additional aspects inspecting each data set. The implementation of the guidelines defined should also improve user participation by encouraging the awareness and reuse of open data, which appears to be one of the most important aspects for each country opening its data, and that is one of the weakest points for Latvia, since the Latvian open data portal is certainly usable as assessed by the participants (6.3 out of 10 points) and demonstrated by the application of framework, however, there is room for improvements listed in this paper.

Although the results of this study are more important mainly for open data portal holders, they could also be useful for users, as these results (1) point to the weakest points to be taken into account using open data portal and (b) provide aspects to be considered when selecting the portal to be used. In addition, potential open data publishers can use the results provided as a checklist when preparing their data for publishing.

This study will be continued to carry out an in-depth analysis of the identified challenges and to propose guidelines to address them, as well as to provide a detailed comparison with more successful open data portals. A detailed literature review will also follow.

ACKNOWLEDGMENT

This work has been supported by University of Latvia Faculty of Computing project AAP2016/B032 “Innovative information technologies". I am also grateful to the participants taking part in the experiment within my workshop “*Open data and data quality*”, which allowed to collect data and led to such results, and Latvian Open Technology Association for sharing information regarding open data hackathons.

REFERENCES

Andrea, P., Alberto, P., & Barbara, R. (2012). E-government Services and User Expectations. In Proceedings of the International Conference on e-Learning, e-Business, Enterprise Information Systems, and e-Government (EEE) (p. 1). The World Congress in Computer Science, Computer Engineering and Applied Computing (WorldComp).

Attard, J., Orlandi, F., Scerri, S., Auer, S. (2015). A systematic review of open government data initiatives. Government Information Quarterly, 32(4), 399-418.

Blank, M. (2019) Open Data Maturity Report 2019, European Data Portal, online: https://www.europeandataportal.eu/sites/default/files/open_data_maturity_report_2019.pdf

Bojars, U., & Liepins, R. (2014). The State of Open Data in Latvia: 2014. Baltic Journal of Modern Computing, pp.160.

Faini, F., & Palmirani, M. (2016). Italian Open and Big Data Strategy. In International Conference on Electronic Government and the Information Systems Perspective (pp. 105-120). Springer, Cham.

Janssen, M., Charalabidis, Y., Zuiderwijk, A. (2012). Benefits, adoption barriers and myths of open data and open government. Information systems management, 29(4), 258-268.

Kim, H. (2019). Analysis of standard vocabulary use of the open government data: the case of the public data portal of Korea. Quality & Quantity, 53(3), 1611-1622.

Máchová, R., Hub, M., Lnenicka, M. (2018). Usability evaluation of open data portals. Aslib Journal of Information Management.

McBride, K., Toots, M., Kalvet, T., Krimmer, R. (2018). Open Government Data Driven Co-creation: Moving Towards Citizen-Government Collaboration. In International Conference on Electronic Government (pp. 184-195). Springer.

Nikiforova, A. (2020a) Definition and Evaluation of Data Quality: User-Oriented Data Object-Driven Approach to Data Quality Assessment. *Baltic Journal of Modern Computing*, 8(3), 391-432.

Nikiforova, A. (2020b) Comparative Analysis of the usability of National Open Data Portals or Whether Your Open Data Portal is Ready to Bring Benefits from Open Data (in print).

Nikiforova, A. (2019). Analysis of Open Health Data Quality Using Data Object-Driven Approach to Data Quality Evaluation: Insights from a Latvian Context, In IADIS International Conference e-Health 2019, Part of the IADIS Multi Conference on Computer Science and Information Systems, pp.119-126, MCCSIS 2019. IADIS.

Sanderson, T., Reeson, A., Box, P. (2019). Optimizing Open Government: an economic perspective on data sharing. In Proceedings of the 12th International Conference on Theory and Practice of Electronic Governance (pp. 140-143).

Saxena, S. (2017). “Usage by stakeholders” as the objective of “transparency-by-design” in open government data. Information and Learning Science.

Smith, G., Sandberg, J. (2018). Barriers to innovating with open government data: Exploring experiences across service phases and user types. Information Polity, 23(3), 249-265.

Zuiderwijk, A., Susha, I., Charalabidis, Y., Parycek, P., Janssen, M. (2015). Open data disclosure and use: Critical factors from a case study. In CeDEM15: Conference for E-Democracy and Open Government (Vol. 197). MV-Verlag.

PLAY THE GAME AND BE AWARE: INFORMATION SECURITY PROJECT WITH SCHOOLS

Regina Schuktomow, Margit Scholl, Peter Koppatz and Denis Edich
Technical University of Applied Sciences Wildau (TH Wildau)
Hochschulring 1, 15745 Wildau, Germany

ABSTRACT

Information security in everyday school life is an area with enormous potential for expansion. Schools are gradually adopting digitization, but there is a lack of knowledge about information security among both pupils and teachers, who have not been trained in appropriate practices. Creative methods such as game-based learning, accelerated learning, and authentic learning are being used to specifically promote the crucial topic of information security and awareness among pupils. In the present study, the use and development of digital simulations in the field of information security for pupils will be examined more closely using concrete examples, providing revealing insights into the process of raising awareness.

KEYWORDS

Information Security Awareness, Digital Simulations, Game-Based Learning (GBL), Accelerated Learning (AccL), Authentic Learning (AuL), Awareness Raising

1. INTRODUCTION

Digital teaching is on the rise, especially in the current state of emergency caused by Covid-19, and schools must adapt ad hoc to the conditions, switch over to distance learning, and find creative solutions. The transfer of knowledge knows no limits in terms of its multifaceted implementation. Frontal teaching in schools, project work in teams, self-study, digital learning platforms, and playful and experience-oriented learning—these modalities all have one goal: the transfer of information. Digitization and the digital learning associated with it are making progress. In the academic world, especially in Germany, there is considerable controversy about the effects of digitization in schools and the possible negative impact on learning success of young people spending significant quantities of time with terminal equipment and the Internet as a regular part of their everyday lives. The JIM study of 2018 shows that young people between twelve and nineteen years of age not only grow up with a wide range of media but also own a smartphone in 97 per cent of cases (Feierabend, et al., 2018, p. 587). The underlying information technologies permeate our lives. Pupils, in particular, need to be familiarized with this topic, because this target group is growing up with digitization and will shape the future. They must be made aware of the dangers lurking on the Internet and given a clear understanding of the basic values of information security (IS). These are *confidentiality*, protection against the unauthorized disclosure and transmission of personal information; *integrity*, ensuring the correctness of information and the correct functioning of systems; and *availability*, the ability to access data, information, services, networks, and components at any time. Depending on the purpose of the application, further protection goals are useful or legally necessary, such as *authenticity* as a guarantee that a person or IT component or an application is actually who or what it claims to be (BAköV, 2016, p. 13). Moreover, data protection is an important issue. This paper defines IS in everyday school life, explains the methods for conveying information security awareness (ISA), and provides examples of analogue and digital learning scenarios.

2. INFORMATION SECURITY AWARENESS AS AN EVERYDAY PART OF SCHOOL LIFE

The "SecAware4school" research project, funded by the Horst Görtz Foundation (HGS) from September 2018 to December 2020, aims to raise awareness of IS among approximately 600 pupils, teachers, and parents from five pilot schools in Berlin and Brandenburg. The goal is to raise awareness among pupils about the topic of IS in everyday school life. This is achieved through awareness training and specially developed analogue and digital learning scenarios. These are based on three learning methods: Game-Based Learning (GBL), Accelerated Learning (AccL), and Authentic Learning (AuL). In addition to being a varied and motivating form of learning, GBL enables pupils to focus on a set goal and direct feedback (Linek & Albert, 2009) (Fang, et al., 2013). AccL, on the other hand, requires pupils to go beyond passive perception to actively create knowledge (Bandura, 1969) (Mataric, 1994) (Rose & Nicholl, 1998) (Boyd, 2004). The approach aims to ensure that learners independently internalize skills over the long term. Among the many learning methods, narrative learning has proved to be particularly effective for children and adolescents. The combination of methods is applied in the form of experience-oriented learning scenarios using a process of emotionalization in the project as well as analogue and digital games that enhance motivation. Starting with information events, followed by IS awareness trainings (ISAT) and creative workshops, and ultimately training pupils as IS advisors, the learning scenarios were developed, tested, and finalized as key elements of the project.

The research work within the project is intended to highlight the fact that inculcating ISA relies on competent education. Schools lack the conceptual foundations and multipliers to teach pupils how to use media and the Internet safely. With the help of analogue GBL scenarios and digital simulations, it is possible to instil in young people a conscious awareness of information security. More than half (58%) of 12- to 19-year-olds use digital games several times a week at least (Feierabend, et al., 2018). The digital GBL simulations developed in the project can be broken down specifically for different age groups and topics. The focus is on the particular interests of the target groups and on concrete everyday situations, one of the aims being to familiarize them with the conscious and careful handling of personal data when using Internet services and social networks. Psychologically based corporate awareness research has shown that awareness-raising measures help emotionalize the topic in question while also enabling an exchange of experience (Scholl, et al., 2016) (Helisch & Pokoyski, 2009) (Haucke & Pokoyski, 2018). The sustainable promotion of awareness thus requires the emotional involvement of the target groups in the discussions about IS issues in concrete situations. The measures were designed as experience-oriented learning scenarios from the everyday lives of the target groups and were developed in analogue and digital form. The awareness raising is carried out in ISAT with the help of experience-oriented learning scenarios as well as coaching and mentoring concepts. Some of these have been modified or freshly developed from previous projects based on concrete everyday situations, a variety of languages, and three different levels of difficulty. A survey linked to the project revealed the following interests among pupils: information security in general, social networks, privacy, encryption, fake news, malware, and programming.

For various reasons and at the wish of the schools—who wanted to have as many classes as possible participate in the project—classes between Years 6 and 11 were included in the project. The school system in Germany comprises the primary and secondary educational sector, i.e. primary schools (grades 1-4) and the schools of the secondary levels I and II. In the latter, pupils of different ability levels are either taught together at one school (comprehensive school, Years 5–12) or taught separately (*Hauptschule*, Years 5–9; *Realschule*, Years 5–10; *Gymnasium*, Years 5–12/13). The particular challenge was to develop and adapt the learning scenarios to three different levels of difficulty. The first, and therefore easiest, level of difficulty covers Years 6 and 7; the second, middle level, Years 8 and 9; and the third and highest level, Years 10 and 11. Dividing the difficulty levels is advantageous, because knowledge transfer between pupils who are more or less the same age as each other is often perceived as more credible and authentic. The three different levels of requirement in the GBL scenarios promote the specific ongoing development of the participants. This is confirmed by Bressler & Bodzin (2013).

The development and testing of various measures tailored to the target groups is based on research into current conditions. An online survey in 2018 served as the basis for identifying relevant topics and the learning scenarios to be developed. Based on this, not only was the project presented to the pupils at information events but their specific needs and questions were also analysed by means of observation and active exchange. The insights gained from this analysis have been used to develop four new learning scenarios and to modify existing

GBL scenarios. The project relates to learning scenarios that have already emerged from previous projects on IS by our research group. This is done by taking into account the concrete everyday situations of the young people, their phraseology, and their age. According to their own self-classification, 481 pupils (63%), 84 teachers (11%), and 204 parents (27%) took part. The topic of fake news was evaluated overall as being of high to medium interest.

This online phenomenon has also become a permanent feature of corporate awareness research, but its significance for the economy and the personal working environment is still largely underestimated (Matas & Pokoyski, 2018, p. 19). A recent study with qualitative field research on the subject shows that disinformation is not a consequence of digital overload, which is why it is not enough merely to check the source of information (Take Aware Events, 2018) (Matas & Pokoyski, 2018, p. 21). Rather, the principle of misreporting must be understood in the context of the institution and situation, and its own mechanisms for dealing with information must be recognized. An awareness-raising measure that takes this into account "goes beyond a mere recognition of right and wrong—it rather requires self-reflection and digital attentiveness". (Matas & Pokoyski, 2018, p. 21). It is also noteworthy from the school survey that when the topic of video games was rated, there was only a 4% variance between the extremes in the level of interest expressed by respondents, ranging from "very" (34%) to "not at all" (30%). Moreover, the answer to this question is school-specific: one secondary school shows significant interest in video games (52% of those surveyed), while a Berlin grammar school (*Gymnasium*) tells a rather different story (36%).

One grammar school in the state of Brandenburg stands out in that 41% of the pupils surveyed showed no interest in video games at all. While the topic "Using video games safely" has to date been underexplored as a research area, it is also characterized by a very specific phraseology and abbreviations that are only known to active video gamers, so that developing a game-based awareness training for everyone (whether they are players or not) with a reduction in complexity represents a considerable challenge. This result can be substantiated by the JIM study, which found that boys with a low level of formal education showed a greater affinity for digital games than boys who attended a high school (Feierabend, et al., 2018). The topics of ISAT dealt with in the analogue and digital learning scenarios are oriented towards the interests of the participants and towards IS situations in everyday school life. For example, the objective of the analogue learning scenario "Behaviour in social networks" is to raise awareness of safe security behaviour. The task within the interactive educational game is to explain and guess certain IS terms in social networks.

The topics selected by the participants were implemented at three levels of difficulty in the experience-oriented learning scenarios that were developed. The learning scenarios in ISAT were tested with the participating pilot schools. Plans are also in place to train about 10% of the pupils at the participating pilot schools as young security consultants within the framework of a mentor/coaching concept. The aim is to enable young safety advisors to pass on their knowledge and experience to their classmates in the lower grades. ISAT, creative workshops, preparatory training, and an examination in line with the internationally recognized computer driving licence (ICDL) in the module "IT security" are milestones in the training of security consultants. The tasks of certified young security consultants include participating in the development of GBL scenarios at three levels of difficulty and moderating the (learning) scenarios for both pupils and parents.

3. DIGITAL SIMULATIONS

Young people use digital media tools to consume information, create videos, or, as the case may be, access and manage data (Ito, et al., 2009). The digital learning scenarios are thus precisely tailored to user behaviour and constitute additional support for self-study as well as independent and sustainable learning and teaching materials. Digital games and game-based scenarios have been associated with the constructivist view of learning. This can be attributed to the sandbox environment in which gamers are allowed to construct scenarios based on their cognitive and emotional experience (Rooney, 2012) (Kark, 2011) (Boyle, et al., 2011). The digitally simulated world has no spatial, material, or temporal limitations. These characteristics make it possible to construct arbitrary digital scenarios that depend only on human creativity and imagination. Digital simulations or scenarios are less expensive to produce because they can be updated and executed more quickly than analogue alternatives. Digital simulations should make learners curious about IS and motivate them to find out more about it, while playfully expanding their existing experience and knowledge (Spinner, 2006, pp. 6-16). Owing to its digital nature, a video game may have features and characteristics that can be used advantageously for learning scenarios (Plarium Team, 2017). The basic elements of a video game are gameplay, entertainment, game storage, repeatability, updatability, history, and information transfer via visual and audio channels. The goals that are defined can include one main goal as well as many secondary goals. The story can be integrated with the gameplay. The game session can be lost or won. Digital simulations—in this case, learning scenarios—are comparable to books, videos, audio podcasts, and lectures, because the same learning goals are pursued.

Digital simulations merely have a different presentation format, with different implementation requirements and other technological possibilities. Depending on the topic, there may be a variety of options for raising awareness in digital learning scenarios: during face-to-face teaching at school with the teachers or via tablets or notebooks—here, digital learning scenarios are integrated as part of the lessons, e.g. as a team or solo task. At this point, the multiplayer capability of the learning scenario can be used—for example, where all the pupils can view the results, statistics, etc., together on the main screen. A learning scenario can be analogue and digital at the same time and the two aspects can support each other, as in the learning scenario "Password Hacking" from a related project on IS, "Gender-Sensitive Study and Vocational Orientation for the Occupation Security Specialist (Security)" (Security, 2020). The previous projects and the related developments of the learning scenarios proved to be successful. An evaluation was carried out in the following way: at the beginning of the project, questions about passwords, for example, were asked in the information events, followed in the survey by *"How many characters must a password have in order to be considered relatively secure?"* The answers showed that a password with eight characters is still considered relatively secure, even if experts recommend more complex sequences with different combinations of characters. A clear majority of 606 people, 84% of 723 participants in this question, chose this correct answer. Only 20 people (3%) chose five characters. This shows that most people seem to be well informed about passwords. However, in further exchanges it became clear that less than half of the respondents (according to our estimate) actually use a password with eight or more characters. This result alone indicates a need for awareness raising, as there seems to be a gap between knowledge and behaviour. This corresponds to the findings of company awareness research (Scholl, et al., 2016) (Haucke & Pokoyski, 2018). When asked again in the awareness training, the students knew the correct answer. Some pupils reported that they had already changed their password to a more secure password. It can therefore be assumed that pupils had memorized the content and implemented the suggested measures. The ISAT using a variety of serious games evidently enabled the pupils to gradually improve their online behaviour and their conceptual understanding of digital security issues.

The digital simulations are well suited to solo learning. Since you usually only need your own computer, it is possible to organize it flexibly in terms of time and space (Engel, et al., 2018). Learning objectives in digital scenarios can be ordered according to complexity and include different cognitive competence levels, such as knowing, understanding, applying, analysing, etc. (Wannemacher, et al., 2016). The expenditure involved in developing and distributing digital simulations and in making such digital scenarios available is much lower than for analogue formats. Regardless of the mode of mediation, digital learning scenarios can be developed for specific topics, or existing sandbox games such as Minecraft (Thiel), Creatives, Skyrim (NewStatesman, 2014) can be used. Virtual Reality games can help to teach material in a creative way. For example, a professor from San Diego showed how fine geometry can be taught during the coronavirus lockdown in the game Half-Life: Alyx (volex24, 2020). In the development of digital simulations, deficits in the classical knowledge transfer of a certain topic need to be identified so that they can be turned to advantage in the process of creating a digital simulation. In general, it is always necessary to find out why digital simulations make more sense in a specific case than their analogue equivalents. This needs to be considered independently of the outlay of time and money. It does not matter what tools are used to implement the learning scenario—what is important is the realization of the learning goal. Furthermore, the circumstances must be taken into account and appropriate adaptations made. For example, not all schools have satisfactory computer room equipment. In developing the digital simulations, it is crucial to check the criteria and requirements in advance. The digital simulations are in a constant phase of testing and evaluation until they reach the specified goals and can be played intuitively.

With the help of digital learning scenarios, it is possible to convey complicated topics in a more understandable, emotional, and age-appropriate way. Various built-in reward systems help motivate pupils to solve the task in question (Webcampus, 2016).

3.1 Data Espionage: Secure Room

The digital simulation and learning scenario "Data Espionage: Secure Room" is intended to enhance recognition of objects with sensitive information, teaching pupils to store them correctly and leave their own workplace "safe and clean" (figure 1 and figure 2). This digital learning scenario can be compared to a "point and click" type of game. In order to achieve the best possible awareness training, this simulation shows the environment as a work office. The workroom or office reflects familiar objects and situations from home and reinforces the idea of a future workplace. A workplace was chosen for the reason that the relevant security objects and situations could occur there in particular. A completely simulated children's room would not have been appropriate, given the information security objects involved. This increases pupils' awareness of the need to pay more attention to security at their own computer workstations.

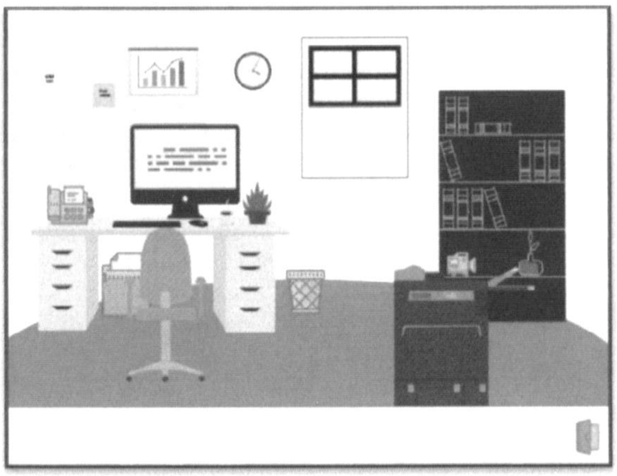

Figure 1. Serious digital game "Secure Room"—game view

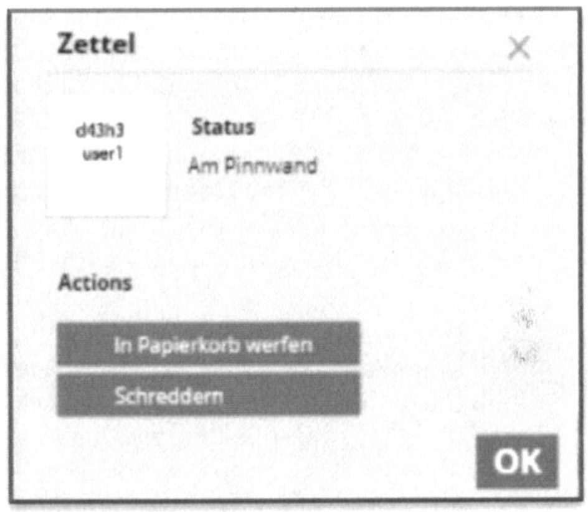

Figure 2. Digital "Secure Room"—Object Info Box

Different objects with sensitive content are distributed in a home office. The task is to recognize them and to select a suitable action with a mouse click. The clickable objects have so-called info boxes to allow a larger view, determine the current status, and select an action. Each object has individual actions, and each action is weighted differently. Here is an example: Object (note with password); Initial state (attached to pinboard); Select and execute action (throw it in the bin: −2 points, shred it: 2 points, hide it in a drawer: 1 point, do nothing: −1 point).

There is a door symbol shown in the bottom right corner, and the game ends when the participants decide to leave the room, at which point all the objects found are listed and the points assigned. Since the objects that were not found are not listed at the end of the learning scenario, the game can be repeated several times to achieve better results. The levels of difficulty depend on the topicality of the issues covered and the age of the target groups. An awareness about how sensitive information can be safely stored is thus instilled using a playful approach and realistic content.

3.2 Image Rights

Almost all schoolchildren have mobile devices that they carry around with them. Many of these devices also have a camera, and with multimedia devices it is not surprising that every event involving friends and acquaintances, no matter how minor, is recorded photographically. In the world of sharing it is often forgotten that there are rules for recording, processing, and sharing photos and videos. This is where the digital simulation "Image Rights" comes in (see https://secaware4school.wildau.biz/de/lernszenarien/bildrechte-digital, German-language version): it uses concrete examples to show what is and is not permitted. This ranges from a simple case to be decided with a yes/no response to multiple-choice questions, the most difficult level, which also includes a basic understanding of the law and legal decisions. The advantage of the digital version as compared to an analogue game is its variability. It is easy to add new questions and adapt the content to new legislation. The success of the awareness-raising will be even better if several young people (three to four) take the test together and discuss each question until a consensus is reached.

The aim of the learning scenario is to raise awareness and knowledge of the motifs that may be photographed without permission being required or without reading house rules or similar documents. This covers knowledge of the right to one's own image. The participants have to decide which motifs may be photographed without permission or which paragraphs in German law are being referred to. In this digital simulation, participants are made aware not only of the uses to which pictures can be put but also, at the third level of difficulty, of the basics of copyright law. The serious digital game "Image Rights" (not shown) sets out to raise awareness that pictures found on the Internet may not simply be used.

3.3 Storytelling

Narration means presenting something in narrative form—telling a story, for example. The ability to read and write is closely related to narratives. Past events are reconstructed as a narrative and linked to memories. The facts reconstructed in the process are reinterpreted, selected, and evaluated through retelling or presentation (Busch, 2013, p. 33). Narratives are based on autobiographical memories, experiences, and expectations. According to Fingerhut (n.d.), narration is a form of learning that contributes to the expansion of linguistic competencies. Thus, children and adolescents develop gender-specific behavioural patterns and anticipate future events in their imagination. Therefore, in narrative learning, the participants of the learning stations are listeners and at the same time affectively involved, whereby the narrative is stored in a way that is almost iconic (Fingerhut, n.d.). It should be noted that active imagination is an important component of narratives. Narration is understood as a language-developing and language-supported learning method. The narrated facts are modelled as events that can be experienced and thus turned into eventful learning.

The game principle for the learning scenario "Storytelling" is simple and effective (see figure 3 and figure 4): symbols must be built into the story. Extending the story to focus on a specific topic or a technical term on the subject of security, data protection, or privacy leads to intensive discussion of the given topic. The story can be funny, serious, or elaborate. What is important is the effect that is known as mnemonic, the ability to memorize many terms and their meaning with the help of a little story. In order to attain the learning goal, it is important for all the given symbols to be included in the story, which should in turn stimulate the imagination. This learning scenario is not limited to the topic of information security and can be used in any context. As an analogue version with pen and paper it may look like the following picture.

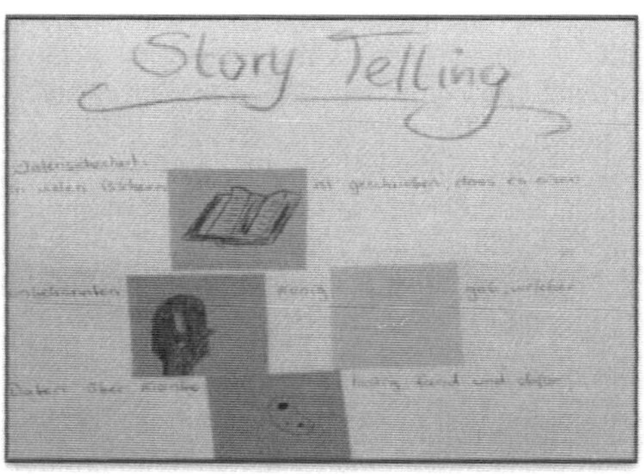

Figure 3. "Storytelling" using analogue storyboard

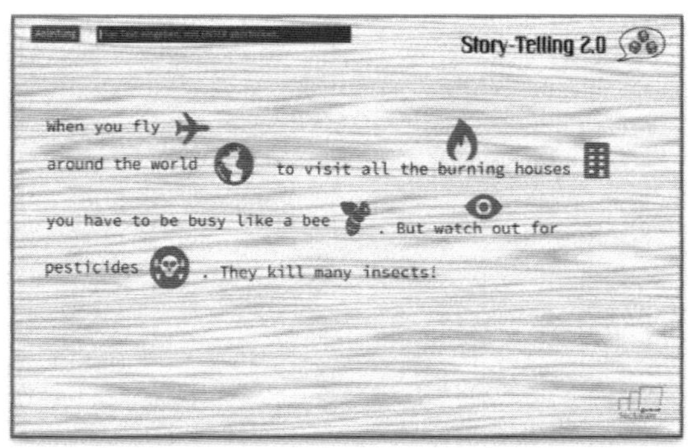

Figure 4. Serious digital game "Storytelling"

The different combinations of images on the dice bring versatility to the game, offering almost infinite variations, as the probability of a repeat combination is very low. In this serious game, awareness of the topic of information security is raised by linking the existing knowledge and experience available to the participants. Storytelling also promotes the repetition of technical terms and an intensification of information security knowledge. The aim of the learning scenario is to instil the basic concepts of information security and promote familiarity with the topic.

The analogue version has the following advantages: no investment in analogue game material and little effort required in terms of preparation if the stories are to be set out in writing. Based on these preconditions, different variants of the game were developed. Using a simple web application (Vue.js), a theme and a number of randomly generated symbols can be defined. The symbols are displayed after the "throw". A screenshot of this can be created and printed out. The preparation time for a course unit is therefore very short, which should be very helpful to moderators, game leaders, and teachers (story-telling, 2017).

The second variant in game development is always connected with the testing of new technologies. In the gaming sector, for example, there has been an increase in the use of 3D visualization. The disadvantages to this in terms of its general application in schools are the demanding requirements, such as high investment and installation costs, often coupled with payment barriers and fee-based licences. The current variant should also allow a form of writing that is similar to writing on paper. The Godot developer tool is used for this. Besides the random selection of symbols, this variant also offers the possibility of using Drag&Drop symbols to arrange text snippets in the same way as with paper, pen, and scissors. Other versions of storytelling can be viewed here: https://story-telling.methopedia.eu/ and https://story-telling-3d.methopedia.eu/.

The advantages are as follows: no preparation of materials is required, and a quick start can be made on the task if computer technology is available and only limited paper corrections are possible—using the digital application, improvements can be made to the text at any time. On the downside, there is no opportunity for pupils to practise their handwriting, which is an important exercise for the brain and enhances motor skills, coupled with the fact that as a group exercise only one team member can use the keyboard at a time, while all the others are passive spectators. This deficiency can be overcome if each team member writes their own story from the pictures that were rolled, after which all the stories can be exchanged as a team and the best story constructed together. Alternatively, after the dice have been rolled, a screenshot of the images on the dice can be turned into a collaborative writing program, with all the group members able to edit the text together. Moreover, there are often data protection regulations in place at schools, and pupils are required to log onto a platform. This is exactly what digital simulations are designed to avoid.

4. SUMMARY AND OUTLOOK

Digital games are a hot topic at the moment and have the potential to be an important addition to traditional knowledge transfer. But they cannot replace the active acquisition of knowledge, which is often referred to as "learning by doing". Thus, for learning to be successful, the digital supplement can be used as a means to get started or as a test at the end of a learning phase. While the rapid availability of digital games is an advantage, this is offset by inadequate technical equipment in many German schools. The costs in terms of technology, energy consumption, and administration should also not be underestimated. Textbook publishers and other providers typically want to make a profit, while politicians are looking to save on costs, which often has an impact on the educational sector. However, new didactic concepts are necessary for the integrative use of digital learning scenarios for IS in school lessons. Therefore, it is extremely important to develop experience-oriented learning scenarios supported by governmental research funds and make these available for free use as open-source material or an open educational resource (OER).

REFERENCES

BAköV (Bundesakademie für öffentliche Verwaltung im Bunbdesministerium des Innern) (Ed.), 2016. *Handbuch IT-Sicherheitsbeauftragte in der öffentlichen Verwaltung.* 5.0 / Federal Academy of Public Administration in the Federal Ministry of the Interior, *Manual IT Security Officer in Public Administration*, Version 5.0, Brühl.

Bandura, A., 1969. Social-learning theory of identificatory processes.. In: *Handbook of socialization theory and research.* p. 262.

Boyd, D., 2004. Effective teaching in accelerated learning programs. In: *Adult Learning (15 (1-2)).* pp. 40-43.

Boyle, E., Connolly, T. & Hainey, T., 2011. The role of psychology in understanding the impact of computer games. In: *Entertaiment Computing.*

Bressler, D. & Bodzin, A., 2013. A Mixed Methods Assessment of Students' Flow Experiences During a Mobile Augmented Reality Science Game. *Journal of Computer Assisted Learning*, 29(6), pp. 505-517.

Busch, B., 2013. *Mehrsprachigkeit.* Wien: Facultas.

Engel, A., Brunn, C., Günther, C., Petersheim, A. & Schenk, S., 2018: *Blended Learning an berufsbildenden Schulen*. Accessed on June 15, 2020.

Fang, X., Zhang, J. & Chan, S. S., 2013. Development of an Instrument for Studying Flow in Computer Game Play. *International Journal of Human-Computer Interaction*, 29(7), pp. 456-47.

Feierabend, S., Rathgeb, T. & Reutter, T., 2018. *Ergebnisse der JIM-Studie 2018.* s.l.:s.n.

Fingerhut, K., n.d. *Narration als Lernform im Fachunterricht und die Eweiterung von Sprachkompetenz im Fachunterricht.* o.O.

Haucke, A. & Pokoyski, D., 2018. *Mea culpa - Schuld, Scham und Opferrolle bei Social Engineering.* kes.

Helisch, M. & Pokoyski, D., 2009. *Security Awareness: Neue Wege zur erfolgreichen Mitarbeiter-Sensibilisierung.* Wiesbaden: Vieweg+Teubner.

Ito, M. et al., 2009. *Hanging out, messing around, and geeking out: Kids living and learning with new media.* Cambridge: MIT press.

Kark, R., 2011. Games managers play: Play as a form of leadership development. In: *Academy of Management Learning and Education 10(3)*, pp. 507-527.

Linek, S. B. & Albert, D., 2009. *Game-based Learning: Gender-specific Aspects of Parasocial Interaction and Identification.*

Mataric, M., 1994. *Reward functions for accelerated learning,* Machine Learning Proceedings.

Matas, I. & Pokoyski, D., 2018. *Von der Ente zur End-Täuschung.* kes.

NewStatesman, 2014. *NewStatesman.* [Online] Available at: https://www.newstatesman.com/culture/2014/11/how-skyrim-teaching-university-students-about-decline-us-empire. Accessed on April 27, 2020.

Plarium Team, 2017. *Plarium.* [Online] Available at: https://plarium.com/de/blog/video-spiele-hilfe-lernen/ Accessed on April 27, 2020.

Rooney, P., 2012. A theoretical framnework for serious game design. *International Journal of Game-Based Learning, 2(4)*, pp. 41-60.

Rose, C. & Nicholl, M., 1998. *Accelerated learning for the 21st century: The six step plan to unlock your master-mind.* s.l.:Dell Books.

Scholl, M., Fuhrmann, F. & Pokoyski, D., 2016. Information security awareness 3.0 for job beginners. In: *Proceedings of the Conference on ENTERprise Information Systems.* s.l.:s.n.

Security, 2020. [Online] Available at: https://security.wildau.biz/en.html. Accessed on April 27, 2020.

Spielekultur, S. D., n.d. *Bildung neu gestalten mit Games.*

Spinner, K. H., 2006. Literarisches Lernen. In: *Praxis Deutsch 200.* s.l.:s.n. story-telling, 2017. [Online] Available at: https://story-telling.methopedia.eu/. Accessed on April 27, 2020.

Take Aware Events, 2018. *Von der Ente zur End-Täuschung. Studie, veröffentlicht anlässlich der 2. Social Engineering-Konferenz BLUFF CITY,* Köln.

Thiel, T., kein Datum *Storytelling mit Minecraft: "Das ist wie Lego".* [Online] Available at: https://magazin.sofatutor.com/lehrer/storytelling-mit-minecraft-das-ist-wie-lego/. Accessed on April 27, 2020.

volex24, 2020. *volex24.* [Online] Available at: http://volex24.com/half-life-alyx-ein-lehrer-hielt-einen-vortrag-ueber-valves-vr-titel/. Accessed on April 27, 2020.

Wannemacher, K., Jungermann, I., Scholz, J., Tercanli, H. & von Villiez, A., 2016. Digitale Lernszenarien im Hochschulbereich. Im Auftrag der Themengruppe "Innovationen in Lern- und Prüfungsszenarien" koordiniert vom CHE im Hochschulforum Digitalisierung, Berlin: Edition Stifterverband - Verwaltungsgesellschaft für Wissenschaftspflege mbH.

Webcampus, 2016. *webcampus.* [Online] Available at: https://www.webcampus.de/blog/22/gamification-in-e-learning-6-wichtige-vorteile. Accessed on April 27, 2020.

A NEUROPHYSIOLOGICAL INVESTIGATION OF DESIGN THINKING PROCESS IN HUMAN-COMPUTER INTERACTION DESIGN

Abhishek Dahiya, Abhijeet Kujur and Jyoti Kumar
Indian Institute of Technology Delhi
UX Lab, IIT Delhi, India

ABSTRACT

This paper investigates the design thinking process of a designer while solving a Human-Computer Interaction (HCI) design problem. HCI design requires a considerable amount of user information to take design-related decisions. HCI designers are often asked to think through the user's mental models and cognitively empathize with the users while designing. Due to this, designers collect and refer user data to develop more user-friendly products. But with increased use and reliance on user data to solve complex interaction design problems, it becomes important to investigate how the design thinking process of a designer is affected by the introduction of user information. The experimental study presented in this paper is aimed to understand the transformations in design thinking process with the introduction of user information.

KEYWORDS

Design Thinking, User Centered Design, HCI Design, EEG, Linkography

1. INTRODUCTION

With the advent of User Centered design philosophy, the design process has become more user focused. The focus of design has shifted from creating more efficient products to more user-friendly products. Hence, designers are encouraged to involve users in the design process and use insights from user research to develop products. With the advancement in design research, new methods and tools are being developed that help designers to understand and empathize with their users. These methods are helpful in getting an in-depth understanding about user needs, behavior, user motivations, pain points etc. Apart from understanding users, designers are also expected to produce novel solutions for design problems at hand(Cross, 2011). Design thinking involves generation of new ideas or concepts for solving complex design problems (Dorst and Cross, 2001). The authors posit that with increased use of user information in design process and design process becoming more user data driven, there are high chances that user information might influence designer's natural design thinking process. This paper investigates the effect of user data on the design thinking process of a designer.

2. BACKGROUND

2.1 User Data in HCI

User-Centered Design (UCD) is defined as "a philosophy based on the needs and interests of the user, with an emphasis on making products usable and understandable"(Norman, 2013). UCD process has advocated the need to understand users before creating design solutions(Ferris, 2004). The need to understand users is argued to be the difference in mental model between a designer and a user(Wykes,1984). Therefore, a design solution produced without understanding users might not solve the actual problem or might be difficult to use(Norman, 2013); (Ferris, 2004); (Wykes,1984);(Corry, Frick and Hansen, 1997). It is due to UCD philosophy that many new design methods have been developed which try to involve users at almost every step of the design process, for example, participatory design, co design etc. HCI design is one the fields of industrial design which has a greater reliance on user information for taking design related decisions. This is due to the fact that products produced in HCI design are highly interactive and cognitively demanding for the users. Hence, designers require in-depth knowledge about the user's cognitive behaviour, mental models, decision making process, information perception, visual ergonomics etc. to design an efficient interacting system. A typical HCI design process follows following steps: identification of problem, user research, specifying needs of the user, ideation for solutions, evaluation, prototyping, user testing, final product. Due to the nature of interaction design problems, designers need to rely more on user data and less on their personal hunch to take crucial design decisions. Therefore, various user research methods have been developed for HCI design which help designers to understand their users. Some of these methods are Usability testing, Card sorting, Interviewing, Eye tracking, Paper prototyping etc. Data collected from these methods is analysed and processed in various formats like persona, scenario, mood boards, UX journey maps, documentary videos etc. But with the use of huge chunks of user information and complexity of HCI design problems the question arises that what happens to the design thinking process of a designer? How does user information affect the design thinking process of a designer?

2.2 User Data Affecting Design Thinking

Design thinking has been extensively studied in literature from various perspectives. Several different terms like intuitive thinking, creative thinking, innovative thinking, novel thinking have been used in a synonymous manner to design thinking. However, design thinking often argued to include two types of thinking processes. These processes are indicated through several terminologies such as ideation and evaluation(Basadur, 1995), vertical and horizontal thinking transformations(Goel, 2014), associative and analytic thought (Gabora, 2010). The two opposite thinking processes indicated above are generally termed as divergent and convergent thinking(Goldschmidt, 2016). The term convergent thinking signifies thinking that brings together information focused on solving a problem. This type of thinking process is found when the person tries to make a sense of some information to arrive at a conclusion. Divergent thinking involves moving away in diverging directions so as to involve a variety of aspects leading to novel ideas and solutions"(Goldschmidt, 2016). This type of thinking process is observed when designers are trying to brainstorm to generate design solutions.

Design thinking is a complex process. Creative outcomes in the design process are influenced by a number of cognitive applications and combinations(Bonnardel,2000). This is primarily because the characteristics of design activities typically present indefinite criteria and constraints, which makes it difficult to study design thinking(Cross, 2001). Research outcomes are used in developing design methods, processes, and design techniques. There are several studies reported in literature that aims to investigate the effect of various stimuli on design thinking. Studies reported in literature indicated differences in design thinking pattern of designers while working with user information(So and Joo, 2017) in various formats(Dahiya and Kumar, 2019), with additional training like empathy exercises((Dahiya and Kumar, 2018.) etc. However, there is a dearth of literature on how user information affects the HCI design thinking process of a designer.

2.3 Mental Processes Involved in Design Thinking

As discussed in the previous section, analysis and synthesis are two distinct mental processes that are involved in design thinking. These two processes serve two functions which are understanding the problem and producing a solution (Gedenryd, 1998). A few mental processes involved in design thinking include:

Analytic thinking: Analysis operation plays a key role in analysing the given problem, task, goal, etc. A designer starts conceptualising from a set of chosen functional requirements that are derived from the problem statement and understanding the needs of the users. Such a type of mental process where it requires a conscious and deliberate attempt to interpret or evaluate information with a set of reflective attitudes is considered an analytical or convergent thinking process.

Creativity: Creativity has been discussed as an essential tool in the process of design thinking, one that designers employ to think of novel ways or produce ideas to solve design problems. Lubart explains the creative process as "a sequence of thoughts and actions leading to a novel, adaptive production'(Lubart, 2001). Plucker explained creative thinking as 'interconnections of ideas that grow into complex, organized mental structures of information'(Plucker and Dow, 2009). Generation of a creative thought or an idea is a result of a designer's intra-mental thinking process with a conscious effort of thinking diverse solutions.

Memory retrieval: Memory retrieval is one the underlying cognitive processes that influence the probability of a creative outcome. Memory retrieval in idea generation processes, have been identified to include retrieval of various types of information, for example specific category exemplars, general knowledge, images, source analogues, etc.(Ward and Kolomyts, 2010). Information from memory not necessarily complete creative solutions to the given design problem, but rather represent possible starting points that can facilitate or create creative outcomes (Ward and Kolomyts, 2010).

2.4 Analyzing Design Thinking

Many studies in literature have studied the design thinking process using qualitative measurement tools like interviewing, think aloud method, retrospective interview methods, analysis of sketching activities etc. Qualitative research methods often have some limitations in capturing design thinking processes. This is due to the fact that mental processes involved in design ideation are very fast and it is hard for researchers to capture such processes using methods like interviewing. Above all, qualitative methods are often criticized for subjective reporting. Therefore, in this study we use a mixed methods approach to observe design thinking and cross validate the results. Linkography is used to qualitatively analyse verbal protocols and EEG as a tool to observe cognitive patterns while designing.

2.4.1 Linkography

Linkography is a technique used in protocol analysis to study a designer's cognitive activities. Verbal protocols are first parsed into design moves which is a 'a step, an act, an operation, which transforms the design situation relative to the state in which it was prior to that move' (Goldschmidt, 2014). Design moves are then linked according to their relationship to form a linkograph. Linkograph produced is thus a graphical representation of cognitive activities involved in solving the design problem. Components of a linkograph include: Link node: point of intersection of two design moves; Backlinks: links of moves that connect to previous moves; Forelinks: links of moves that connect to subsequent moves; Critical move: design moves that are rich in links, they can be either forelinks, backlinks, or both; Web: a large number of links among a relatively smaller number of moves; Chunk: a group of moves that are almost exclusively linked to themselves; Link index: ratio between the number of links and the number of moves. An example of a linkograph is shown in Figure 1.

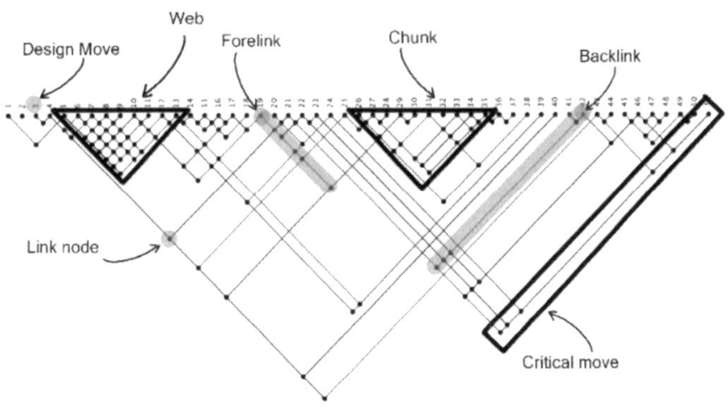

Figure 1. Example of a Linkograph with its constituents

2.4.2 Electroencephalography (EEG)

Electroencephalogram or EEG is a tool that helps in recording brain activities. EEG works on the principle that functioning of brain cells in the form of neural impulses are detected and recorded using EEG electrodes. EEG electrodes are placed on the scalp to record electrical signals in microvolts. The placement of electrodes is generally followed by 10-2- International System of Electrode Placement. The electrical signals recorded using EEG are in the form of waves which are categorised on the basis of frequency. The four frequency bands are delta (1-4Hz), theta (4-8Hz), alpha (8-13Hz) and beta (13-30Hz). Delta and theta bands are commonly found during sleep or calm state of brain. Alpha is evident mainly during the low mental activity whereas beta and gamma are produced when the brain is involved in higher cognitive functions. Human brain regions are divided into lobes, namely frontal lobe, parietal lobe, temporal lobe, and occipital lobe. Each lobe is responsible for performing a different type of function. For example, frontal lobe is responsible for planning, judgement, decision making, emotions and concentration. Parietal lobe performs functions like verbal understanding, texture and shape interpretation. Temporal lobe is responsible for auditory processing and storing auditory memory. Occipital lobe is responsible for visual processing. Before moving further in analysing design thinking, it is important to review the mental process involved in design thinking from a neurological perspective. Alpha synchronisation and creativity: The phenomenon of increased alpha power has been labelled as synchronization of EEG. It is argued in literature that alpha synchronization especially in frontal and posterior parietal brain regions of the right hemisphere is related to creative task demands (more creativity-related tasks are accompanied by more alpha activity) e.g.(Fink, Benedek, et al., 2011),and originality of ideas (the generation of more original ideas is accompanied by higher alpha activity (Fink, Grabner, et al.,2006) (Benedek et al., 2011). Memory retrieval: Cognitive resources in memory retrieval are devoted to effective memory search and retrieval. It is found that parietal alpha synchronization is an indicator of efficient memory processing(Fink and Benedek, 2014). Convergent thinking: Convergent or analytical thinking in the brain is associated with theta band power. Razoumnikova argues that convergent thinking-induced coherence is increased in the caudal regions of the cortex in the theta band(Razoumnikova, 2000). Power in the theta band is increased over frontal recordings during convergent thinking in comparison with divergent thinking(Mölle et al., 2010, Liu et al., 2018)

3. OBSERVING DESIGN THINKING PROCESS FOR HCI DESIGN

3.1 Experiment Methodology

To investigate design thinking process, designer's solution generation approach to a given HCI design problem was studied. This method is used in various studies aiming to understand creativity, design thinking, problem solving process etc. In this study, the participant was asked to design conceptual solutions for two design problems. One design problem was introduced without any information about the user. The other problem was given with the user information. While the participant ideated for solutions, brain mapping tool (EEG) recorded changes in brain activities the process. The participant was asked to think aloud while sketching for design solutions. Verbal data along with EEG data was used to observe design thinking process. The experiment was conducted on one participant. The participant was right handed, 26 yrs. old male student of post-graduate course in industrial design program. It was ensured that participant is in healthy mental and physical condition.

3.2 Design Problem

Two HCI design problems were given to the participant. Participant was asked to design a mobile application in both design tasks. It was ensured that both design problems are different. This was done to ensure that the participant do not get biased towards the solutions proposed earlier. However, it was also ensured that both the problems are not very different from one another so that results might get affected due to difference in complexity of the design problem. The two design problems given to the participant were management applications which will be used to perform similar type of tasks. The design problems given to the participant were: Design problem 1 (DP1): Design a mobile application for time management which can help a person to keep a track of their events, get reminders, schedule meetings etc. Design problem 2 (DP2): Design a mobile application for money management which can help a person to keep a track of their credit, debit, and other expense related records. User data provided to the participant was in form of a persona. was displayed on the screen in front of the participant. Figure 2 shows the persona information shown to the participant.

Manoj (32) is daily wage labour from Bihar. He is working in Gurgaon on a building construction site. Manoj gets Rs. 450 (approx. 6USD, very low income) for working 8 hrs a day. He sends most of his savings back home in Bihar. Manoj could not get formal education. However he can read and write and has a very basic understanding of simple mathematics. He suffers loss in money because of his inability to do simple calculations. His son made him buy a simple smartphone which helps him remain connected to his family and also helps in his entertainment. Manoj is able to use simple applications like WhatsApp, YouTube, wynk etc. He can do basic conversation in Hindi using English alphabets on WhatsApp and is able to feed keywords to generate content for YouTube and wynk. He also has an understanding of basic mathematical symbols like +, -, x, /.

Figure 2. Persona given to the participant

3.3 Experiment Procedure

The experiment started by getting a consent form signed by the participant. A brief of the experiment procedure was explained. The participant was then moved to the experimental setup location where EEG cap was put. Eye tracker glasses were put and calibrated. It was ensured that experiment room is quiet, and free from other visual distractions. Participant was given A3 sheets and sketch pens for ideation and designing. Instructions for the design task were displayed on a screen in front of the part.

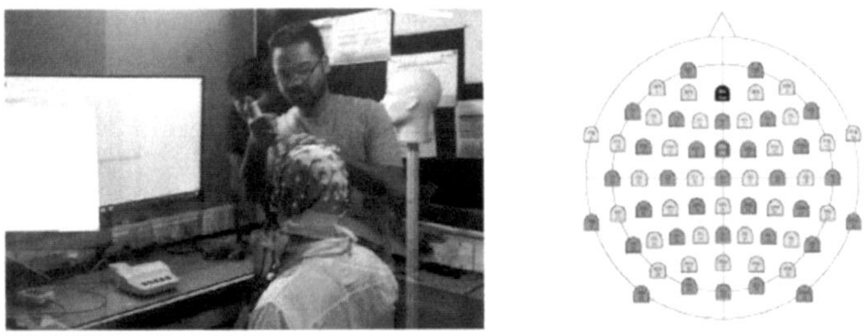

Figure 3. Experimental setup(left), EEG electrode positions(right)

Before starting the experiment the participant was asked to sit and relax for two minutes. This was done to get brain signal data of the participant in the resting state. Next, first design task 1 was displayed on the screen. The participant was given 20 minutes for completing the task. The participant was free to ask any question/queries related to the design task, though he didn't ask any. While the participant was also thinking aloud while sketching the solutions for the first design task. After the first design task, the participant was again asked to relax for five minutes. After five minutes, the participant was asked to thoroughly read the information about a user which was displayed in form of a persona. As the participant finished reading persona, the second design task was introduced and participant was asked to again design conceptual solutions for the given design task. The time given for this design session was 20 minutes. The participant was allowed to refer the user information displayed on the screen as many times as he wanted. After 20 minutes, the experiment was completed and the participant was thanked with a gift for his participation.

3.4 Data Collection and Processing

Verbal protocols were recorded when the participant was thinking aloud during ideation. The protocols were first transcribed into text and then separated to identify the design moves. Along with the verbal protocols, designer's behavioural data and eye tracker data were used to document designer's micro activities along the timeline. EEG data was recorded and analysed for following brain regions: frontal left (FP1, FC9, F3, F7), frontal right (FP2, FC10, F4, F8), fronto-central left (FC1, FC5), fronto-central right (FC2, FC6), centro-temporal left (C3, T7), centro-temporal right (C4, T8), centro-parietal left (CP1, CP5), centro-parietal right (CP2, CP6), parieto-temporal left (P3, P6), parieto-temporal right (P4, P8), occipital left (O1), and occipital right (O2). Eye tracker was also used to track eye movements of the participant while performing the tasks. The raw EEG signals were analysed using Brain Vision Analyser 2.2 (Brain Products.). Brain activity during the performance of experimental tasks was quantified by means of spectral frequency changes using Fast Fourier Transform (FFT) in the EEG. First, EEG data were captured and collected through the Brain Product LiveAmp-64 from the participant while they were carrying out the design tasks. All the operations were executed via Analyser 2.2 software using 8th order Infinite Impulse Response (IIR) filter with cut-off frequency from 0.5 Hz to 40 Hz. Sampling frequency was changed to 250 Hz using spline interpolation method. Accelerometric channels in the EEG were de-selected. Independent component analysis was done for the Ocular correction using mean slope blink detection algorithm and both horizontal and vertical ocular activities were removed. The recorded EEG data was then segmented into four parts according to the tasks done by the participant using the manual segmentation method. The frequency spectrum of alpha, beta and theta bands were obtained using Fast Fourier Transform (FFT) to extract a statistical feature such as spectral power.

3.5 Data Analysis

The data collected was analysed in two phases. First phase - Generating linkographs: As explained in previous section, verbal protocols along with notes on designers behavioural data were identified as design moves. Next step was to code these design moves. The coding scheme was generated taking references from literature along with the participant's behaviours identified during the session. The design moves were primarily coded into three activities i.e. Analysis, Synthesis and Evaluation. Analysis refers to the act of understanding and formulation of the problem. Synthesis refers to the act of generating solutions or creating ideas. Evaluation refers to the act of rechecking the created design solution against design requirements. These codes were subdivided further into more categories. Analysis involved Requirement Formulation(RF), Referring Requirements(RR). Design moves where the designer was formulating design requirements from the design brief were coded into RF. Design moves when the designer is referring the design requirements which were either given or formulated by him were coded into RR. Synthesis activity was divided into Solution Generation (SG) i.e. design moves where designer is creating a new solution, new solution, Solution Addition (SAN) i.e. adding a new feature to a design solution and Solution Alteration (SAE) which means altering an earlier created solution. Evaluation (SR) mostly involves the act of reflecting back on previously created designs. The coded design moves were then used to create linkographs for further analysis.

The second phase of analysis involved analysing the brain signal data recorded using EEG. Total recording time for both the sessions was 45 minutes i.e. 20 minutes for first design session, 20 minutes for second design session and 5 minutes when the participant was not performing any activity. Recording from both the sessions were divided into segments. These segments were identified on the bases of design moves which were coded earlier. Design moves which were having similar codes and were adjacent to each other were grouped into a single segment. This step was taken assuming that adjacent design moves with similar codes would show little differences in the brain signal data as the participant is involved only in type of cognitive activity for a prolonged period of time. An example showing the extraction of a segment is shown below. A total of 22 segments were identified in first session and 17 segments were identified in second session.

Table 1. An example of segmentation process from design activity

Design Move	Start time	End time	Activity	Code	Segment
16	02:02:00	02:09:00	adds events/festivals in layout	RF	7
17	02:09:00	02:22:00	thinks of what more can be added in layout	RF	
18	02:22:00	02:27:00	went back to note and adds "space"	SAN	8
19	02:27:00	02:29:00	looks at screen, utters what more can come	RF/RR	9
20	02:29:00	02:34:00	looks at screen	RR	
21	02:34:00	02:50:00	looks back to the sheet of what all he has written	RR	
22	02:50:00	03:03:00	started sketching screen layout, draws rectangle for screen	SG	10
23	03:03:00	03:09:00	draws side panel of the screen	SG	

3.6 Observations and Results

Figure 4 shows linkographs created for both design sessions. The linkograph on left shows the design thinking process while solving design problem without user data. Linkograph on right shows design thinking process for design problem with user data. The design moves for these linkographs are colour coded on the basis of design activities performed by the designer during the session.

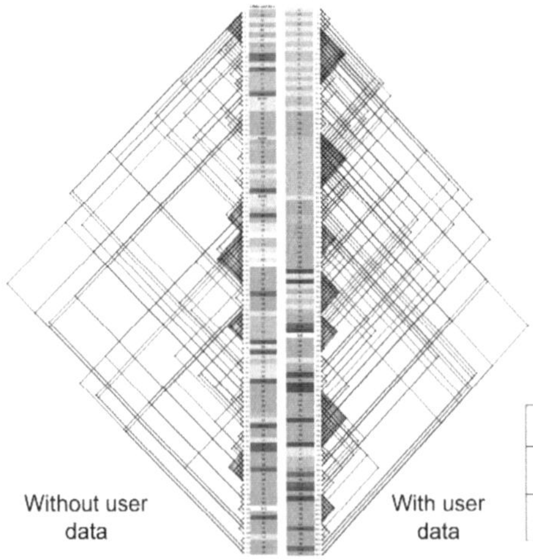

Coding Distribution of Design Activities in Linkographs

		Without User Data		With User Data	
Design Activity	**Code**	No. of moves	% share	No. of moves	% share
Analysis	RF	20	17.9	25	22.5
	RR	30	26.8	22	19.9
Synthesis	SG	47	42.0	48	43.2
	SAN	6	5.4	5	4.5
	SAE	1	0.9	1	0.9
Validation	SR	8	7.0	10	9.0

Quantitative data from Linkographs

	No. of Critical moves (CM^5)	**Link Index**	**Forelink entropy**	**Backlink entropy**	**Horizontal Link entropy**
Without user data	8	1.57	21.39	27.11	9.79
With user data	11	2.43	28.97	36.33	14.12

Figure 4. Linkographs for both design sessions(left), Coding distribution and quantitative data(right)

Qualitative assessment of Linkograph: From the physical characteristics of both the linkographs, it can be observed that idea links in case where designer is working without user data are much coarser than the other case. This feature indicates that the designer was able to hold his initial ideas/design moves more in the case where user data was provided. Further, the initial region of linkograph for design session where the participant was working with user data is denser. Design moves in this region are mostly Requirement Formulation(RF), and Referring Requirements(RR). These codes are associated with Analysis activity of the design problem solving process. Hence the designer was majorly involved in analysing the design problem in the initial part of the problem solving process. While in the other case, the initial part of the linkograph does not have much cohesiveness in the design moves. The design moves in this region are mostly Requirement Formulation (RF), and Solution Generation (SG). This indicates that the designer was shifting from Analysis to Synthesis and again to Analysis in this case. Requirements were formulated along with creating solutions for the design problem.

Quantitative assessment of Linkograph: Critical moves in linkographs are important turning points in the thinking process (Kan, Bilda and Gero, 2007). A higher value of link index and more number of critical moves in a linkograph is an indicator of a more productive design process (KAN, BILDA and GERO, 2006). Quantitative data table shown above shows a rise in the number of critical moves and link index for session where the designer was working with the user data. This indicates that the designer underwent a more productive design thinking process while working with user data as compared to the other case.

Entropy of idea links in a linkograph is helpful in indicating the creative thinking behaviour of the individual. The table showing quantitative data from the linkograph indicates rise in fore link entropy, backline entropy and horizontal link entropy the designer working on design problem with user data was provided to them. Forelink entropy in the first design session could indicate weak ideas or more idea fixation (Kan, Bilda and Gero, 2007). Low fore link entropy value of designers working without user data could be a result of weak ideas or more idea fixation (Kan, Bilda and Gero, 2007). This result explains the coarse nature of idea links that was observed in qualitative assessment of linkograph. Low backlink entropy value is indicative of a new idea generation process (Kan, Bilda and Gero,2007). This indicates that designer working without user data was able to take more novel design moves as compared to the session when the design problem was given with user information. High value of horizontal link entropy in the second design session is indicative of cohesiveness in design thinking process. Designer working on design problem after providing user data tend to reflect back on his initial thoughts about user requirements which resulted in more cohesive design thinking process and high horizontal link entropic value.

Table 2. Spectral power values for alpha, beta and theta band for both design sessions

	ANALYSIS						SYNTHESIS					
Brain region	ALPHA		BETA		THETA		ALPHA		BETA		THETA	
	Without data	With data	Without data	With data	Without data	With data	Without data	With data	Without data	With data	Without data	With data
Frontal left	2.08	1.67	4.22	4.31	3.18	2.93	1.89	1.78	5.67	3.96	3.15	2.83
Fronto central left	1.22	1.26	5.79	4.15	1.41	1.80	1.55	1.11	7.33	2.56	1.75	1.80
Centro temporal left	3.99	4.29	54.31	40.28	2.23	3.99	4.67	2.24	7.00	5.65	2.96	3.52
Parietal left	1.43	1.82	3.68	3.33	2.21	3.43	1.84	1.89	4.14	2.90	2.49	3.40
Parieto temporal left	6.56	9.14	22.00	18.35	15.25	12.25	6.45	7.62	11.95	14.15	7.20	11.32
Occipital left	4.68	4.27	12.40	6.50	4.05	7.59	4.75	5.92	12.54	11.12	4.08	7.31
Occipital right	5.42	4.56	15.58	6.53	3.92	7.59	5.10	5.79	13.79	12.51	3.82	7.19
Parietal right	1.83	4.17	6.96	6.53	2.38	7.26	3.00	4.75	8.42	6.13	2.70	6.97
Centro parietal right	2.39	1.73	4.52	2.84	3.25	3.68	2.58	2.17	4.17	3.08	3.38	3.40
Centro temporal right	1.33	1.87	4.35	3.35	1.68	3.99	1.37	1.97	4.56	3.89	1.70	3.58
Fronto central right	1.51	1.44	6.06	6.97	1.57	2.48	1.22	1.37	7.02	6.13	1.61	2.10
Frontal right	1.06	1.69	2.69	3.40	1.90	2.71	1.15	1.68	3.53	3.39	1.82	2.41

EEG Data Analysis: EEG data shown in Table 2 shows difference in alpha, beta and theta power spectral bands at various brain regions. From the table it can be observed that there is rise in alpha and theta band power values where the designer was working on the given design problem with user data. However, drop in beta band power is observed when the designer is working on the design problem user data.

Alpha synchronisation: Literature reports that rise in alpha band power in the right frontal region of the brain is associated with the creative thinking process (Benedek et al., 2011). This indicates that designers working on the design problems with user data underwent a more creative thinking process as compared to the other case. Nguyen (Nguyen and Zeng, 2014) proposed a relationship between creative performance and mental effort. It is argued that creative performance is associated with high mental effort ability while low mental effort is associated with low creative ability. Liu (Liu et al., 2018) explains mental workload as the total use of cognitive resources. Mental workload is positively correlated with alpha and theta band power and negatively correlated with beta band power (Liu et al.,2018). From the table given above it can be seen that there is a rise in alpha and theta bands and drop in beta band power when the designer is working on a design problem with user data. Hence, the designer while working with user data underwent a greater mental workload as compared to the case where no user data was provided with the design problem.

Analytical thinking: Convergent or analytical thinking in the brain is associated with theta band power. It was observed that there was a rise in theta band power in the case where the designer was working on the design problem with user data. This behaviour indicates that the designer working on the design problem with user data took more efforts in analysing the given data. In design thinking, analysis operation is observed in defining requirements, design task, goal, etc. This observation is in line with the linkography results, it was observed that there was a rise in the percentage share of requirement formulation (RF) design moves.

Memory retrieval: Parietal alpha synchronization is an indicator of efficient memory processing. As shown in table 2, alpha synchronisation was observed in parietal locations like parietal left, parietal right, parieto-temporal left and parieto-temporal right in the case where the designer was working with user data. This indicates that the designer working on the design problem with user data was able to perform design moves that originated from parietal memory locations. Table 2 also compares alpha, beta and theta power bands for two types of design activities, i.e. activity including problem analysis, problem synthesis. Spectral power for each frequency band was observed at different brain regions. It was observed that power was higher in analysis activities in left brain regions including left centro-temporal and left parieto-temporal. Similarly, for synthesis activities spectral power was observed higher in almost all right brain regions including occipital right, parietal right, centro parietal right, centro temporal right, and frontal right. Figure 5 graphically represents the data shown in table 2.

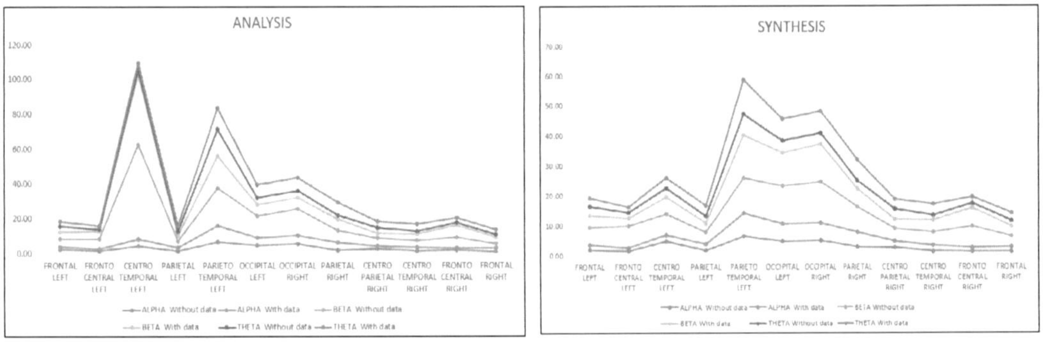

Figure 5. Graphical representation of spectral power values for alpha, beta and theta band for both design sessions

4. CONCLUSION AND DISCUSSION

With the increased use of user information in HCI design, many design related decisions are dependent on data facts. Thus, while creatively thinking about design solutions, designers have to keep a track of various user related issues. The preliminary study reported is aimed to observe changes in design thinking process of a designer with the introduction of user information. Study results indicate that providing user information to the designer results in a more productive design process, despite increasing the mental workload. The authors would like to admit that the observations were limited to only one participant and it will be too early to the generalize the findings. Through an increase in number of participants and exploring the effect of user information on different types of design problems the results can be validated.

The study presented in this paper aimed to understand how increase in user information affects the design thinking process of a designer. Investigations in this area can be helpful in design domains where design decisions are heavily dependent on user research. Findings from such studies can provide answers to questions like how much user study is beneficial? What should be the format in which the user data can be presented to a designer? Which is better: Providing user data before introducing the design problem or after the design problem? How to help designers to think more creatively while working with user data? etc.

REFERENCES

Basadur, M. (1995) "Optimal Ideation-Evaluation Ratios," Creativity Research Journal, 8(1).

Benedek, M. et al. (2011) "EEG alpha synchronization is related to top-down processing in convergent and divergent thinking.," Neuropsychologia, 49(12), pp. 3505–3511.

Bonnardel, N. (2000) "Towards understanding and supporting creativity in design: analogies in a constrained cognitive environment," Knowledge-Based Systems, 13(7–8).

Corry, M. D., Frick, T. W. and Hansen, L. (1997) "User-centered design and usability testing of a web site: An illustrative case study," Educational Technology Research and Development, 45, pp. 65–76.

Cross, N. (2001) "Design Cognition," in Design Knowing and Learning: Cognition in Design Education. Elsevier, pp. 79–103.

Cross, N. (2011) Design Thinking. Understanding how designers think and work. Oxford; New York.

Dahiya, A. and Kumar, J. (2019) "Do Design Outcomes Get Influenced by Type of User Data? An Experimental Study with Primary and Secondary User Research Data," in Human Systems Engineering and Design: Proceedings of the 1st International Conference on Human Systems Engineering and Design 2018, Springer International Publishing, pp. 191–197.

Dahiya, A. and Kumar, J. (2018) "Observations on Design Thinking in Novice Designers While Empathizing With Persona," in Handbook of Research on Human-Computer Interfaces and New Modes of Interactivity. IGI Global, pp. 21–39.

Dorst, K. and Cross, N. (2001) "Creativity in the design process: Co-evolution of problem-solution," Design Studies, 22(5), pp. 425–437.

Ferris, T. L. J. (2004) "User-Centered Design: An Integrated Approach," IEEE Transactions on Professional Communication, 47(1).

Fink, A., Benedek, M., et al. (2007) "Creativity meets neuroscience: experimental tasks for the neuroscientific study of creative thinking.," Methods (San Diego, Calif.), 42(1), pp. 68–76.

Fink, A., Grabner, R. H., et al. (2006) "Divergent thinking training is related to frontal electroencephalogram alpha synchronization.," The European journal of neuroscience, 23(8), pp. 2241–2246.

Fink, A. and Benedek, M. (2014) "EEG alpha power and creative ideation.," Neuroscience and biobehavioral reviews, 44, pp. 111–123.

Gabora, L. (2010) "Revenge of the 'Neurds': Characterizing Creative Thought in Terms of the Structure and Dynamics of Memory," Creativity Research Journal. Taylor & Francis Group, 22(1), pp. 1–13.

Gedenryd, H. (1998) How Designers Work, Lund University Cognitive Studies. Stockholm: Lund University Cognitive Studies.

Goel, V. (2014) "Creative brains: designing in the real world.," Frontiers in human neuroscience, 8, p. 241.

Goldschmidt, G. (2014) Linkography: unfolding the design process. MIT Press.

Goldschmidt, G. (2016) "Linkographic Evidence for Concurrent Divergent and Convergent Thinking in Creative Design," Creativity Research Journal. Routledge, 28(2), pp. 115–122.

KAN, J. W., BILDA, Z. and GERO, J. S. (2006) "Comparing Entropy Measures of Idea Links in Design Protocols," in Design Computing and Cognition '06. Springer Netherlands, pp. 265–284.

Kan, J. W. T., Bilda, Z. and Gero, J. S. (2007) "Comparing entropy measures of idea links in design protocols: Linkography entropy measurement and analysis of differently conditioned design sessions," Artificial Intelligence for Engineering Design, Analysis and Manufacturing, 21(4).

Liu, L. et al. (2018) "An EEG study of the relationship between design problem statements and cognitive behaviors during conceptual design," Artificial Intelligence for Engineering Design, Analysis and Manufacturing, 32(3).

Lubart, T. I. (2001) "Models of the Creative Process: Past, Present and Future," Creativity Research Journal. Lawrence Erlbaum Associates, Inc., 13(3–4), pp. 295–308.

Mölle, M. et al. (1999) "EEG complexity and performance measures of creative thinking.," Psychophysiology, 36(1), pp. 95–104.

Nguyen, T. A. and Zeng, Y. (2014) "A physiological study of relationship between designer's mental effort and mental stress during conceptual design," Computer-Aided Design, 54.

Norman, D. A. (2013) The design of everyday things: Revised and expanded edition. Basic books.

Plucker, J. A. and Dow, G. (2009) "Attitude Change as the Precursor to Creativity Enhancement: (606092009-001)," PsycEXTRA Dataset. APA.

Razoumnikova, O. M. (2000) "Functional organization of different brain areas during convergent and divergent thinking: an EEG investigation.," Brain research. Cognitive brain research, 10(1–2), pp. 11–18.

So, C. and Joo, J. (2017) "Does a Persona Improve Creativity?," The Design Journal. Routledge, 20(4), pp. 459–475.

Ward, T. B. and Kolomyts, Y. (2010) "Cognition and Creativity," in Kaufman, J. C. and Sternberg, R. J. (eds) The Cambridge Handbook of Creativity. Cambridge University Press, pp. 93–112.

Wykes, T. (1984) "Mental Models. By P. N. Johnson-Laird. Cambridge University Press: Cambridge. 1983.," Psychological Medicine, 14(2).

AMAZON ECHO: A BENCHMARKING MODEL REVIEW

Dietmar Jakob and Sebastian Wilhelm
Deggendorf Institute of Technology, Technology Campus Grafenau
Grafenau, Germany

ABSTRACT

Smart speakers are becoming increasingly popular. The market leader for smart speakers are the products of the *Echo* family from *Amazon*. There are currently 9 different models with different technical specifications available in Germany. With this paper, the models was benchmarked against each other in terms of (i) speech recognition reliability, (ii) output sound pressure and (iii) power consumption in a laboratory experiment. Previous works in this area has only considered individual models of the product family. Significant differences in speech recognition accuracy, output sound pressure and power consumption were identified between the models. In general it was observed, that the *Echo Show 8* model was the most efficient in terms of the above criteria.

KEYWORDS

Echo, Alexa, Voice User Interface, Speaker Recognition, Usability, Human Computer Interaction

1. INTRODUCTION

The global smart speaker market grew by 44.9% in the third quarter of 2019 compared to the third quarter of 2018. In the third quarter of 2019, 28.6 million units were sold globally. *Amazon* dominates the market alongside *Alibaba*, *Baidu*, *Google*, *Xiaomi* and others with 10.4 million smart speakers sold in the third quarter of 2019. Therefore, *Amazon* was able to increase its market share from 6.3% to 10.4% (Canalys, 2019).

The smart speaker family from *Amazon* is known as *Echo*-devices and relies on the voice user interface *Alexa*. In Germany there are currently (per February 2020) 9 different models available: (i) *Echo Show (2. Gen)* (ii) *Echo Show 8* (iii) *Echo Show 5* (iv) *Echo (2. Gen)* (v) *Echo (3. Gen)* (vi) *Echo Plus* (vii) *Echo Flex* (viii) *Echo Dot* (ix) *Echo Studio*.

The market leadership of *Amazon* and the variety of its available smart speakers, is the motivation to examine the individual products of the company in more detail from a technical point of view, as well as the reliability of speech recognition. The main contribution of this paper is, to examine the differences between the available models of the *Echo* family in the aspects of: (i) how precisely does it follow the recognition of the deposed voice commands (ii), at what distance do the devices still understand the voice commands (iii) , what is the power consumption of the individual models (iv) , how does the sound pressure change as output volumes increase.

The remaining of the paper is structured as follows: The work begins with an overview of similar scientific studies in section 2. The theoretical and experimental benchmarking of the *Amazon Echo* devices will be presented and discussed in section 3 before the work ends with a summary of the results and an outlook for future research in section 4.

2. RELATED WORK

2.1 Speech and Voice Recognition

A key feature of smart speakers is the recognition of voice commands and the execution of corresponding actions. *Gao et al.* investigated the speech recognition and understanding of the *Echo* devices based on customer reviews at the *Amazon* website. They found that customers often complain about the precision of speech recognition and/or the ability of *Echo* devices to answer questions correctly (Gao et al., 2018). In contrast *Hellwig et al.* summed up that the recognition of the language was 'relatively good', however they although noted that *Echo* could not understand all commands so that the interaction is aborted (Hellwig et al., 2018). *Lopatovska et al.* found that for advanced users 89% of commands are understood, while for non-advanced users the rate is only 56% (Lopatovska et al., 2018). By asking 25 Japanese about their experiences with language assistants, *Yamada et al.* found that 50% had encountered problems with speech recognition (Yamada et al., 2018). Further investigation of *Shalini et al.* showed in an experimental way, that some words of 12 different sentences was misinterpreted. For example, commands containing the terms 'health', 'pulse', 'what', 'an hour', 'vacation', or 'early' were understood and interpreted as other terms (Shalini et al., 2019).

All the studies mentioned above came to the conclusion that the voice commands were not reliably recognized. However, none of them quantified the precision of speech recognition. Further, the individual *Echo* models were not examined and compared individually.

2.2 Power Consumption

None of the current *Echo* device own a power switch. Therefore, the device are continuously in a standby operating mode. Up to now, less investigations was made on analyzing the power consumption of individual Echo devices. *Lloyd* analyzed the power consumption data from the Echo Dot, Echo (1st Gen.), *Echo (2nd Gen.)*, *Echo Plus* and *Echo Spot* models in standby-mode and while playing music. His findings are shown in Table 1 (Lloyd, 2018). His investigations lacks the models *Echo Show*, *Echo Show 8*, *Echo Show 5*, *Echo Flex* and *Echo Studio*. Furthermore, the methodology are not very resilient, since *Lloyd* only made a comparison in standby operation and music playback.

Table 1. Power consumption data (in W) (Lloyd, 2018)

action	Echo Dot	Echo (1. Gen.)	Echo (2. Gen.)	Echo Plus	Echo Spot
standby	1.75	2.95	1.95	2.4	1.9-2.25
playing music	2.1-2.4	3.1-3.4	2.4.3.4	3.0-4.3	2.6-3.2
average playing music	2.25	3.25	2.9	3.65	2.9

Frawley determined the power consumption of several *IoT* devices from different manufacturers. In the smart speaker category, he examined the *Echo Dot* and the *Echo Show*. Each smart speaker is prompted to read the weather, read the news, and play music every time it is used. Once a week, he asked the speakers to set a reminder for the future. Each speaker was also muted for a few minutes to see, if there are any noticeable changes in power consumption during the period where the device is not listening for. He noted that when the environment darkens, the LEDs of the devices light up brighter. This causes the *Echo Dot* to consume about 2200mW of power rather than its usual 1500mW (Frawley, 2018). The trial period of one week and the small number of different models do not allow meaningful conclusions to be drawn about power consumption under loads.

3. TECHNICAL BENCHMARKING OF *ECHO* MODELS

In order to benchmark the *Echo* models with each other in the fields of speech recognition, output volume and power consumption, all currently available models in Germany (per February 2020) was investigated.

In the following, first the general technical specifications of each model are presented in subsection 3.1. With subsection 3.2 the power consumption of the devices is reviewed over a 24-hour period during which the devices received commands continuously. Next, in subsection 3.3, the precision of speech transcription based on the data self-disclosure from *Amazon* is examined. subsection 3.4 investigates the speech recognition of the devices based on two different voice profiles (male and female) and a varying distance to the output speaker, before the output sound pressure of the individual Echo devices are finally compared with each other in subsection 3.5.

(a) Setup for testing all models simultaneously

(b) Setup for testing the individual devices with variable distance to the output speaker

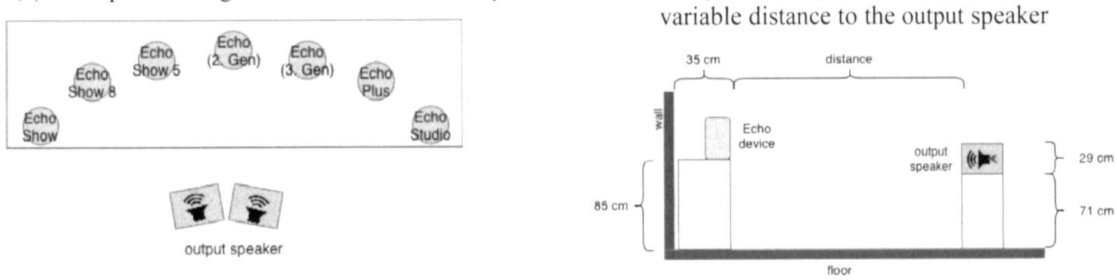

Figure 1. Setups of the test environment

For the investigations of subsection 3.2 and subsection 3.3 all *Echo* devices are placed in a semicircle in front of two output speakers, so that the distance between the *Echo* devices and the output speaker was almost identical (see Figure 1a). We then played out test sequences, listed in Table 2, over the output speaker for 24 hours. This sequences was previously generated with three different voices profiles (2x Female; 1x Male) using the *Any Text to Voice*[1] service from *AnywaySoft Inc.*. In order to minimize resonances, the devices were placed on a sound-absorbing mat and the room was additionally equipped with sound-absorbing foam.

Table 2. Commands played during a test period of 24 hours including translation. The sequences was repeated every hour, where the column time indicates when the command was played within an hour. The output voices profiles used also changed randomly every hour

name	time	original command	translation
volume	hh:01	Alexa, stelle die Lautstärke auf X. *(X changed hourly)*	Alexa, set the volume to X *(X changed hourly)*
news	hh:06	Alexa, was sind die Nachrichten?	Alexa, what's the news?
appointment	hh:11	Alexa, wann findet mein nächster Termin statt?	Alexa, when is my next appointment?
weather	hh:16	Alexa, wie wird das Wetter heute?	Alexa, what's the weather like today?
lotto	hh:21	Alexa, sag mir die Lottozahlen.	Alexa, tell me the lotto numbers.
shopping list	hh:26	Alexa, was steht auf meiner Einkaufsliste?	Alexa, what's on my shopping list?
foreign word	hh:31	Alexa, was bedeutet kongruent?	Alexa, what does congruent mean?
capital	hh:36	Alexa, was ist die Hauptstadt von Osterreicht?	Alexa, what is the capital of Austria?
DAX	hh:41	Alexa, wie steht der DAX?	Alexa, how's the DAX?
skill	hh:46	Alexa, öffne Glückskeks.	Alexa, open fortune cookie.
sun	hh:51	Alexa, wann geht die Sonne auf?	Alexa, when does the sun come up?
football	hh:56	Alexa, auf welchen Tabellenplatz steht Dortmund?	Alexa, which place is Dortmund in the table?

[1] https://www.anywaysoft.com/text-to-voice/download.html

3.1 Technical Specifications

Table 3 shows the differences between the individual *Echo* models based on their specification.

The models differ especially in the existence of display, camera and ZigBee-hub and the number of microphones and speakers. This technical information can influence the quality of speech recognition, the output sound pressure and the power consumption of the devices.

Table 3. Technical specification of each model according to Amazon product website

	Echo Show	Echo Show 8	Echo Show 5	Echo (2. Gen.)	Echo (3. Gen.)	Echo Plus	Echo Flex	Echo Dot	Echo Studio
display	10.1''	8''	5.5''	None	None	None	None	None	None
camera	5MP	1MP	1MP	None	None	None	None	None	None
number speaker	2	2	1	2	2	2	1	1	5
microphone characteristi	far field	far field	far field	far field	far field	far field	far field	far field	far field
number microphone	4	2	2	7	7	7	2	4	7
ZigBee	yes	no	no	no	no	yes	no	no	yes
firmware (per 20/04/2020)	651614220	3725204100	3725204100	653621620	3658075268	3658075268	3658075268	3658075268	3725203076

3.2 Power Consumption

During the 24 hour test period, we recorded the power consumption of the individual *Echo* device by using *ALL3075v3* single power measure tools from *ALLNET GmbH*, Germering. These devices allows measurements in a resolution of up to 7Hz, which can be accessed via a local network interface (API). We stored and resampled the data to a frequency of 1Hz and then calculated the average value and the maximum value for power consumption of the individual *Echo* device over the entire test period of 24 hours.

Further we analyzed the power consumption data during playing radio (station: 'Bayern 1', Volume: 8) and in standby mode. We also investigated a period of 24 hours in each case. This values are listed in Table 4.

Table 4. Average (avg) and maximum (max) power consumption during playing the test sequences, while playing radio and in standby mode over a test period of 24 hours per model (in W)

power consumption	Echo Show	Echo Show 8	Echo Show 5	Echo (2. Gen.)	Echo (3. Gen.)	Echo Plus	Echo Flex	Echo Dot	Echo Studio
test sequences (avg)	6.7	4.7	3.6	2.1	2.6	3.0	1.7	1.7	4.1
test sequences (max)	13.5	8.6	6.1	6.7	13.8	15.7	2.8	7.5	35.2
play radio	11.4	8.4	5.1	2.1	4.9	5.6	2.1	2.6	6.5
standby	9.3	6.3	4.3	2.8	3.5	4.6	2.0	2.2	6.2

Even if all *Echo* devices received the same test sequences at the same time, some commands could not be understood or processed (see subsection 3.3). This can have a direct impact on the power consumption.

In general, it can be observed that the *Echo Show* has the highest average power consumption (6.7W), followed by the *Echo Show 8* (4.7W) as well by playing the test sequences, playing radio or in standby mode.

This can be explained by the displays of these devices, which consumes constant power. The highest peak consumption was received by the *Echo Studio* (35.2W) which corresponds to the higher number of included speakers and the integrated 330W amplifier.

3.3 Speech Transcription

To check how accurately speech recognition was performed during the 24 hour test phase, a data self-disclosure from *Amazon* was requested and analyzed for all devices. The data self-disclosure lists all commands understood by the device and contains transcriptions of the spoken phrases or 'Data not Available' entries. 'Data not Available' indicates that the activation word ('Alexa') was understood but not the command. Further the transcripted entries must be checked whether the command was interpreted correctly - i.e., if the device transcribed the spoken text correctly.

The transcriptions were analyzed in detail and compared with the expected values (see Table 2). For the individual *Echo* devices the number of correct entries is shown in Table 5.

Table 5. Number of correctly understood commands during testing all devices simultaneously for 24 hours according to the data self-disclosure. Maximum possible per command: 24 / sum: 288

command	Echo Show	Echo Show 8	Echo Show 5	Echo (2. Gen.)	Echo (3. Gen.)	Echo Plus	Echo Flex	Echo Dot	Echo Studio
volume	12	20	16	13	18	16	17	13	15
news	15	18	17	18	19	14	12	18	10
appointment	11	13	11	12	9	12	11	10	13
weather	16	17	13	12	17	17	16	14	17
lotto	12	18	15	17	17	18	12	15	12
shopping list	13	20	15	14	18	14	15	18	12
foreign word	8	7	3	9	6	11	4	9	3
capital	13	13	19	13	14	11	16	13	17
DAX	14	17	18	12	16	14	14	17	14
skill	18	18	17	19	20	13	16	16	19
sun	15	17	15	11	16	11	11	12	16
football	7	12	13	8	11	14	19	10	9
SUM	154	190	172	158	181	165	163	165	157

None of the tested *Echo* models was able to interpret all commands correct. The most reliable model was the *Echo Show 8*. It is particularly notable that the foreign word was often not or not correctly understood. The word 'kongruent' (transl. congruent) was often interpreted as 'Konkurrenz' (transl. competition).

3.4 Distance Based Speech and Voice Recognition

In a second test setup, the *Echo* devices were tested individually. It was the intend to investigate how the distance of an audio source to the Echo device affect on the number of commands are understood or misunderstood. Therefore, the *Echo* devices and an output speaker was placed as shown in Figure 1b and the distances between them was varied. The *Echo* device was constantly standing on the front edge of a shelf - 35cm away from a wall and set to volume 5. The output speaker was set to 50dB[2]. We varied the distances and played an automated test sequence which was again created using the *Any Text to Voice* service from *AnywaySoft, Inc.*. The sequence asked ten times with a female voice and ten times with a male voice 'Alexa, wie viel ist eins plus ein' (transl.: Alexa, how much is one plus one). The number of correctly understood and answered commands was counted. The results are shown in Table 6.

[2] DBA - measured 50cm in front of the device

Table 6. Number of correctly understood commands based on the distance between the Echo device and output speaker. Maximum possible per command: 10

distance in *cm*	voice profile	Echo Show	Echo Show 8	Echo Show 5	Echo (2. Gen.)	Echo (3. Gen.)	Echo Plus	Echo Flex	Echo Dot	Echo Studio
200	female	10	10	10	8	9	8	10	9	9
200	male	1	10	10	0	0	2	10	1	8
400	female	10	9	8	9	8	9	9	8	9
400	male	9	9	9	5	5	6	9	4	7
600	female	10	9	8	4	5	5	9	6	9
600	male	5	8	8	6	0	5	8	1	7
800	female	8	9	9	1	1	4	7	3	9
800	male	5	9	9	2	0	1	7	1	4
SUM	female	38	37	35	22	23	26	35	26	36
SUM	male	20	36	36	13	5	14	34	7	26
SUM	both	58	73	71	35	28	40	69	33	62

It can be generally stated that, if the output speakers are closer to the *Echo* device, the speech recognition will be more accurate. However, it is noteworthy that in some models there are significant differences in the precision of the male and female test sequences. On average, the male voice is recognized far less frequently than the female voice.

The *Echo Show 8* can again be identified as the most reliable model.

3.5 Output Volumes

In order to determine the individual output volume of each *Echo* device, the devices have again considered individually. The devices were placed on a sound absorbing mat and the room was equipped with sound absorbing foam (no anechoic chamber). The devices are then asked 'Alexa, wie viele Menschen leben auf der Erde?' (transl. Alexa, how many people live on earth?) and the sound pressure of their response was measured. For this purpose the measuring device '*DEM202*' from the company '*Vellemann*' was used, which was placed 100cm in front of the *Echo* device and 30cm above table height in the DBC-mode. This measuring device promises an accuracy of +/- 1.4dB.
The measurements are listed in Table 7.

Table 7. Output volume in dB (DBC) measured 100cm in front of the Echo device depending on the set volume

Volume Echo	Echo Show	Echo Show 8	Echo Show 5	Echo (2. Gen.)	Echo (3. Gen.)	Echo Plus	Echo Flex	Echo Dot	Echo Studio
1	51.2	54.8	58.3	40.8	55.2	54.6	38.0	41.5	51.4
2	50.7	56.9	58.6	39.5	59.8	59.6	43.8	55.4	53.2
3	58.0	62.4	64.7	55.9	65.1	64.9	46.3	61.7	58.9
4	61.5	68.3	70.9	63.3	71.2	71.4	46.7	67.2	64.7
5	67.0	71.3	71.4	67.5	73.8	73.8	50.6	70.0	67.4
6	69.6	74.0	72.0	72.3	74.9	75.6	51.6	74.5	70.1
7	75.2	77.2	74.0	76.9	78.3	78.1	53.8	75.8	72.0
8	78.3	78.4	74.8	82.4	81.3	81.3	58.1	76.1	76.1
9	80.6	84.5	74.9	83.2	83.0	82.6	58.7	77.0	78.2
10	82.5	84.4	76.0	83.8	82.7	82.4	59.1	76.7	78.1

4. CONCLUSION AND FUTURE WORK

The goal of this work was to investigate how the individual *Echo* models differ from each other in the aspects of speech recognition precision and output volume in a laboratory environment. Furthermore, we investigated how the power consumption of the models differs.

In two different test setups for measuring the speech recognition precision, it was observed that the model *Echo Show 8* correctly recognized the most commands by comparison to the other Echo devices.

In general it is worth mentioning that none of the tested models was able to interpret all commands correctly. When testing 288 sequences in maximum 190 (= 66%) was correctly understood.

For the models *Echo 2. Gen*, *Echo 3. Gen*, *Echo Plus* and *Echo Dot*, it was found that male voice sequences can not be recognized reliable. Similar can be observed for the models *Echo Show* and *Echo Studio*, but not in the significance. Specific problems interpreting the male voice did not occur with the *Echo Show 8*, *Echo Show 5* or *Echo Flex* models.

A correlation between the number of installed microphones and the number of correctly recognized commands could not be detected.

In investigations on the output sound pressure, we discovered that the model *Echo Show 8* reaches the highest output sound pressure (round 84dB). The models Echo Show, Echo 2. Gen, Echo 3. Gen, *Echo Plus* each at about 83dB. The most silent model is *Echo Flex*. Conversely, however, it could not be observed that the *Echo Studio*, even if it had the highest number of integrated speakers, reached the highest sound pressure level. This can be attributed to the fact that this model is designed for 3D audio systems and the large number of speakers required to implement this.

With subsection 3.2 we have compared the average and maximum power consumption of the *Echo* models. We found that the display models consume on average more power than the non-display models (with the exception of the *Echo Studio*).

Our work showed that the voice profile of the person speaking with *Echo* is highly relevant for the reliability of speech recognition. In further work, the reliability of speech recognition with more different voice profiles (possibly also with dialect) has to be investigated. In addition, external factors such as background noise must be taken into account in further work.

ACKNOWLEDGEMENT

This work was founded by the Bavarian State Ministry of Family Affairs, Labour and Social Affairs.

REFERENCES

Canalys. (2019). Canalys: Amazon smart speaker shipments crossed 10 million mark in q3 2019. Retrieved 3/6/2020, from https://www.canalys.com/newsroom/worldwide-smartspeaker-Q3-2019

Frawley, R. J. (2018). Logging and analysis of internet of things (IoT) device network traffic and power consumption (Doctoral dissertation). doi: 10.15368/theses.2018.60

Gao, Y., Pan, Z., Wang, H., & Chen, G. (2018, October). Alexa, my love: Analyzing reviews of amazon echo. In 2018 IEEE SmartWorld, ubiquitous intelligence & computing, advanced & trusted computing, scalable computing & communications, cloud & big data computing, internet of people and smart city innovation (SmartWorld/SCALCOM/UIC/ATC/CB- DCom/IOP/SCI). IEEE. Retrieved from https://doi.org/10.1109/smartworld.2018.00094 doi: 10.1109/smartworld.2018.00094

Hellwig, A., Schneider, C., Meister, S., & Deiters, W. (2018). Sprachassistenten in der pflege - potentiale und voraussetzungen zur unterstützung von senioren. Retrieved from http://dl.gi.de/handle/20.500.12116/16665 doi: 10 .18420/MUC2018-MCI-0341

Lloyd, C. (2018). How much electricity does the amazon echo use? How-To Geek. Retrieved 6/3/2020, from https:// www.howtogeek.com/348219/how-much-electricity-does-the-amazon-echo-use/

Lopatovska, I., Rink, K., Knight, I., Raines, K., Cosenza, K., Williams, H., ... Martinez, A. (2018, March). Talk to me: Exploring user interactions with the amazon alexa. Journal of Librarianship and Information Science, 51(4), 984–997. Retrieved from https://doi.org/10.1177/0961000618759414 doi: 10.1177/0961000618759414

Shalini, S., Levins, T., Robinson, E. L., Lane, K., Park, G., & Skubic, M. (2019). Development and comparison of customized voice-assistant systems for independent living older adults. In Lecture notes in computer science (pp. 464–479). Springer International Publishing. Retrieved from https://doi.org/10.1007/978-3-030-22015-0_36 doi: 10.1007/ 978-3-030-22015-0 36

Yamada, S., Kitakoshi, D., Yamashita, A., Suzuki, K., & Suzuki, M. (2018, November). Development of an intelligent dialogue agent with smart devices for older adults: A preliminary study. In 2018 conference on technologies and applications of artificial intelligence (TAAI). IEEE. Retrieved from https://doi.org/10.1109/taai.2018.00020 doi: 10.1109/taai.2018.00020

PERCEIVED USABILITY OF LEARNING MANAGEMENT SYSTEMS AND UNIVERSITY WEBSITES: A SYSTEMATIC REVIEW

Prokopia Vlachogianni[1], Nikolaos Tselios[1] and Michalis Xenos[2]
[1]*Department of Educational Sciences and Early Childhood Education*
[2]*Computer Engineering and Informatics Department*
University of Patras, 26500 Patras, Rio, Greece

ABSTRACT

This paper presents the findings of a systematic meta-analysis of perceived usability evaluation studies of Learning Management Systems (LMS) and University Websites used in the context of higher education. The research was conducted after studying, organizing, and analyzing the results of 33 research papers, which report evaluation of the perceived usability of LMS and websites using the System Usability Scale (SUS). The results obtained were organized and analyzed according to the following: (a) the usability score obtained by the SUS questionnaire, (b) the type of educational technology used (LMS or University website), (c) the type of participant (student or teacher), (d) the age and (e) the number of participants in each study. Statistical analysis demonstrated a satisfactory level of perceived usability both for LMS and for University Websites respectively. Moreover, participants' age was found to be significantly associated with SUS score as well as the number of participants in the LMS context. However, as far as university websites are concerned, the number of participants does not seem to be related with SUS score. In addition, no significant difference was derived in the LMS context between SUS score and the type of participant (student - teacher). Finally, there was no significant improvement of the perceived usability over time both for the Learning Management Systems and for the University Websites. The reported findings will provide useful benchmarks for teachers and educational technology designers.

KEYWORDS

System Usability Scale, Learning Management Systems, University Websites, Higher Education, Review, Meta-Analysis

1. INTRODUCTION

During the recent years, educational technology has been widely adopted in every aspect of the educational process. In particular, in higher education it seems that various forms of educational technology are widely used. As a consequence, significant opportunities are provided for the improvement of quality and accessibility of university teaching while at the same time reducing some costs (McCann et al., 1998). An important aspect, when it comes to technology, is its perceived usability. In an educational setting, students' learning experience and, in turn, academic performance is greatly affected by the usability of educational technology systems provided by an institution. A user interface which meets users' needs in an intuitive way will lead to more frequent use and increased adoption. On the contrary, it will require more time to learn how to operate it at the expense of focusing on the actual learning content (Ardito et al., 2006).

The main goal of the research reported in this paper was to provide a standardized frame of reference to all stakeholders regarding usability in educational technology used in the context of higher education; specifically, for Learning Management Systems (LMS) and university websites. In specific, usability levels of the abovementioned systems are examined and compared with the criteria set by Bangor et al. (2009). In addition, all existing information individual researches provided are summarized in an unbiased, systematic way so to extract more compact conclusions about usability in higher education. Furthermore, a quantitative analysis followed up in order to investigate possible correlations among variables.

LMS allow asynchronous and synchronous communication, delivery of learning content, assessment and class management (Coates et al., 2005). A rather overlooked form of educational technology used in higher education is university websites. University websites are key components for institutions because they are cost and time efficient and communicate the university's vision, goals, values and culture to various stakeholders (students, alumni, prospective students, parents, faculty, staff, Mentes & Turan, 2012). In this context, it should meet in the same time all stakeholders' needs. A usable university website should be considered as an asset and a competitive advantage for attracting prospective students. According to Smith and Oliver (2000) the adoption of technologies that provide flexibility, access and convenience will be the cornerstone to institutions' continued viability in the frame of the competitiveness of the world market.

In this systematic review, perceived usability of two categories of educational technology systems used in higher education, namely Learning Management Systems (LMS) and University Websites was examined. The results of 33 research papers are organized and analyzed evaluating the perceived usability using the System Usability Scale (SUS).

SUS is a questionnaire which is used for evaluating perceived usability. It is well received as a highly valid and reliable tool (Orfanou et al., 2015) and is the most widely adopted questionnaire for perceived usability evaluation of software and products (Tullis & Albert, 2008). However, there is no universal consensus, as it is reflected upon the number of questionnaires used for usability evaluation of products and/or software currently (Brooke, 1996; Lewis 1991, 1992, 1995; Tullis & Albert, 2008). Surprisingly, usage of questionnaires for the evaluation of the perceived usability of educational software is quite limited as it is demonstrated to the research data. Only in recent years SUS has begun to be used for ICT's usability evaluation in Education (Orfanou et al., 2015). It is therefore reasonable to have an overview of these studies in order to investigate the levels at which LMS and university websites score and to identify the frequency SUS scale is used.

The available research data regarding the relation of gender with SUS score seem quite contradictory. On the one hand, in a dataset of 213 surveys Bangor et al. (2008) found no significant difference between the mean SUS scores obtained from females (M=71.6) and males (M=70.2, p=0.586, ns). Ituma (2011) evaluating the perceived usability of Blackboard WebCT came into the same conclusion. Orfanou et al. (2015) also found no significant difference in SUS score between women (mean=76.30, SD=13.16) and men (M=76.21, SD=13.40). Similar results were provided by Georgsson and Staggers (2015) who found that males rated higher than females a diabetes mHealth system (males, M=83.13, SD=2.39, females, M=79.69, SD=14.98).

Concerning age, the research data obtained are also not conclusive. Granić and Ćukušić (2011) found a significant negative correlation between SUS score and age (r=-0.467, p=0.001, s); thus younger participants tend to assign a higher SUS rating than the older ones. In a sample of 213 participants Bangor et al. (2008) found that younger participants tend to give higher SUS scores too (r=-0.203, p=0.03, s). Binyamin et al. (2016) found no correlation between SUS score and age which comes in line with the findings provided by Orfanou et al. (2015). A recent research (Mujinga et al., 2018) revealed a significant relation between age and SUS score (r=0.036, p=0.09, s).

Thus, this literature review and meta-analysis has been guided by the following research questions:

RQ1. Which is the level of perceived usability of Learning Management Systems (LMS) and University websites in the context of higher education as it is reflected upon System Usability Scale (SUS)?

RQ2. Is there a significant difference in usability between the two types of technology?

RQ3. Which factors are related to SUS score (e.g. age, type and number of participants)?

RQ4. Is there a significant difference in usability at LMS and university websites over time?

2. METHODOLOGY

Firstly, this paper presents the findings of a systematic review of usability evaluation of LMS and University Websites used in higher education. The research was conducted after studying, organizing, and analyzing the results of 33 research papers evaluating the perceived usability of LMS and websites at university settings using the System Usability Scale (SUS). The methodology for this systematic review followed the guidelines proposed by Kitchenham (2004). Our search was conducted using the keywords at Google Scholar: sus, usability, learning management system or university website. The reported research papers were published from 2007 to 2019. The data were collected from October 2019 until January 2020. In the cases of inadequate or ambiguously reported data, we contacted the corresponding researchers.

Some inclusion and exclusion criteria were set at the beginning of the search. The inclusion criteria were a) Research papers which evaluate usability for LMS and university websites by using the SUS b) Research papers which were written in English. The exclusion criteria were: a) Research paper is not written in English, b) another scale or method was used for evaluating usability and c) the SUS scale is not used for educational purposes.

The results of the literature review were organized on a basis of (a) the usability rating as derived from the SUS questionnaire, (b) the type of educational technology (LMS or university website), (c) the number of participants in each sample, (d) the age and (g) the type of participants (e.g. teachers, students). The obtained data were analyzed with IBM SPSS Statistics v25.0. Possible correlations were investigated between independent variables and SUS score regarding the research questions. We have also taken into consideration possible variations at SUS score which may exist due to different sample sizes by reporting weighted means.

3. RESULTS

RQ1. Level of Perceived usability of LMS and University Websites

The Learning Management Systems (LMS) category comprised 40 studies and its mean SUS score was 66.88 (SD=10.88, see Table 1). The University websites category comprised 12 studies and its mean SUS score was 63.81 (SD=16.51, see Table 2). Possible variations in perceived usability score regarding the sample size of each survey were taken into consideration. Weighted SUS mean score for LMS is (M=60.14, SD=15.02) and for university websites (M=65.83, SD=16.86). Considering the criteria set from Bangor et al. (2009), LMS and University websites seem to have good usability levels but with some design flaws.

Table 1. Overview of the studies included evaluating LMS

Study	**Number of participants**	**Mean SUS**	**Mean Age**	**Participants** (S: Students/ T:Teachers, U: Unknown)
Pirker et al. (2019)	14	70.63	23.43	S
Rosato et al. (2007)	13	59.00		S
	13	64		S
	16	72.50		S
Ivanović et al. (2018)	96	74.70		S
Lehong et al. (2019)	9	63		T
Erdoğmuş et al. (2015)	10	50.75		S
Katsanos et al. (2012)	45	74.50	21.04	S
	191	70.48	20.44	S
	44	71.48	37.2	S
Rahimi et al. (2015)	57	60.61	34.7	U
Alshammari et al. (2016)	39	79.46	22.21	S
	36	71		S
Kaewsaiha (2019)	41	56.83		T
Gutiérrez-Carreón et al. (2015)	24	83.3		S
	32	76		S
Srimarong & Achalakul (2017)	9	57.22		T
Harrati et al. (2017)	180	72.83	36.70	T
Al-Sumaty & Umar (2018)	45	83.60		T

Binyamin et al. (2016)	50	69.30		S
Erdoğan et al. (2017)	204	67.14		S
García-Peñalvo et al. (2019)	43	65.23	21	S
Tsironis et al. (2016)	31	66.30	31.5	S
	31	76.50	31.5	S
	31	65.90	31.5	S
Al-Omar (2018)	347	38		T
	893	39		S
Blecken et al. (2010)	60	72		T
	440	56		S
Vertesi et al. (2018)	182	58.60		U
Thuseethan et al. (2014)	201	67.50		S
Harrati et al. (2016)	50	69.30	37	T
Orfanou et al. (2015)	769	76.27	21.78	S
Shi et al. (2013)	10	75.75		S
Marco et al. (2013)	10	89.50	23	S
Luo et al. (2014)	49	58.10		S
	24	65.93		S
	9	74.45		T
Granić & Ćukušić (2011)	47	59.36		S
	23	53.15	40	T
Total	**4418**	**66.88**		

RQ2 comparison between LMS's and University Websites' SUS score

An independent samples t-test was conducted to investigate possible statistical differences between SUS score and the category of educational technology (LMS and university websites). No statistically significant difference was observed (p=0.454, ns).

RQ3. Attributes which may relate to SUS score

In a dataset of 40 surveys of LMS' evaluation of perceived usability a moderate negative correlation between age and SUS score (r=-0.33, p=0.05, s) and between the number of participants and SUS score (r=-0.364, p=0.021, s) was found. It should be noted that in the study conducted by Alshammari et al. (2016) it is not completely clear if the mean age of the participants refers to the total number or for each group of the two reported studies. Thus, the second hypothesis was adopted and these two studies were not excluded from the analysis. For university websites, no data were provided for the variable age. Regarding the number of participants of the university websites' evaluation studies, no statistically significant correlation was found between SUS score and the number of participants (r=0.347, p=0.269, ns).

Table 2. Overview of the studies included evaluating University Websites

Study	Number of participants	Mean SUS	Participants (S: students, U: Unknown)
Alnasser et al. (2017)	14	80.2	U
Demir & Parraci (2018)	6	68	S
Benaida et al. (2018)	20	91	S
	20	52.9	S
	20	90.8	S
	20	46.4	S
	20	73.4	S
	20	57.4	S
Sengel (2014)	10	43.75	U
	10	54.38	U
Şengel (2013)	8	54.06	S
NaifJabli & Demir (2018)	10	53.5	S
Total	**178**	**63.81**	

In addition, an independent samples t-test was conducted to investigate possible statistical differences between SUS score and the type of participant (student - teacher). There was no significant difference in the LMS context (p=0.165, ns). The sample referring to university websites' evaluation comprised students only.

RQ4: Evolution of SUS ratings over time

Perceived usability ratings over time were examined by using Repeated measures ANOVA. The years 2007, 2012 and 2019 were used as reference points for the LMS category (p=0.261, ns) and 2014, 2018 for the University Websites category (p=0.128, ns). Thus, a non-significant improvement was observed for both categories.

4. CONCLUSIONS AND DISCUSSION

The purpose of the research presented in this paper was to provide a summary of the findings regarding the perceived usability's evaluation of two core educational technologies used mainly in the context of higher education: LMS and University Websites. Their perceived usability was assessed using the System Usability Scale (SUS). It is argued that the significance of the reported research is significant by providing usability benchmarks for educational technology used in higher education to all stakeholders. As a result, those working in the field of Educational Technology will be knowledgeable at what levels the evaluation of systems varies. In addition, it will be proved useful for educational technology system designers as a basis for reporting and comparing results by raising the level of awareness of those involved.

Regarding the research questions, both LMS and University Websites seem to have a good usability level, but with some issues. It seems that in recent years special attention is given to the evaluation of the perceived usability of LMS but not to that of university websites. Perhaps this fact on the one hand implies a shift in distance asynchronous education, with emphasis on LMS as a complement to learning and on the other hand University websites may be neglected because they do not directly contribute to learning. Although LMS are considered "old technology", they are mainly used when users reach higher education stage. On the other side, the University websites do not aim directly at learning a particular subject, so they are a quite unrecognized dimension in the learning process. They are frequently a product of in-house development and their perceived usability may not be sufficiently taken into account as it is demonstrated by the research data. However, no significant difference was observed between the two categories concerning the usability ratings.

Furthermore, a strong negative correlation between age and SUS score was found for LMS (r=-0.533, p=0.05). This is in line with the findings reported by Bangor et al. 2008 (r=-0.203, p=0.03, s) and Granić and Ćukušić (2011) (r=-0.467, p=0.001, s), but contradicts the findings reported by Orfanou et al. (2015, r=-0.061, p=0.09) and Mujinga et al. (2018, r=0.036, p=0.09). For the university websites category, no data were provided for the "age" variable. In addition, the number of participants does not seem to affect SUS score for the University websites category. Nevertheless, a moderate negative correlation was found between the number of participants and SUS score at the LMS context (r=-0.364, p=0.02, s). This is a useful first record which needs further research to reach definitive and meaningful conclusions. Moreover, in LMS settings no statistically significant difference was observed (p=0.165, ns) concerning the type of participant (student or teacher). In university websites category the studies consisted only of students. It is noteworthy that there is a slight non-statistically significant improvement at usability levels over time. This result is encouraging because the importance of usability is now more apparent and necessary than ever.

This research is not without limitations. Even though SUS is considered as a highly valid and reliable tool for evaluating the perceived usability (Orfanou et al., 2015), there is no universal consensus regarding the psychometric tool for evaluating usability. In addition, only the studies using System Usability Scale were included. Other usability parameters such as findability (Katsanos, Tselios & Avouris, 2008) should be taken into consideration. Moreover, usability evaluation of websites was conducted by students. The results might be differentiated if other users such as prospective students, teachers or parents were taken into account. In addition, only 12 surveys were included at the usability's evaluation of university websites and most of them (7 out of 12) were carried out in 2018.

As for future research, it would be useful to conduct a study which will consider other stakeholders for evaluating the perceived usability of university websites such as alumni, prospective students and parents. In addition, it should be examined if there are any differentiations in the perceived usability depending on the academic discipline of the stakeholders involved (i.e. Humanities, Applied Sciences, Natural Sciences). For the LMS's, it would be useful to investigate possible relationships between SUS score and a) the learning object, b) the internet competency, c) the delivery method d) the information architecture of the LMS (Katsanos et al., 2008) and e) whether the participants are undergraduate or postgraduate students. Finally, the scope of the presented study can be expanded to take into account the perceived usability's evaluation of other types of educational technologies adopted in all educational stages.

ACKNOWLEDGEMENT

Part of the work presented in this paper has been completed in the context of the project: "ERMIS-F: Web services for environmental risk–Floods". Funding: Interreg V-A Greece – Cyprus.

REFERENCES

Alnasser, A., Alnabit, N., & Alanazi, W. (2017). Usability Evaluation of Prototypes Designed for a Saudi University Website. *International Journal of Computing & Information Sciences*, *13*(1), 15-25.

Al-Omar, K. (2018). Evaluating the Usability and Learnability of the" Blackboard" LMS Using SUS and Data Mining. In *Proceedings of the 2018 Second International Conference on Computing Methodologies and Communication (ICCMC),* February 15-16, Erode, India, pp. 386-390. IEEE.

Alshammari, M., Anane, R., & Hendley, R. J. (2016). Usability and effectiveness evaluation of adaptivity in e-learning systems. In *Proceedings of the 2016 CHI conference extended abstracts on human factors in computing systems,* May 7-12, San Jose, California, USA, pp. 2984-2991. ACM.

Al-Sumaty, R. M., & Umar, I. N. (2018). Design and Evaluation of Cloud-Based Students Data Management System Usability. In *Proceedings of the 2018 International Conference on Smart Computing and Electronic Enterprise (ICSCEE),* July 11-12, Kuala Lumpur, Malaysia, pp. 1-8. IEEE.

Ardito, C., Costabile, M. F., De Marsico, M., Lanzilotti, R., Levialdi, S., Roselli, T., & Rossano, V. (2006). An approach to usability evaluation of e-learning applications. *Universal access in the information society*, *4*(3), 270-283.

Bangor, A., Kortum, P. T., & Miller, J. T. (2008). An empirical evaluation of the system usability scale. *Intl. Journal of Human–Computer Interaction, 24*(6), 574-594.

Bangor, A., Kortum, P., & Miller, J. (2009). Determining what individual SUS scores mean: Adding an adjective rating scale. *Journal of usability studies*, *4*(3), 114-123.

Benaida, M., Namoun, A., & Taleb, A. (2018). Evaluation of the Impact of Usability in Arabic University Websites: Comparison between Saudi Arabia and the UK. *Evaluation*, *9*(8), 365-375.

Binyamin, S., Rutter, M., & Smith, S. (2016). The utilization of system usability scale in learning management systems: A case study of Jeddah Community College. In *Proceedings of the 9th International Conference of Education, Research and Innovation (ICERI2016),* November 14-16, Seville, Spain, pp. 5314-5323, International Academy of Technology, Education and Development (IATED).

Blecken, A., Bruggemann, D., & Marx, W. (2010). Usability evaluation of a learning management system. In *Proceedings of the 2010 43rd Hawaii International Conference on System Sciences,* January 5-8, Honolulu, Hawaii, USA, pp. 1-9. IEEE.

Brooke, J. (1996). SUS-A quick and dirty usability scale. *Usability evaluation in industry*, *189*(194), 4-7.

Coates, H., James, R., & Baldwin, G. (2005). A Critical Examination of the Effects of Learning Management Systems on University Teaching and Learning. *Tertiary Education and Management, 11*(1), 19-36.

Demir, F., & Parraci, W. (2018). The more complex the less success in online library services: Evaluating the user experience for international students. *Issues and Trends in Educational Technology*, *6*(2), 50-64.

Erdoğan, T., Yıldırım, O. G., & Çiğdem, H. (2017). The Investigation of the Usability of Web-Based Assignment System. *Journal of Theory and Practice in Education, 13*(1), 1-9.

Erdoğmuş, F., Kokoç, M., Pinal, E., Bilgi, Ş., & Murat, Z. (2015). Investigation of an Online Learning Environment in Terms of Usability. *Participatory Educational Research, 2*(3), 55-66.

García-Peñalvo, F. J., Vázquez-Ingelmo, A., García-Holgado, A., & Seoane-Pardo, A. M. (2019). Analyzing the usability of the WYRED Platform with undergraduate students to improve its features. *Universal Access in the Information Society*, *18*(3), 455–468.

Georgsson, M., & Staggers, N. (2016). Quantifying usability: an evaluation of a diabetes mHealth system on effectiveness, efficiency, and satisfaction metrics with associated user characteristics. *Journal of the American Medical Informatics Association, 23*(1), 5-11.

Granić, A., & Ćukušić, M. (2011). Usability testing and expert inspections complemented by educational evaluation: A case study of an e-learning platform. *Journal of Educational Technology & Society*, *14*(2), 107-123.

Gutiérrez-Carreón, G., Daradoumis, T., & Jorba, J. (2015). Integrating learning services in the cloud: An approach that benefits both systems and learning. *Journal of Educational Technology & Society*, *18*(1), 145-157.

Harrati, N., Bouchrika, I., & Mahfouf, Z. (2017). Investigating the uptake of educational systems by academics using the technology to performance chain model. *Library Hi Tech*, *35*(4), 629–648.

Harrati, N., Bouchrika, I., Tari, A., & Ladjailia, A. (2016). Exploring user satisfaction for e-learning systems via usage-based metrics and system usability scale analysis. *Computers in Human Behavior, 100*(61), 463-471.

Ituma, A. (2011). An evaluation of students' perceptions and engagement with e-learning components in a campus-based university. *Active Learning in Higher Education, 12*(1), 57-68.

Ivanović, M., Milicević, A. K., Ganzha, M., Bădică, A., Paprzycki, M., & Bădică, C. (2018, January). Usability and Quality Parameters for E-Learning Environments and Systems. In *CEUR Workshop Proceedings*.

Kaewsaiha, P. (2019). Usability of the Learning Management System and Choices of Alternative. In *Proceedings of the 2019 International Conference on Education, Psychology, and Social Sciences (ICEPS),* August 22-24 Tokyo, Japan, pp. 252-259.

Katsanos C., Tselios N., & Avouris N. (2008). AutoCardSorter: Designing the Information Architecture of a Web Site using Latent Semantic Analysis. In *Proceedings of the SIGCHI conference on Human factors in computing systems, CHI 2008*, Florence, Italy, pp. 875-878. ACM Press.

Katsanos, C., Tselios, N., & Xenos, M. (2012). Perceived usability evaluation of learning management systems: a first step towards standardization of the System Usability Scale in Greek. In *Proceedings of the 2012 16th Panhellenic Conference on Informatics,* Piraeus, Greece, pp. 302-307. IEEE.

Kitchenham, B. (2004). Procedures for performing systematic reviews. *Keele, UK, Keele University, 33*(2004), 1-26.

Lehong, S., van Biljon, J., & Sanders, I. (2019). Open-distance electronic learning environments: Supervisors' views on usability. In *Proceedings of the 2019 Conference on Information Communications Technology and Society (ICTAS),* March 6, Durban, Africa, pp. 1-7. IEEE.

Lewis, J. R. (1991). An after-scenario questionnaire for usability studies: psychometric evaluation over three trials. *ACM SIGCHI Bulletin*, *23*(4), 79.

Lewis, J. R. (1992). Psychometric evaluation of the post-study system usability questionnaire: The PSSUQ. In *Proceedings of the Human Factors and Ergonomics Society Annual Meeting,* October 1, Santa Mónica, California, USA, pp. 1259-1263, Human Factors Society

Lewis, J. R. (1995). IBM computer usability satisfaction questionnaires: psychometric evaluation and instructions for use. *International Journal of Human-Computer Interaction, 7*(1), 57-78.

Luo, G. H., Liu, E. Z. F., Kuo, H. W., & Yuan, S. M. (2014). Design and implementation of a simulation-based learning system for international trade. *International Review of Research in Open and Distributed Learning, 15*(1), 203-226.

Marco, F. A., Penichet, V. M. R., & Gallud, J. A. (2013). Collaborative e-Learning through Drag & Share in Synchronous Shared Workspaces. *J. UCS, 19*(7), 894-911.

McCann, D, Christmass, J, Nicholson, P & Stuparich, J (1998). *Educational technology in higher education.* Occasional papers series (Australia. Department of Employment, Education and Training. Higher Education Division), DEETYA, Canberra.

Mentes, S. A., & Turan, A. H. (2012). Assessing the usability of university websites: An empirical study on Namik Kemal University. *Turkish Online Journal of Educational Technology-TOJET, 11*(3), 61-69.

Mujinga, M., Eloff, M. M., & Kroeze, J. H. (2018). System usability scale evaluation of online banking services: A South African study. *South African Journal of Science, 114*(3-4), 1-8.

NaifJabli, H., & Demir, F. (2018) The Usability of King Khalid University Website: Assessing Effectiveness, Efficiency, And Satisfaction. *International Journal of Arts Humanities and Social Sciences, 3* (7), 10-16.

Orfanou, K., Tselios, N., & Katsanos, C. (2015). Perceived usability evaluation of learning management systems: Empirical evaluation of the System Usability Scale. *International Review of Research in Open and Distributed Learning, 16*(2), 227-246.

Pirker, J., Holly, M., Almer, H., Gütl, C., & Belcher, J. W. (2019). Virtual Reality STEM Education from a Teacher's Perspective. In *Proceedings of the Immersive Learning Research Network Conference (iLRN),* June 23-27, London, UK.

Rahimi, A., Embi, M. A., & Rahimi, A. (2015). Evaluation of the e-Learning developed for casemix and clinical coding: Quality of the material and usability of the system. *Argos Special Issue 2*, 130-143.

Rosato, J., Dodds, C., & Laughlin, S. (2007). *Usability of course management systems by students.* Dept. Computer Information Systems/Computer Science, College of Scholastica, Duluth.

Şengel, E. (2013). Usability level of a university web site. *Procedia-Social and Behavioral Sciences, 106*, 3246-3252.

Sengel, E. (2014). Discovering How Students Search a University Web Site: A Comparative Usability Case Study for PC and Mobile Devices. *Turkish Online Journal of Educational Technology-TOJET, 13*(4), 12-20.

Shi, L., Awan, M. S. K., & Cristea, A. I. (2013). Evaluating system functionality in social personalized adaptive e-learning systems. In *Proceedings of the European Conference on Technology Enhanced Learning,* September 17-21, Paphos, Cyprus, pp. 633-634. Springer.

Smith, J., & Oliver, M. (2000). Academic development: A framework for embedding learning technology. *International Journal for Academic Development, 5*(2), 129-137.

Srimarong, S., & Achalakul, T. (2017). Usability evaluation of outcome-based education tool. In *Proceedings of the 2017 IEEE 9th International Conference on Engineering Education (ICEED),* November 9-10, Kanazawa, Japan, pp. 233-237. IEEE.

Thuseethan, S., Achchuthan, S., & Kuhanesan, S. (2014). Usability evaluation of learning management systems in Sri Lankan universities. *arXiv preprint arXiv:1412.0197.*

Tsironis, A., Katsanos, C., & Xenos, M. (2016, April). Comparative usability evaluation of three popular MOOC platforms. In *Proceedings of the 2016 IEEE Global Engineering Education Conference (EDUCON),* April 10-13, Abu Dhabi, UAE, pp. 608-612. IEEE.

Tullis, T., & Albert, B. (2008). Measuring the user experience: Collecting. *Analyzing, and Presenting Usability Metrics*, 124.

Vertesi, A., Dogan, H., Stefanidis, A., Ashton, G., & Drake, W. (2018). Usability Evaluation of a Virtual Learning Environment: a University Case Study. In *Proceedings of the 15th International Conference on Cognition and Exploratory Learning in Digital Age (CELDA),* October 21-23, Budapest, Hungary, IADIS.

A PILOT STUDY ON VIDEO COLOR TRANSFER: A SURVEY OF USER-TYPE OPINIONS

Mairéad Grogan*, Emin Zerman*, Gareth W. Young* and Aljosa Smolic
V-SENSE, School of Computer Science, Trinity College Dublin,
College Green, Dublin 2, Dublin, Ireland

ABSTRACT

Multimedia software products can be used to create and edit various aspects of online media. Recently, the affordances of mobile devices and high-speed mobile data networks mean that these editing capabilities are more readily available for mobile devices enabling a broader consumer-base. However, the precise role of the user in creative practice is often neglected in favor of reporting faster, more streamlined device functionality. In this paper, we seek to identify high-level human-computer interaction issues concerning video recoloring interfaces that are driven by the needs of different user-types via a methodological and explorative process. By conducting a pilot study, we have captured both quantitative and qualitative responses that formatively explore the role of the user in video recoloring tasks carried out on mobile devices. This research presents a variety of user responses to a video recoloring application, identifying areas of future investigation for explorative practices in user interface design for video recoloring visualization. These findings present important information for researchers exploring the use of state-of-art video recoloring processes and contribute to dialogues surrounding the study of mobile technology in use.

KEYWORDS

Color Transfer, User Study, Opinions, Usability

1. INTRODUCTION

In recent years, advances in mobile technology and the popularity of image and video sharing applications such as Instagram and Flickr have seen the platform for image and video editing tools shift from PCs to mobile phones. Editing tasks previously carried out by artists using software applications such as Adobe Photoshop and Premiere Pro are now achievable by casual creatives using simpler tools such as Instagram filters and Google Photo's in-app editing facilities. As these mobile editing tools rise in popularity, we must strive to understand the motivations and expectations of these new casual users when editing images and videos. For this purpose, a pilot study was undertaken to gain insight into how people with different levels of editing expertise use mobile applications when recoloring videos, assessing the users' interactions with the application interface, and exploring other measures such as user expectations and usability. In this paper, we outline the related work in this area (Sec. 2), describe the design of our recoloring application (Sec. 3), detail the methodology behind our user study (Sec. 4), present the results and data gathered (Sec. 5), and discuss these results (Sec. 6). Finally, the conclusions that can be drawn (Sec. 7).

2. RELATED WORK

One recoloring approach that has become very popular in recent years is palette-based image recoloring. These methods allow users to edit a small palette of colors to indicate what color changes they would like to see in their recolored images. Since these applications allow for more interactive experiences during the recoloring process, user studies are often undertaken to assess usability and quantify the overall user experience. In the work of Chang et al (2015), novice users were given an allotted time to recolor an input

* These authors contributed equally

image to match a target image using different pieces of software. The difference between the recolored image and the target was then computed, along with the time taken to edit the image, and both were used to assess the usability of the applications. When assessing new tools, others compared the results generated by novice users using the proposed approaches to those generated by professional artists using tools available in Adobe Photoshop, such as the Replace Color tool, or image keying tools such as Keylight and Primatte (Aksoy et al., 2017, Chang et al., 2015, Zhang et al., 2017). These studies give an insight into how different pieces of software compare to professional tools for specific tasks, as well as providing an insight into the usability of these tools and whether the correct level of control is provided to recreate particular image results.

Another popular approach to image and video recoloring is example-based recoloring, where an example image provides the color palette used to recolor the input image (Arbelot et al., 2017, Ferradans et al., 2013, Grogan & Dahyot, 2019, Reinhard et al., 2001) or video (Bonneel et al., 2013, Frigo et al., 2015, Grogan & Dahyot, 2015) While the quality of example-based image recoloring approaches have been assessed subjectively and user studies implemented to determine which example-based method creates the most appealing results (Grogan & Dahyot, 2019, Hristova et al., 2015), little research has considered how "usable" these methods are for different user-types, whether this type of approach allows users to create their desired results, whether more complex control is required by users, and what types of palette images should be provided. In terms of example-based video recoloring, many methods simply extend image techniques to video data by applying the color transfer function estimated for a single frame to all frames of the video (Frigo et al., 2015, Grogan & Dahyot, 2015). While the quality of image recoloring techniques has been assessed through subjective experiments, their extensions to video data often have not (Grogan & Dahyot, 2019).

With the continuous advances in mobile hardware, many state-of-the-art image editing tools have been transferred to mobile platforms, raising new questions about how such applications should be designed (Isenberg, 2016). These tools include image recoloring, neural style transfer and filtering methods (Ryffel et al., 2017, Dürschmid et al., 2017, Reimann et al., 2019, Semmo et al., 2017). Ryffel et al. extended their soft segmentation approach to an augmented reality application, allowing users to virtually recolor a select number of paintings in a museum (Ryffel et al., 2017). Paintings were decomposed into layers in a preprocessing step which meant that at runtime, paintings could be recolored and displayed on the user's mobile device in real time. A recent neural style transfer approach proposed using a network with a reduced number of layers to reduce computation time, relying on upsampling to create high resolution results from the low resolution network output (Semmo et al., 2017). Other neural style transfer mobile applications consider the usability of the application, devising methods to increase the learnability of the application through user driven redesigns (Reimann et al., 2019) and allowing users to manipulate different style parameters and presets, and even share styles between users (Dürschmid et al., 2017). In this paper, we propose a pilot study to formatively assess user interactions with an example-based mobile video recoloring application, and to explore potential differences in user opinion and usability in terms of both the recoloring interface and the video results.

3. MOBILE COLOR TRANSFER APPLICATION

In this paper, we consider the color transfer method proposed by Grogan et al. (Grogan & Dahyot, 2015, 2019, Grogan et al., 2015). Proposed first by Grogan et al. (2015) and extended by Grogan & Dahyot (2019), this method enables the color transfer of the source image to a targeted color distribution by selecting a palette image. The method uses an L2 based cost function and transforms the colors in the input image to that of the target image by estimating a thin plate spline transfer function φ, see Figure 1. Although the original method was proposed for images, it is shown by Grogan & Dahyot (2015) that applying the same transfer function which was estimated between a single frame of the source video and a target image, the method could also easily be extended to video. For this purpose, a single random frame can be selected from the source video, and the same φ can be applied to all the frames of the said source video to avoid temporal inconsistencies.

Figure 1. Example based color transfer used in this work

For this pilot study, the state-of-the-art video color transfer technology described was implemented by way of an Android application, see Figure 2. The application recolors video via the following steps. First, the user selects a source video from the phone gallery (Figure 2(a)) and a target color palette (Figure 2(b)) immediately after that. Although the application allows users to select a custom target image from the phone's gallery, in this study, the participants were asked to select from a predefined list[†] of palette images (Figure 2(c)) from famous movies that have a strong color feel, for example, The Revenant, 300, Alice Through the Looking Glass, etc. After users have selected both source video and target palette, they are brought to a preview screen that displays their selected video and target palette (Figure 2(d)). The color transfer process can then start after the user presses the 'Color Transfer' button. The resulting video is displayed after the color transfer process is completed (Figure 2(e)). On this last screen, users are given the option to download the resulting video.

The implemented application was a prototype and was designed as a front-end to back-end processing system residing on a remote server of a public university. In this framework, once users selected the input video and target palette, both video and palette were uploaded to the back-end where the color transfer function (φ) was estimated and used to recolor the video. The recolored video was then sent back to the device and displayed to the user. The duration for uploading both source video and target palette to the server was 3.8 seconds on average for a video with 960×540 resolution. To accelerate the recoloring, source videos were resized to a resolution of 320×180 server-side to decrease processing times and reducing the download time for the result. The whole process took 8.6 seconds on average from pressing "Color Transfer" to the download of the resulting video.

(a) Video selection (b) Palette selection (c) Color palettes (d) Preview screen (e) Results screen

Figure 2. The user interface of the mobile color transfer application

4. PILOT STUDY

To collect data concerning the usability of the recoloring application a controlled pilot study was conducted. In this section, we discuss the methodologies applied.

4.1 Apparatus & Setup

A Huawei P9 Plus smartphone (with 1080×1920 display resolution) was used to run the Android application described previously. All participants used the same device under the same network conditions. Pretesting was undertaken to ensure that there were no network-related delays reported during the test. The study was conducted in a dedicated quiet and well-lit room with no windows. A total of 16 source videos and 12 target palettes[†] were used in this study. Source videos were selected considering various features such as camera movement (tripod, drone, handheld), focus (all-in-focus, low depth of field), and theme (personal, professional, touristic). Target palettes were selected from famous movies in which the photography was color graded by industry professionals. Moreover, quantitative metrics such as color variation and spatial information were considered for the selection of source videos and target palettes. All source videos were of 10 seconds duration. This device set up ensured that we could identify which video and palette images were selected by each user for the reproducibility of results.

4.2 Methodology

Participant recruitment took place in the Republic of Ireland via an online call advertised in December 2019 on the mailing lists of the university and social media accounts of the research project, etc. Therefore, the cohort comprised of staff and students from the departments of engineering, computer science, and members of the university from outside of these disciplines. The study was then conducted within the latter part of January 2020. To avoid any bias which may have been caused by differences in device and location, the participants were invited to attend the laboratory at a time and date that suited their schedule. To preserve anonymity, participants were assigned a four-digit alphanumeric code. Following this, they were asked to report their age, gender, and occupation. To identify user-types within the cohort a user-cube approach (Nielsen, 1993) was implemented, therefore, participants were asked to self-identify their *(i)* ability to use new technology, *(ii)* familiarity with the video and image editing domain, and *(iii)* expertise in the application and use of video and image editing applications on a fully labeled 5-point Likert scale.

To ensure all participants received the same instruction, they were presented with a scripted demonstration on how to use the mobile color transfer application. During this instruction, participants were shown each step of the color transfer procedure, and they viewed the resulting recolored video. After this, the test was conducted in two stages. In the first, participants were asked to complete at least two color transfer operations by themselves, selecting from pre-installed source videos and target palettes. During this time, participants were instructed to remain seated and hold the device at a comfortable distance. In the second stage of the study, the participants were asked to fill in a questionnaire. To collect user opinions related to the mobile recoloring application, this questionnaire included a Single Ease Question (SEQ) (Sauro & Dumas, 2009), application-specific questions with fully labeled 5-point Likert scales, and open-ended answer options. Each session took no more than 30 minutes.

4.3 Participants

A total of 21 participants volunteered to take part in the study (Male = 14; Female = 7), with an average age of 31.5 (M=31.50; SD=5.50). The cohort was comprised of students (n=10), researchers (n=9), and others (n=2). The participants self-reported that their ability to use new digital technology is "Good" to "Excellent" (M=4.29; SD=1.01; CI=0.43), their familiarity with the video and image recoloring domain is "Moderately Familiar" to "Very Familiar" (M=3.71; SD=1.01; CI=0.43), and their expertise in the use of video and image recoloring applications is "Average" (M=2.95; SD=1.07; CI=0.46). Using the three dimensions of technical ability, familiarity, and expertise, the participants were identified as different user-types. These user-types were novices (users with some simple experiences with the technology), primary and secondary end-users (users who routinely use this technology in their daily work activities or who are motivated by occasional, contextual, or intrinsic interests), and advanced users (tech-savvy professionals with a broad knowledge of related activities and tools, a high degree of competency, and comprehensive expertise). All participants were

[†] For replicability, all the pre-selected source videos, target images, and their selection procedure are shared on our project webpage: https://v-sense.scss.tcd.ie/research/vfx-animation/mobile-video-color-transfer-project/.

sufficiently versed in the use of digital technology to contribute meaningful discourse on the topic and the participant group could be considered as containing broad perspectives from novices to advanced users who were discreetly familiar with the recoloring domain. From this data, user-groups were logically formed as novices (n=5), end-users (n=9); and advanced users (n=7), see Figure 3. The participant group size for a usability study remains a matter of debate; however, for studies related to problem discovery, a group size of 3-20 participants is typically valid, with 5-10 participants being a sensible baseline range (Macefield, 2009). Therefore, in the case of the presented study, the user-type groups were considered of large enough size for a pilot study to discover any severe problems in our video recoloring prototype design and not a direct user-type comparative study. Additionally, further limitations in the participant pool were found in gender type and employment sectors, constraining our extrapolation of results to the broader population.

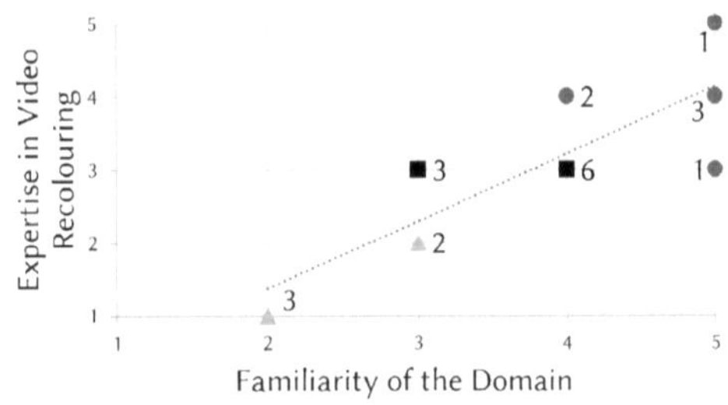

Figure 3. User-cube identifying user-groups: advanced (blue circles); end-users (black squares); novices (yellow triangles); numbers represent the number of users

5. RESULTS

Our pilot study sought to explore and identify elements of the video recoloring task that was of concern to our users. Both quantitative and qualitative data were collected, and areas of interest are reported below concerning the user interface. To begin, we assessed how difficult the recoloring task was to complete. The SEQ revealed that all users considered the application to be easy to use (M=5.9, SD=1.31), see Figure 4(a). The results of a Kruskal-Wallis Test (a non-parametric method for comparing independent samples) indicated that there were no statistically significant differences in how difficult the user-types found the task, with x^2 (2, n=21) = 0.49, p = 0.78. Therefore, all users found the task “Easy” to complete (Md=6).

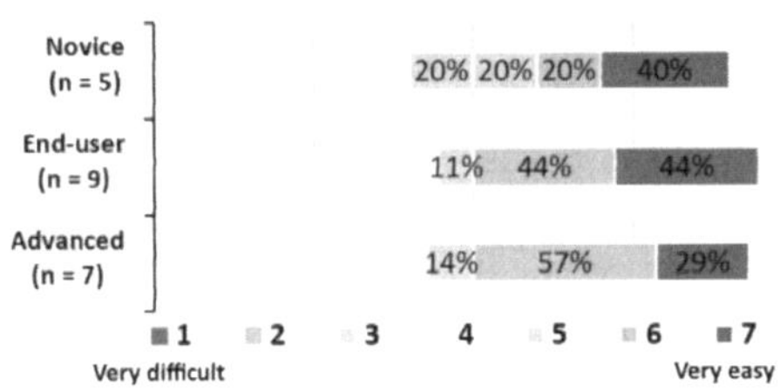

(a) The Single Ease Question (SEQ)

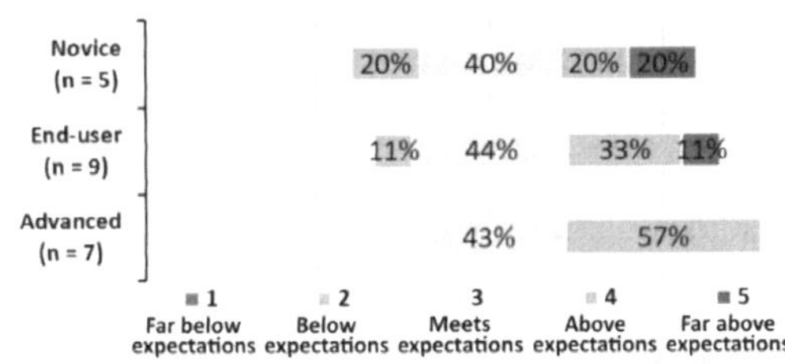

(b) User opinions about the number of palettes

Figure 4. Participant responses for SEQ and number of palettes

In response to the question *"Were there enough palettes to get the results you wanted?"* a median score of “Above Expectations” (Md=4) was measured. A Kruskal-Wallis test revealed no statistically significant differences in palette choices across the three different user groups, with x2 (2, n=21) = 0.248, p = 0.88. When asked to expand upon their answers, users openly expressed that there were more than enough palettes provided for an exploratory task, with only two participants indicating that they would like more (a score of 2) and two others believing that the application gave more options far above their expectations (a score of 5). The advanced group recorded a median score of “Above expectations” (Md=4), and the novice and end-user groups both recorded median values of “Meets expectations” (Md=3), see Figure 4(b).

When asked *"Which palette representation do you prefer?"* from a selection of three choices, see Figure 5, most participants preferred the combined representation of the movie frame and color palette (18/21). When asked to expand upon their preferences, users expressed their partialities for the movie still (2/21) as it was "simple", and felt that "[the palette] doesn't mean much to me" – KI74 (novice) and that the movie frame "gives a good example of the color palette" – MC75 (end-user). Statements for the color palette alone (1/21) highlighted that there was "no bias in terms of content." – ZA60 (advanced user). With the color palette and movie still combined, the participants were able to understand how the image and colors related to the recolored video output, giving them a better understanding of how the color transformation would look.

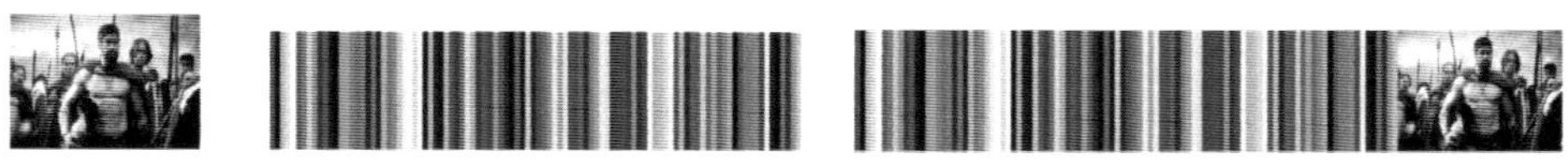

(a) Movie frame only (b) Color distribution only (c) Movie frame and color distribution combined

Figure 5. Palette representation

Participants were also asked *"Would you prefer to use a recoloring application that provides color palettes or one that uses example images of the filters? Please explain why."*, referring to Figure 6(a). Most participants preferred having example images as they seemed "more intuitive" and expressed that users "can directly evaluate the result". Moreover, the examples images were said to be helpful for users "to contextualize and visualize the result" – HM41 (advanced user). Some of the participants expressed that they liked the color palette representations in the application as "[I] prefer color palettes, because filters don't give much idea about the outcome, and they may not match our expectations" – IS42 (novice). Similarly, as mentioned by one advanced user, their preference was dependent on what they wanted to achieve: "When I know what look I want, color palettes. When I don't know what look I want, then example images" – CT77 (advanced user). Many of the participants would have liked to have seen example images when recoloring was taking place so they could get a better idea of what the output would look like. It was felt that it would be easier to directly evaluate the result and would be more intuitive to use.

To compare different types of interaction possibilities, the participants were asked *"Do you think it would be easier to use this recoloring application rather than other types of existing filters? Please explain why."*, see Figure 6(a). Participants' responses were mixed and not distinctly indicative when comparing user-type profiles. Many participants were in favor of the current recoloring application, while other members of the cohort were in favor of using existing user interfaces from familiar recoloring systems. Some participants also expressed that their opinions would be influenced by specific task factors, while other participants said that there were no distinguishing differences between the current recoloring application and other recoloring filter user interfaces. From the analysis of the qualitative user feedback, those in favor of the recoloring application thought that the current recoloring application was "less complicated", or it made "results more unique". One participant commented: "this recoloring application does most of the work for you if you want to quickly change the mood of an image/video" – BG78 (novice). Participants who were in favor of other, existing filter user interfaces said that they liked the instant feedback and "a preview down below" these interfaces provided "to give a quick idea of what the result might look like" – KI74 (novice). If provided with instant feedback, users "can test different filters very easily" – XC97 (advanced user). Users' opinions that were based purely upon the circumstances of the experiment stated that "if I want to change the mood, I will use the recoloring app. If the change I want is very small, maybe I would prefer a filter." – BV46 (end-user). Regardless of their personal preferences, many participants indicated that it was important to be able to control the effects and to tweak parameters, as "I often change the parameters of the filters when I do use them" – SQ34 (end-user).

(a) Instagram filters (b) Complex controls

Figure 6. Visual representations of different image and video editing tools

The participants were asked *"Would you like more complex control over the recoloring application to create more appealing or custom looking videos? Please explain why."*, referring to Figure 6(b). More than half of the participants declared that they would like more complex controls over those provided in the current recoloring application. Most of the participants stated that it would be great to "tweak the results" and to "correct errors" for "refinement" after initial results were processed, as "the application provides a great initial result but with refinement, it could be even better" – HM41 (advanced user). Although being more positive, some users suggested that "otherwise it does not add much to preset filters" – SK56 (end-user) or "it's good to have the option. However, I probably wouldn't use the advanced controls often!" – XC97 (advanced user). One user believed that it could be useful "if I were using it with professional software, but not for a social media app" – WD79 (advanced user). Participants that gave negative responses declared that they either "prefer a simple interface" or that it currently is "[a] little too complicated". The remainder of the participants were indecisive. One novice user acknowledged that "it might be nice to have in the rare case I want fine adjustment, but I rarely use these controls or keep the results from using them" – KI74 (novice). On the other hand, participants also wanted to have access to both options as "I will have a simple version, and for advance users let them customize it" – BV46 (end-user).

When asked *"Do you think that a color palette is easier to use than the more traditional image and video editing tools that offer more custom color change options? Please explain why."*, referring to Figure 6(b), participants mostly agreed that the recoloring application was easier to use but that this comes at a trade-off since they also have less control. These participants expressed that it was "more intuitive" and "it's easier to imagine the results without being an expert" – GS24 (end-user), while some users said that the current application was "easier because there are fewer parameters to tune" – MU69 (novice). It was also suggested that "it is less effort but leaves you feeling you don't have full control over the results" – YG89 (end-user). Participants also commented that the "feel" of the video was easier to change with the recoloring application, as "choosing a palette is more like choosing a mood" – JN33 (end-user). Some participants were indecisive on how difficult the current recoloring application was and answered the question without giving any explicitly positive or negative responses. These participants balanced how the recoloring results would change concerning the user's level of expertise and experience. For example, one end-user noted that "the color palette is quick and easy for social media use, but I still prefer full control for professional use" – HL75.

In the last section of the questionnaire, participants were asked to provide their opinions and suggestions regarding the ease of use of the user interface or discuss possible improvements that could be made. In general, advanced users were more critical of the layout and the technical limitations that they presented. On the other hand, participants who identified as end-users and novices suggested more practical changes, for example, changes in the color palettes or visualizations of the selected video and palette combination. Furthermore, positive comments regarding the application – "impressive" and "easy to use" – were also from this cohort. The three main areas of improvement were identified from participant comments on layout, technical limitations, and ease of use.

6. DISCUSSION

This Android-based, mobile phone video recoloring application was designed as a prototype, and as such, the questions asked of the participants were aimed at highlighting possible research directions and improvements in the initial user interface design. The SEQ demonstrated how the mobile color transfer application was easy to use by all user-types. The task was clear and straightforward for novices, encouraged end-users to try new things, and proved adequate for most advanced users' needs. Furthermore, the user interface was considered easy to use when compared to other filter interfaces too. Participants' responses to other areas of the user interface were mixed regardless of the user-types and were often described as being task-dependent. Although the color transfer application had fewer parameters to tune and gave "a unique film look", the example images provided by filters gave instant feedback, which was sought after by users. The results of the study also indicated that the number of palettes provided either met expectations (for novices and end-users) or was above expectations (for advanced users). This suggests that 12 different target palettes would be enough for a mobile recoloring application. Moreover, participants preferred the combined palette representation, stating that they could understand how the color transfer would take place since the combined representation showed both the dominant colors and how they might be distributed in the recolored video. Regarding complex controls, participants noted that it would be good to have the option to tweak the results although these complex controls would probably not be used often. This shows the need for a simple interface for novice users and an expanded user interface option to satisfy end-users or advanced users. Regarding the interaction, most users preferred the example images that filters provided as it allowed the user to quickly evaluate the recolored result compared to the current recoloring application. Nevertheless, they also preferred the current recoloring application over the more traditional image and video editing tools, as the application was found easier to use. This shows that using simple interfaces that provide fast feedback is appealing to most of the users and user-types.

7. CONCLUSION

In this paper, we report on a pilot study that identifies human-computer interaction issues related to a state-of-the-art video recoloring application. For three different user-types, we formatively explore key aspects of the video recoloring application related to usability, design choices, and user-type expectations from such a mobile application. We found that the color transfer application was easy to use by all user-types. Moreover, the different user-types also agreed that the number of palettes and the palette representation met their expectations. While praising its simplicity, the users also requested additional features such as optional complex controls and instant feedback options. The results show that there are some qualitative differences among user-types. The novices we engaged with scored more broadly when compared to the other user-types, which can be analyzed in future work relating to motivations for knowledge building and advanced user interactions.

We believe that these results can help developers and researchers expand existing dialogues to improve user experiences and create new user interfaces for video recoloring applications. Particularly, we believe that user-types vary in their motivations, expectations, satisfaction, and perceived usability of mobile applications, as various factors impact their confidence when concerning their previous knowledge and experiences with video editing software. Therefore, future application developments and usability studies will focus on the addition of advanced "accelerator" options for more complex recoloring control, the development of sample-based feedback in the form of cell images and palettes, and explore the perceived usability and users' experiences of existing user interfaces (e.g. Instagram, Google Photos, etc.) that take different approaches to these issues.

REFERENCES

Aksoy, Yagiz et al, 2017. Unmixing-based soft color segmentation for image manipulation. *ACM Transactions on Graphics*, Vol. 36, No. 2, pp. 19:1-19:19.

Arbelot, Benoit et al, 2017. Local texture-based color transfer and colorization. *Computers & Graphics*, Vol. 62.

Bonneel, Nicolas et al, 2013. Example-based video color grading, *ACM Transactions on Graphics*, Vol. 32, No. 4.

Chang, Huiwen et al, 2015. Palette-based photo recoloring. *ACM Transactions on Graphics*, Vol. 34, No. 4.

Dürschmid, Tobias et al, 2017. ProsumerFX: Mobile Design of Image Stylization Components. *Proceedings of SIGGRAPH Asia 2017 Mobile Graphics & Interactive Applications*, Bangkok, Thailand.

Ferradans, Sira et al, 2013. Regularized discrete optimal transport. In: Kuijper, Arjan, Bredies, Kristian, Pock, Thomas, & Bischof, Horst eds, *Scale Space and Variational Methods in Computer Vision*, Berlin: Springer Berlin, pp. 428–439.

Frigo, Oriel et al, 2015. Optimal transportation for example-guided color transfer. In: Cremers, Daniel, Reid, Ian, Saito, Hideo, & Yang, Ming-Hsuan eds, *Computer Vision – ACCV 2014*, Cham: Springer, pp. 655-670.

Grogan, Mairéad & Dahyot, Rozenn, 2015. L2 registration for colour transfer in videos. *Proceedings of the 12th European Conference on Visual Media Production (CVMP)*, London, UK.

Grogan, Mairéad & Dahyot, Rozenn, 2019. L2 divergence for robust colour transfer. *Computer Vision and Image Understanding* Vol. 181, pp. 39-49.

Grogan, Mairéad et al, 2015. L2 registration for colour transfer. *23rd European Signal Processing Conference (EUSIPCO)*. Nice, France, pp. 1-5.

Hristova, Hristina et al, 2015. Style-aware robust color transfer. *Proceedings of the Workshop on Computational Aesthetics (CAE),* Goslar, Germany, pp. 67–77.

Isenberg, Tobias, 2016. Interactive NPAR: What type of tools should we create? *Proceedings of the Joint Symposium on Computational Aesthetics and Sketch Based Interfaces and Modeling and Non-Photorealistic Animation and Rendering*, Lisbon, Portugal, pp. 89-96.

Macefield, Rich, 2009. How to specify the participant group size for usability studies: a practitioner's guide. *Journal of Usability Studies*, 5(1), 34-45.

Nielsen, Jakob, 1993. *Usability engineering.* Academic Press, Boston.

Pitié, François et al, 2005. N-dimensional probability density function transfer and its application to color transfer. *Tenth International Conference on Computer Vision (ICCV)*, Beijing, China, pp. 1434-1439.

Reimann, Max et al, 2019. Locally controllable neural style transfer on mobile devices. *The Visual Computer* Vol 35, pp. 1531-1547.

Reinhard, Erik et al, 2001. Color transfer between images. *IEEE Computer Graphics and Applications*, Vol. 21, No. 5.

Ryffel, Mattia et al, 2017. AR Museum: A mobile augmented reality application for interactive painting recoloring. *In Multi Conference on Computer Science and Information Systems 2017*, Lisbon, Portugal.

Sauro, Jeff & Dumas, Joseph S., 2009. Comparison of three one-question, post-task usability questionnaires. *Proceedings of the SIGCHI conference on human factors in computing systems*, pp. 1599–1608.

Semmo, Amir et al, 2017. Pictory: Combining Neural Style Transfer and Image Filtering. *Proceedings of ACM SIGGRAPH 2017 Appy Hour*, Los Angeles, California.

Zhang, Qing et al, 2017. Palette-based image recoloring using color decomposition optimization. *IEEE Transactions on Image Processing*, Vol. 26, No. 4, pp. 1952-1964.

EXAMINING THE EFFECTIVENESS OF GAMIFICATION AND GAME-BASED LEARNING IN THE CONTEXT OF BLOCKCHAIN

Nicholas Abela and Owen Sacco
Malta College of Arts, Science and Technology, Malta

ABSTRACT

In the world of gaming, there has been a shift from games being used solely for entertainment, to games being used as a medium to educate. For this matter, there are two methods of making a game which are gamification or game-based learning. The former is the use of game elements, such as health points or leader boards, and they are applied to a non-gaming platform. The latter, game-based learning, includes developing a full-fledged game where the means towards the end, that is to say victory are set in a world where the player has to apply the teachings given to advance. Since this is an IT-related research, the topic chosen for this study is Blockchain, an ever-expanding sector over the past decade. Different parts of Blockchain's makeup have been dissected into small, comprehensible pieces of information in the applications created, which a brand new student to the form can take in at their own pace. Should this study go beyond this research, it would be beneficial for the experiments to have two games designed and created by someone who has the artistic and technical capabilities of creating their own assets. This would leave a better impression with the test subjects and ideally receive a better data set for examination.

KEYWORDS

Blockchain, Gamification, Game-Based Learning, Education

1. INTRODUCTION

This research will be investigating the effectiveness of combining teaching with video games to produce a learning environment for vast and complex topics. To conduct the experiments needed, the topic of Blockchain was selected, due to its prominence in many spheres of influence in the world. In order to educate students about the vastness of Blockchain, there needs to be a system in place. To determine which method would be most beneficial for the education of this topic, there will be a game implemented using Gamification elements, and another game that will make use of a Game-Based Learning system. In other words, this research focuses on determining whether gamification or game-based learning is most effective for teaching concepts about Blockchain. The remainder of this paper is structured as follows: section 2 provides core information about gamification, game-based learning and blockchain and reviews current work in these research areas. Section 3 provides an explanation of our methodology and Section 4 presents our results from our user study. Section 5 concludes the paper by providing an overall discussion and the future steps of this work.

2. RELATED WORK

In order to understand how education can be improved, there needs to be an understanding on the methods of education. (Zeng, et al., 2006) discussed an analysis of classroom-teaching in order to verify its quality at a given time. They observe how the different factors present in the classroom affect the end-result, which is how much the student learned. Among the factors that (Zeng, et al., 2006) concluded was that the need for the quality of teaching and how to motivate the students to learn better should be given its due importance, which will result in better education overall.

2.1 Gamification

To understand what is needed to create a gamified application, one must understand what the term Gamification means. Coined for the digital media industry, (Deterding, et al., 2011) explains how the concept was constructed without an actual clear definition of its content. It was coined by Nick Pelling in 2002, according to (Tóth & Tóvölgyi, 2016), but became widely known in 2010. Its most common feature is that it makes use of game-elements in a context that is not usually attributed to games, which lead this feature to become its widely accepted definition. (Deterding, et al., 2011) said that it is a concept that relates to the "game" part of a system, instead of the "play" portion. These two elements are what defines a game created for leisure or a system created with game-elements added on top of it to be made more appealing to customers or students.

As stated before, in order for a system to be considered as a gamified one, it cannot be design as a full game, but rather as a system that takes certain elements into itself to make the functional aspects of the system less tedious or more educative. (Tóth & Tóvölgyi, 2016) gives various examples of what elements can be considered for such a system. The examples below are just a few from the ones mentioned:

- **Points**: The most basic of reward systems, points are given when the user performs an action that reflect the application's functionality.
- **Badges**: A symbol of achievement, the badge is used to display the successes of the player's actions. These are comparable to the badges handed out by Boy Scouts.
- **Avatar**: The virtual representation of the player online, this element is used for the social aspect of such systems.
- **Progress Bar**: A system that records the experience gained by actions completed, and translates it into visual feedback for the player to follow.

As outlined by (Codish & Ravid, 2014), in order for a system to properly implement gamification, the system itself must show a degree of adaptability, so that each player feels comfortable within the community of the service. This adaptability must be taken from different angles, between elements such as game mechanics and dynamics, or personality and social demographics.

There are multiple sectors in society that make use of such systems. Once again, (Tóth & Tóvölgyi, 2016) offers some examples, some of which are:

- **Education**: This can be seen in Duolingo and Codecademy, where the former is a language teaching system, whereas the latter is used by programmers to learn their craft. These two systems make use of the aforementioned game elements that (Tóth & Tóvölgyi, 2016) listed, which include experience points, points that are presented as currency and badges to showcase progress.
- **Tasks**: Gamification helps people accomplish their goals on the Habitica platform just as their slogan is: Inspire yourself to do something. The website does this rewarding active members with gold and experience, and inactive ones with loss of health. Furthermore, every user can build an avatar on the website, but some features are only available via coins and gold. Thus users can "spend" the gold they have collected.

2.2 Game-Based Learning

Contrary to Gamification, Game-Based Learning is the use of a serious game in order to create a learning environment. (Dunwell, et al., 2011) discusses the use of serious game and explains what needs to blend the game with education. It is very important to note that a serious game cannot fully be a permanent replacement of traditional methods of education. The crucial aspect of such a type of game is that it can add to the learning environment of students, and aid teachers in explaining better their subject.

In their report, (Dunwell, et al., 2011) create a case study which was EU-Funded in order to showcase how effective a game is at teaching its participants. The game featured a 3D simulation of an evacuation scenario, where the player needs to escape from a burning building. Alternatively, 3D games are not the only way of creating an educative game. (Hung, et al., 2014) created a multi-touch puzzle which teaches primary school students the geographical concepts of Taiwan. In his research, (Petrov, 2014) looked at using Minecraft's educational features to see how effective they truly are. In his research, he collaborated with different teachers who made use of this game in order to teach younger students.

2.3 Blockchain

In 2008, Satoshi Nakamoto released the paper "Bitcoin: A Peer-To-Peer Electronic Cash System", which paved the way for the popular blockchain system. (Srivastava, et al., 2019) gave a detailed rundown on how the system works.

A blockchain is an increasing set of data blocks that are connected in the form of a single long chain. These blocks are connected by a secure cryptographic hash. This chain of linked data blocks is viewed as a general ledger and is spread over a peer to peer network. Every computer that is connected to the network has an updated copy of the same general ledger. Most importantly, the ledger itself is secure, and the database can be extended only by adding new blocks into the chain. Changing records which have already been assigned to the chain is impossible.

In order to understand how blockchain works, (Srivastava, et al., 2019) explain the 4 main points of its security.

- **Data encryption**: There are two types of encryption schemes for various purposes: Symmetric and Asymmetric. In asymmetric algorithms, various keys are used for plaintext encryption and ciphertext decryption. Sender and receiver in this form of encryption both have a key pair of a public and private key. Because the data is encrypted by public key recipients, it is only the recipient who can decrypt the data.
- **Modification prevention**: The data stored in the chain is not easy to change. Using a Hash Reference, the blocks are locked together and each new block contains previous block's hash value. A hash function's main property is that if anyone changes a single bit in the input, the entire value will change in output.
- **Inserting new blocks**: Bitcoin mining is the process of adding transaction records to the public ledger of past transactions. The miners solve a complex mathematical problem referred to as 'Proof of Work' to add a new block. In the same network, there may be many miners, but only one can be successful at any given time.
- **Data verification in blocks**: Inside a block the data or transactions are stored in the form of a hash-based tree data structure called a Merkle Tree. If someone does not follow the structure of the tree, and a single transaction is already manipulated, then the entire hash output will be different. Only those transactions that have been tampered with will be incorrect, whereas the rest will be the same.

The most famous use of blockchain is the cryptocurrency Bitcoin which was released in 2009. Bitcoin operates under blockchain technology and follows the same regulations and rules. In order to store money a user needs an online wallet, which contains a collection of software-controlled Bitcoin addresses and private keys. A private key is a cryptographic hash of 64 characters which proves ownership of a specific address.

(Latifi, et al., 2019) also provide a practical use for blockchain, this time within the sphere of Real Estate. The currency used by this research is not Bitcoin, but Ethereum, which makes use of Ether. Ethereum is another cryptocurrency that stemmed from Bitcoin. The value of this cryptocurrency is far less than its predecessor.

3. METHODOLOGY

In the proposed experiment, the implementations created will be used to lead the study towards an understanding on how effective the games are in actuality. The first step is to create a design which will benefit the respective game's genre. Each game has its own unique function, one assigned to Game-Based Learning and another to Gamification. The implemented Gamification-based learning game is accessible here[1] and the Game-based learning game is accessible here[2].

[1] Gamification-based learning game: https://bit.ly/2YJNhWG
[2] Game-based learning game: https://bit.ly/37CTsQc

3.1 Technologies Used

As this is a game related experiment, the choice of game-engine is paramount. The final choice of engine needs to be taken with respect to the experience the developer has with it, the effectiveness of the game-engine in the given two scenarios and the ease of which a game can be built and published to be distributed among the test subjects. After careful consideration of these facts, Unity was the choice of engine.

The games were created on a WebGL Unity build option which, by the end of the development life cycle, allows for a deployment on an online website. The WebGL build option creates a folder with an index.html link, compiled build data and Unity's TemplateData, which can be seen at the start of the game. This choice was taken because of the ease of distribution a game hosted on a website offers.

3.2 Gamification Design

(Anam Fathoni & Delima, 2016) explained that game elements can be re-purposed to achieve the goal of educating a person in a given subject. In this implementation, the elements that were added were progression through multiple stages, points awarded for correct questions, collection of resources, randomly generated avatars and an end screen showing what was achieved and what was not. Added to these elements was a narrative that gave movement to the game. As (Palomino, et al., 2019) discussed, the use of narrative can be implemented in order to help the user build their own experience, within the logic of the game. To create the game, an asset called Fungus was used to create objects such as menus and another asset called "2000+ Faces" was used to create a randomly generated avatar for the player. The player is then introduced to a brief history of what is currently trending around the world. The narrative has a negative undertone, suggesting that the avatar's system is being hacked. This gives the player the sense of being part of the situation by being the character themselves. It also gives the game a more interactive feel, rather than having to rely on simple instructions. This is followed by an explanation of the game's reward system. The game's winning and losing conditions are tied to the player's health points, and the keys received.

The following rules are applied to the game:

- A player has up to three chances to guess a question wrong throughout the game.
- A player can progress to the next level if at least two keys are attained.
- If at any given level, the player misses two keys, even if they still have 3 chances, the game is over. This gives the player a sense of urgency to make sure that the game is played attentively.

The player is given three sections of information, each section given at different stages of the game. They are then given the choice to either attempt the questions, or re-read the information. Each question was given two variables, later used as part of the data set, which were the "Attempted" and "Correct" variables. If the three questions were attempted but only one was correct, it can be safely assumed that the player lost the game. If two of the questions were correct, the player could proceed without having to answer the third question. The result sheet also highlights what keys the player managed to attain, so that when the game is played again, extra attention is given to the sections that were not fully understood. The game will go through the loop of supplying information, waiting for answers and progressing three times.

3.3 Game-Based Learning Design

Compared to the Gamification section, this game was made possible using a complex game engine which can be imported into Unity, called TopDown Engine, where the character within the game is an orange rectangular blob. Instead of having a start button, the game launches playing already, with two simple instructions given to the player. These are "Press WASD to move" and "Press SPACE to interact with doors." In this game, the player is transported to another room, where an instruction sheet is given. The questions are are allocated to a set of coloured doors, which are used as the modes of transport between rooms. Green and Blue doors offer progress forward or backwards, whereas Red doors offer either victory or defeat. This setup was made to assess how well the player does when faced with familiar information, given that proper implementation was given previously. The player can move on the instructions and read at their own pace, and a timer starts counting up, which will be used in the final analysis of the data.

This game has a different set of rules:

- A player can go back and forth through questions and instruction sheets to read at their own pace.
- If a player answers incorrectly, they are transported to a room with a red door, which will end the game in defeat.
- The game is won if the player makes it through all 9 questions and goes through the red door at the end, which means victory this time round.

3.4 Data Collection

In order to collect data, the subjects chosen all varied in age, education and IT experience as much as possible. The chosen subjects will be ranging from 18 to 35 years of age, with different IT experience, as well as different takes on gaming itself. The design of the game was done with the intention that someone with no prior gaming or IT expertise could pick up and play till the end. Gender was not a criteria that would be mentioned in any questionnaire, due to gender not being a factor considered in the results. For both games, if the method of distribution was chosen correctly, then the Gamification portion should prove a high attempted is to correct ratio. The Game-based learning portion should provide with low timer numbers.

After trying both games, a questionnaire was supplied to the test subjects, targeting both quantitative and qualitative data. The former was targeted using a 10-point rating scale, where 1 indicated the least favourable outcome and 10 for the best outcome. The latter was gathered using two opinion based questions.

4. RESULTS AND DISCUSSION

In this section, the results for both games are defined and examined.

4.1 Gamification

Table 1 shows the frequency of the attempts and correct answers throughout the whole experiment. Overall, the results show a positive number of attempts, and a high number of correct answers as well. Based on this data, since the game required player to answer two questions correctly to progress, it can be deducted that only one player failed the game, and that this player failed during the first section.

According to the data, only 44\% of the questions had an attempt rate equal to the correctly answered rate, whereas 33\% of the questions had a two more attempts than correct answers, and 23\% had only a one attempt difference to correct answers.

Table 1. Frequency of attempts and correct answers

Question ID	Attempted	Correct
S1_Q1	9	7
S1_Q2	9	8
S1_Q3	10	8
S2_Q1	9	9
S2_Q2	8	8
S2_Q3	9	8
S3_Q1	9	9
S3_Q2	9	7
S3_Q3	8	8

4.2 Game-Based Learning

Table 2 below shows the frequency of the type of message which was shown, as well as the amount of time taken to be displayed said message. In the table, the victory screen will be an represented by the letter "V", and the losing screen will be represented by the letter "L". Through the data gathered, it can be deduced that something was amiss in the experiment. Having only 10\% of the dataset being victorious, it can be concluded that the game did not successful deliver all the information it was capable of. Each player took an average of 195.4 seconds, around 3-4 minutes, to play the game.

Table 2. Player's duration in the game and the result

Player ID	Time (Seconds)	Message Shown
Player 1	170	V
Player 2	76	L
Player 3	237	L
Player 4	139	L
Player 5	165	L
Player 6	125	L
Player 7	370	L
Player 8	152	L
Player 9	192	L
Player 10	278	L

4.3 Discussion

The results provided by the test subjects prove that, based solely on this test between Gamification and Game-Based Learning, it is Gamification that ought to be implemented when tackling a new, complex subject. This deduction is made in light of the two systems being implemented as they were in the experiment. Had further design and development choices been made, such as the ones provided by the opinions of the test subjects, the results would have surely been very different.

5. CONCLUSION

In this study, two implementations were applied and tested to determine what is more effective, Gamification or Game-based learning. The games where handed out to random people from different backgrounds, in order to determine if the developed systems could provide a good enough basis for the topic chosen, which was Blockchain.

Based on the results, Gamification managed to elicit an overall better result from the test subject than Game-Based Learning. In the experiments provided, gamified system managed to have better overall scoring than its counterpart. The Gamification system managed to have a 90\%-win rate from the test subjects, while the direct opposite was observed in Game-Based Learning, with only a 10\%-win rate achieved. The reason for this discrepancy in victories for the second system can be found within the opinions of the test subjects, who gave substantial feedback in ways to improve the system.

The Game-Based learning implementation received praise on its aesthetic qualities. It did not fulfil the functional requirement of teaching someone or provide enjoyment for the player. More RPG (Role Playing Games) elements, such as questing, monster killing and NPC transactions could be made to distribute the information, which makes it more interesting.

Gamification was developed to have multiple text areas the student must click through. Future implementations need to address the reading issue of these types of games. In reality, reading is an essential part of learning, but the way the players are made to read can make or break the game.

REFERENCES

Anam Fathoni, A. F. C. & Delima, D., 2016. Gamification of learning kanji with "Musou Roman" game. *2016 1st International Conference on Game, Game Art, and Gamification (ICGGAG),* pp. 1-3.

Codish, D. & Ravid, G., 2014. Adaptive approach for gamification optimization. *IEEE/ACM 7th International Conference on Utility and Cloud Computing,* pp. 609-610.

Deterding, S., Dixon, D., Khaled, R. & Nacke, L., 2011. From game design elements to gamefulness: defining" gamification. *Proceedings of the 15th international academic MindTrek conference: Envisioning future media environments,* pp. 9-15.

Dunwell, I. et al., 2011. Blended Game-Based Learning Environments: Extending a Serious Game into a Learning Content Management System. *2011 Third International Conference on Intelligent Networking and Collaborative Systems,* pp. 830-835.

Hung, C.-Y., Kuo, F.-O., Sun , J. C.-Y. & Yu, P.-T., 2014. An Interactive Game Approach for Improving Students' Learning Performance in Multi-Touch Game-Based Learning. *IEEE Transactions on Learning Technologies,* pp. 31-37.

Latifi, S., Zhang, Y. & Cheng, L.-C., 2019. Blockchain-Based Real Estate Market: One Method for Applying Blockchain Technology in Commercial Real Estate Market. *2019 IEEE International Conference on Blockchain (Blockchain),* pp. 528-535.

Palomino, P. T. et al., 2019. Narrative for Gamification in Education: Why Should you Care?. *2019 IEEE 19th International Conference on Advanced Learning Technologies (ICALT),* pp. 97-99.

Petrov, A., 2014. Using Minecraft in Education: A Qualitative Study on Benefits and Challenges of Game-Based Education. *Master Thesis, University of Toronto, Toronto, Canada.*

Srivastava, G., Dhar, S., Dwivedi, A. D. & Crichigno, J., 2019. Blockchain Education. *2019 IEEE Canadian Conference of Electrical and Computer Engineering (CCECE),* pp. 1-5.

Tóth, Á. & Tóvölgyi, S., 2016. The introduction of gamification: A review paper about the applied gamification in the smartphone applications.. *7th IEEE International Conference on Cognitive Infocommunications (CogInfoCom),* pp. 213-218.

Zeng, Z., Huang, C. & Yue, D., 2006. Research on Classroom-Teaching Quality and Its Evaluation index System of Higher Education. *IEEE International Conference on Service Operations and Logistics, and Informatics,* pp. 118-122.

REQUIREMENTS FOR DESIGNING EFFECTIVE CLIMATE CHANGE GAME

Nurlieda Ellyanna Munirrah Razali[1], Nor Azan Mat Zin[1], Mohamad Pauzi Zakaria[2],
Tengku Siti Meriam Tengku Wook[1], Norizan Mat Diah[3] and Fadhilah Rosdi[1]
[1]*Faculty of Technology and Information Science, Universiti Kebangsaan Malaysia*
43600 UKM BANGI, Selangor, Malaysia
[2]*Institute of Ocean and Earth Sciences(IOES), University of Malaya, Malaysia*
[3]*Faculty of Computer Science and Mathematics, Mara University of Technology, Malaysia*

ABSTRACT

Climate continues to change as a result of global warming but awareness and positive behavior are still low despite efforts to educate and engage the public through campaigns and education. Therefore, interactive games which provide simulated experience can be effective to promote engagement, especially among youth who are less concerned about the environment and less likely to engage in environmentally responsible actions. This paper presented a study on the requirements gathering for a serious game design on climate change (CC) that contextualize the processes in carbon cycle as the main story. Further literature analysis on CC issues and existing CC games that have the element of climate change were carried out to identify gaps and propose a design solution for a new CC game. The findings show that the requirements for CC game include correct information (content), aesthetic pleasure, quizzes, rewarding mechanisms, rules, goals leaderboard, performance graph and badges.

KEYWORDS

Serious Game, Climate Change, Carbon Cycle, Requirements, Game Design

1. INTRODUCTION

Global climate continues to change over the past 50 years as a result of global warming. Climate system data show that human activities rapidly change many aspects of the global climate and that the Earth is warming (Walsh et al. 2014). Nevertheless, awareness of climate change issues among Malaysians is still low, therefore there is a need to enhance awareness which should start at an early age (Shahiddan 2014; Aqilah 2018, Shahino 2018). Some society leaders suggested education at primary school level to change citizens' attitude and empower importance of green technology among the people (Aqilah 2018). Global warming, energy issues and greenhouse effect are interdependent environmental issues that lead to climate change thus need to be addressed for sustainability.

Locally, here have been increasing efforts by the government, private sectors and non-governmental organisations (NGOs) to educate and engage the public on environmental issues through various campaigns and formal education approach, such as the Annual program for 3R -waste to Art competition sustainable green campus convention, setting-up an annual National level recycle day on 11th November, School recycling competition (PerKiSS) and community driven programs like recycling bank in community (3R@com). The ministry of Science and Innovation (MESTECC) together with Education ministry, Department of Society Progress (Kemas) and the National Department for Integration (JPNIN) developed a Teaching and learning module for 3R practices and solid waste management for preschool which is used in 5,228 preschools across the nation starting 2018. For the primary and secondary schools, SWCorp has introduced a training module for recycling since 2014. However, awareness and behavior change regarding positive responses to climate change is still low among the population.

Recent studies also confirmed that many climate communications efforts have failed due to uni directional transmission of information that made audience passive consumers of information, lack of contextualization which cause confusion with other environmental issues and the negative and alarmist tone of the content, which often evokes paralysis or apathy instead of motivating people to take action (Ouariachi, Olvera-Lobo, & Gutiérrez-Pérez 2017). Serious Games are digital games that providing the purpose to create awareness of a certain issue, to change behavior or to teach simultaneously with entertainment (Alonso-fernandez et al. 2017). In addition, gaming increases the sense of personal responsibility, the confidence in politics for climate change mitigation, and makes players more optimistic about international cooperation in climate politics (Meya, & Eisenack 2018). It is important to start teaching young people to bring change regarding the CC issues using the current technology such as games to engage them. Furthermore, quantitative evidence on the effectiveness of a simulation game for communicating and teaching international climate politics showed that the game facilitates experiential learning about the difficulties of international climate politics.

Young people have the potential to trigger an ambitious and long-term societal change, adopting sustainable attitudes and behaviors in energy use from early ages and influencing their parents' decisions (Ouariachi, Olvera-Lobo, & Gutiérrez-Pérez 2017). However, Bofferding and Kloser (2015) opined that awareness and commitment are still limited with 'Youth' who is even less concerned about the environment than older age-groups and less likely to engage in environmentally responsible actions. 'Youth' belongs to digital generation, hence interactive games which can provide immersive, real time simulated experience, should be employed for climate change engagement, complementing factual persuasion - presenting climate change facts through conventional methods such as school curriculum, campaigns using printed materials or mass media which fail to change many people's actions due to ideological and other intractable resistances.

Available games have content issues in the way games model the human-environment relationship, either environment as backdrop, resource, antagonist or text are only frameworks for players action and aesthetic pleasure (Abraham & Jeyamanne 2017). Most games focus on practices such as recycling or reducing waste but very few focuses on mechanisms and processes that cause anthropogenic climate change although some games discuss long-term climate effects. However, only recently there have been a few games employing carbon cycle as the content for CC games Hence our research aims to gather requirements for effective CC game, focusing on game elements that contextualize the process of carbon cycle disruptions as the main story of the game.

2. CARBON CYCLE

Climate change occurs due to the release of excess greenhouse gases such as carbon dioxide (CO^2), nitrous oxide and methane as a result of industrial and agricultural waste. The effect of greenhouse gases in the atmosphere captures heat, which in turn causes an increase in the temperature of the earth. Consequently, extreme weather and global warming are due to excessive greenhouse gas emissions (Sau, Weng, & Ahamad 2016). Global CO^2 emissions from human activities have increased by 400% since 1950 [https://www.theccc.org.uk/tackling-climate-change/the-science-of-climate-change/climate-variations-natural-and-human -factors /] and more than 40% compared to pre-industrial levels (Galloway et al.2014).

Furthermore, rapid urbanization in pursuit of a better quality of life has led Malaysia to shift towards environmental degradation as a result of some challenges from environmental issues (Sau, Weng, & Ahamad 2016). Extreme climates can affect the structure, composition and function of inland ecosystems and can therefore affect regional carbon cycles, potentially leading to the transition from carbon sequestration to carbon sources (Frank 2015). One of the main causes of global climate change has been identified as increasing carbon emissions and our daily actions are among the contributors to the greenhouse gas collection process in the atmosphere (Zou, Mustafa, & Eid 2015). CO^2 remains the major anthropogenic greenhouse gas that accounted for 76% of total gas emissions in 2010 (Rolle 2018).

In addition, the ocean absorbs about 30% of the anthropogenic CO^2 released into the atmosphere to help mitigate the effects of climate change. However, CO^2 hydrolysis in seawater results in an increase in the concentration of hydrogen ions and this would result in the progressive acidification of the oceans (Rolle 2018). The global action to address the issue of climate change (known as the Paris Agreement) aims to ensure that global warming in this century is below 2 degrees Celsius above pre-industrial levels and will continue efforts to limit temperatures to as low as 1.5 degrees Celsius (Wyrwa 2018).

The challenge of designing a carbon cycle CC game is to understand and then contextualize the fundamental processes of carbon cycle that contribute to the CC. As further game requirements, previous and available games were also analysed.

3. GAME ANALYSIS

None of the 'environmental games' apply the whole carbon cycle as the main context of the game, as indicated in Table 1. Among the 11 games, Carbon Command represented one process in the carbon cycle but only focused on CO^2 and photosynthesis of plants. While neglecting other elements in carbon cycle such as respiration and decomposition which are necessary to understand the causes of CC. Carbon on our planet is stored in the major sinks which are atmosphere, soil organic matter, ocean, marine sediments and sedimentary rocks, terrestrial plant and fossil fuel deposits (Pidwirny, 2006). The CC game should implement all processes of carbon cycle to further players' understanding. Many CC games focus on climate protection with a major focus on international consultation and local technology for greenhouse gas reduction and there are less games that consider adaptation to climate change (Reckien & Eisenack 2015). Thus, one requirement of CC game is to contextualize the whole processes of carbon cycle as the main story of the game.

The effectiveness of a game to convey useful information to the players doesn't necessarily depend on a mesmerizing design solely but the accuracy of the game content itself and how it is represented to the players. The correct information given to the players are of concern to the game developers (Foltz et al. 2019). A combination of good design and context will strengthen the effectiveness of the game. Foltz et al. stated that to communicate the complexities of climate change, a simulation type of game is especially well suited as it permits for the simulation of a complex system and allows players' interaction with the system. Games can be a medium to educate people about the carbon cycle and climate change. People can have fun while learning so that they will not feel pressured to process the knowledge all the way through the game. The overall games as mentioned in Table 1 possess the aesthetic pleasure and good context in the game design. the relevancy of a game design for education is how it can be abstracted to convey project curriculum development more widely, apart from creative, communication and project management competencies exposed in the game design process (Shoop & Lucas 2019). Sailer et al. (2017) also stated that aesthetic value and quality of the design implementations in the game design can affect the players' psychological need satisfaction. Table 1 shows that On Thin Ice, Climate Cards and Urban Climate Architect are among of the examples of simple games yet meaningful as it explains the effect of global warming to the Earth through the game. Hence, the second requirement for CC game is to possess the combination of aesthetic pleasure and a good information on the whole processes of carbon cycle.

Moreover, players need motivation to play a game on their own will. Without the motivation players will neglect the game and the game failed to achieved its goal. Enjoyment is not the factor that can motivate players willingness to learn while playing serious game but expectations of usefulness and ease of use are the factors that will raise their motivation, in this way serious game should be fun and engaging (Iten & Petko 2016). In order to get the players' motivation to play CC game, the game should provide ease of use and expectations of usefulness to the players. The players will learn about Carbon cycle while engaging and having fun throughout the game. The use of quizzes in the game may increase the players' motivation and understanding according to the issues that become the focus of the game. A quiz game can be a tool to boost reflection process which is considered as an important bridge between learning and knowledge (Videnovik et al. 2018). Games as indicated in Table 1 which applying quiz in the game designs are Carbon Runner and Carbon Command. These games also rewarding the players if they answer the quiz correctly. Due to the fact, the next requirement for CC game is to apply the quiz concept into the game in order to stimulate players' motivation and understanding.

Furthermore, the character design is important in a game design because the character carry the role as an ambassador of the message and the idea that is portrayed by the game makers (Zufri, Hilman & Pratama 2016). Zufri, Hilman and Pratama also stated that the game character is the representation of ourselves as a part of the game and the success of a game is usually determined by it. For example, Carbon Runner and Carbon Command use 'Green Ninja' as the avatar of the game while Oxygen Not Included provide 'duplicants' as the avatar. Players emotional state is very important to be considered in the CC game design process as it is the element that can promote players' engagement while playing the game. Sekhavat stated that rewarding mechanism is a crucial part of the game design which can directly affect the game experience in order to promote a desired behavior in serious game. Players' playing experience can be improve by rewarding framework as it can affect the players' emotional state and their behavior (Sekhavat 2019). To stimulate desired learning outcomes, the use of design elements, such as narrative context, rules, goals, rewards, multisensory cues, and interactivity seems necessary (Dondlinger 2014). Hence, CC game's requirement is to add rewarding mechanism, rules and goals to improve players' emotional state and behavior.

In addition, competence, satisfaction and perceived task meaningfulness of the players can be triggered by the use of leaderboards, performance graphs and badges while experiences of social relatedness can be affected by the use of meaningful stories, avatar and teammates in the game design (Sailer et al. 2017). As mentioned in Table 1, games such as Block'Hood, Eco, Carbon Runner, Carbon Command, Rise of Industry, Oxygen Not Included, Cities Skyline, and SimCity 4 provide the players with the rewarding mechanism, rules, goals, leaderboards and more to stimulate players' learning outcomes. Therefore, there is a requirement for the CC game to implement leaderboard, performance graph and badge in the game design in order to trigger players' satisfaction, and perceived task meaningfulness.

Table 1. Game with Climate Change Analysis

Game	Story	Gameplay	Challenges	Carbon Cycle Element
Bock'Hood, by Plethora Project (Plethora Project, 2016)	"Player creations will attract inhabitants, both humans and animals, that will populate your neighborhood. It is the hands of the player to provide a positive environment for inhabitants to prosper"	"Envision a neighborhood, by building structures out of a catalog of 200+ blocks"	"The player is challenged to maintain an ecological balance as each block placed will consume and produce resources of different kinds Blocks that are not provided of their required input, will slowly decay and deteriorate to a point of collapse"	Block'hood doesn't specifying about carbon cycle, the gameplay that is produced by the developer can educate player on what is the effect of their action on the available resources
ECO, by Strange Loop Games (Strange Loop Games, 2017)	"Eco is an online game where players must collaborate to build a civilization in a world where everything they do affects the environment. All resources come from a simulated ecosystem, with thousands of plants and animals simulating 24/7"	Creating virtual planet's civilization	"Work together through the player-run government and economy to build the technology to stop a meteor on a collision course with the planet, without polluting the world and killing it off in the process before that even happens"	"Like the real world, the environment is fragile. Chop down forests and wildlife faces extinction; pollute the air and temperatures will rise" (Wallis, 2017). The element of carbon cycle is not clearly shown but the effect from players' action in the game shows that it contributes to climate change
Carbon Runner by Pew Pew studios (Green Ninja, 2018)	"Carbon Runner is a fast-paced game focusing on how personal decisions positively or negatively affect the environment"	"The endless runner game lets players jump and punch as a green ninja sent to make the world a greener place to live. They encounter things that are both good for the environment (worth collecting) and bad for the environment (for punching). Quizzes and databases teach students eco facts while also helping them to make environmentally friendly decisions" (Wyers, 2016)	"Collect or destroy items, which can be good or bad for the environment Correctly answering questions allows the player to gain the powers to advance to higher levels"	"Carbon Runner helps teach kids about climate change and implementing sustainable practices to make the Earth a better place". It does not focus on carbon cycle process, but it did teach the players by giving quiz when they hit the wrong element for the environment

Urban Climate Architect, by Clisap (Games4 sustainability)	"Urban Climate Architect is an educative flash game that allows you to create your own environmental-friendly city."	"Design the city by building houses, streets and green spaces, employ citizens in offices and industrial plants while observing the effect of these actions on the climate of the city"	The player is challenged to make a critical decision to make an environmental-friendly city	The evaluation of the city will give the information to the player about the impact of the city that they have created. With the evaluation given, player will gain knowledge about suburbanization and its effects on environment. The game does not specify on carbon cycle process but it teaches the players about the effect of their action to the city
Carbon Command (Green Ninja, 2018)	"Carbon Command is a simplified model of the influence of human activities on climate change"	"The game starts with carbon raining down through the atmosphere (and ocean), while the player uses the photosynthesis of plants to control the uptake of atmospheric carbon"	Players need to shoot the CO^2 particles that are released to the environment. As too much CO^2 that the player missed, the temperature will rise and it will make the Earth flooded	By playing this game player will gain knowledge about the effect of CO^2 to the environment. It is a good game that display the carbon cycle to the player but it does not represent the whole carbon cycle process
Climate Cards by Hopeless Production (Hopeless Production, 2018)	"A deck-building game where you play cards to exploit a small ecosystem while avoiding destruction as long as possible"	The player is given a deck of cards containing resources, utilities, and tools. Cards such as farms and industry produce money, utilities like generators and power plants provide energy that some cards need as requirements to be picked	Player need to carefully making decision before picking their card in order to avoid destruction in the ecosystem	Even though, it does not cover about carbon cycle process but by playing this game, player can gain knowledge on the relationship between the actions committed by humanity and its effect on the change in temperature. The player has a choice between exploiting the planet and destroying the ecosystem with risks of flooding or stall it as long as possible with environmentally friendly options.
On Thin Ice by Karn Bianco (Karn Bianco, 2018)	"On Thin Ice is a short game about the climate crisis, what its impacts might look like, and what we can do to stop the worst of it right now. With the help of a time-travelling polar bear (Nanuq)"	The player must reflect sunlight back into space. If sunlight strikes the surface, the heat bar will go up. When the bar is full, the game is over	As the game progresses to the next level, the number of CO^2 particles spawned increases and the ice platform the player use decreases in size. Making it harder to reflect back light or causing the reflected light to still raise the heat level	Player can learn about albedo phenomenon while playing this game. On Thin Ice is a simple yet meaningful game as it explains the effect of global warming to the Earth. It explains the effect of excessive intake of carbon to the Earth
Rise of Industr by Dapper Penguin Studio (Kasedo Game: 2018)	"Rise of Industry is a strategic tycoon game that puts player in the shoes of an early 20th-century industrialist"	"Player need to build and manage their growing empire in a living, breathing, and procedurally generated world that is constantly evolving and adapting to their playstyle"	Once hit a specific level, pollution will destroy housings and reduce the product output of farms. Player need to control the pollution by adding environmental	It does not focus on carbon cycle process but it is up to the player to choose a path for their own world, with this player will learn that every move or choice that they made will have an impact to the environment

			building in order to reduce pollution	
Oxygen Not Included by Klei Entertainment (Klei Entertainment, 2017)	"In the space-colony simulation game Oxygen Not Included player will find that scarcities of oxygen, warmth and sustenance are constant threats to player colony's survival"	The player will need to set up a proper base by ordering the workers to start harvesting resources, build a fully functional base, install the necessities such as wiring, plumbing, and controls by themself. Once a proper base is up and running, the player shall begin work on researching new equipment and upgrades	The game has several mechanics that the player must be aware of such as workers' needs like food, health, and mental state, the base's temperature, switches, and electricity, and other mechanics like gas cycles"	The focus of this game is not about carbon cycle but it does simulate the relationship between gas type, pressure, humidity and temperature on an immensely complex scale. With this simulation it is best suited to carbon cycle which is important to understand in order to know the causes of climate change. Player can gain knowledge on the importance of proper management and planning to handle harmful gas production and elimination. The game also describes multiple harmful substances that contributed to pollution including carbon dioxide, sulfur, and pollutants like smoke
Cities: Skylines by Colossal Order Ltd. (Paradox Interactive, 2015)	"The game introduces new gameplay elements, allowing player to experience the thrill and hardships of creating and maintaining a real city"	The player starts by designing road layouts for their city and managing city zones by residential, economical, and industrial. The player shall then implement and handle basic demands of their citizens such as power, water supply, sewage, traffic congestion, pollution, and policies	Player need to be in control of the city that they had built in order to avoid pollution rising because it will cause the citizens to become ill and potentially die	The game mechanic teaches how a well-planned city and living area is necessary for a clean and healthy environment. While it does not focus on carbon cycle process but player can relate it with real life situation of what will happen to the people if the rate of pollution in the world is worsen.
SimCity 4 by Maxis (Electronic Art 2003)	A city builder simulation game that allows the player to plan and build a city with a more freeform ancasual intensity	A city simulation game that allows the player to plan, build, and manage their own city	The player must fulfill the demands of their citizens such as residential needs, workplaces, and industry	Air pollution is a mechanic that exists in this game. Factories and oil or coal power plant release an area of pollution around them. As pollution rises, the land value in that area will lower. If the pollution becomes too strong, acid rain will start forming. These rains will cause damages to other buildings and infrastructures

To summarise, the requirements for CC game gathered from analysis of literature and available games are; 1) Contextualize the whole processes of carbon cycle as the main story, 2) Apply a combination of aesthetic pleasure and a good information of carbon cycle process, 3) Embed quiz into the game, 4) Add reward mechanism, rules and goals into the game, 5) Implement leaderboard, performance graph and badge in the game design.

4. CONCLUSION

In conclusion, the first requirement of CC game gained from further literature analysis on CC issues and existing CC games is to contextualize the whole processes of carbon cycle as the main story of the game. The CC game must have a decent game design in a way that the carbon cycle information that is abstracted can be convey to the players effectively. A good game design can benefit players to understand its content that is portrayed through the game. The game design that is effective does not only depend on its fascinating art but there are also other elements that will strengthen it. Therefore, the next requirement for CC game is to adopt the combination of aesthetic pleasure and a good information on the whole processes of carbon cycle.

In addition, the use of quiz can motivate players to play CC game, motivate players' willingness to learn while playing serious game Thus, there is a requirement for CC game to apply the quiz concept in order to stimulate players' motivation and understanding. Moreover, the use of different kind of elements in the game design can trigger different psychological experience to the players. Elements in a good game design can bring satisfactions to the players when they play the game. Different elements in a game design such as stories, characters and leaderboards can bring different positive psychological experience to the players. Hence, there is a requirement for the CC game to add leaderboard, performance graph and badges in the game design in order to give a positive impact to the players' psychological needs.

The players might become more motivated to play and learn if they earn a reward after accomplishing a certain task in the game. Rewarding mechanism is a crucial part of the game design in order to promote a desired behavior or attitude in serious game that can directly affect the game experience (Sekhavat 2019). The CC game must have rewarding mechanism, rules and goals stimulate players' emotional state and behavior. For future work, we will formulate a CC game framework for climate change game based on the requirements, elements, factors and criteria, and to propose a new climate change game concept before constructing prototypes.

REFERENCES

Alonso-fernandez, C., Calvo, A., Freire, M., Martinez-ortiz, I. & Fernandez-manjon, B. 2017. Systematizing game learning analytics for serious games (April), 1111–1118.

Alyson Wyers. 2016. Carbon Runner is an Endless Runner Video Game About Climate Change https://www.trendhunter.com/trends/carbon-runner [access on 1 May 2020]

Aqilah Mior Kamarulbaid. 2018.Kesedaran teknologi hijau masih rendah. http://www.utusan.com.my/sainsteknologi/teknologi/kesedaran-teknologi-hijau-masihrendah-1.729413 [access on 17 Feb 2019]

Bofferding L., Kloser M. (2015). Middle and high school students' conceptions of climate change mitigation and adaptation strategies. Environmental Education Research, 21, 275-294. doi:10.1080/13504622.2014.888401

Dondlinger, M. J. 2014. Educational Video Game Design : A Review of the Literature (January 2007), 20–31.

Electronic Arts. 2003. https://www.ea.com/games/simcity/simcity-4 [access on 7 May 2020]

Foltz, A., Williams, C., Gerson, S. A., Reynolds, D. J., Pogoda, S., Begum, T., Walton, S. P. et al. 2019. Game Developers' Approaches to Communicating Climate Change 4(June). doi:10.3389/fcomm.2019.00028

Frank, D., Reichstein, M., Bahn, M., Thonicke, K., Frank, D., Mahecha, M. D., Smith, P. et al. 2015. Effects of climate extremes on the terrestrial carbon cycle : concepts , processes and potential future impacts (January), 2861–2880. doi:10.1111/gcb.12916

Games4Sustainability. Urban Climate Architect https://games4sustainability.org/gamepedia/urbanclimatearchitect/ [access on 4 May 2020]

Galloway, J. N., W. H. Schlesinger, C. M. Clark, N. B. Grimm, R. B. Jackson, B. E. Law, P. E. Thornton, A. R. Townsend, and R.Martin. 2014. Ch. 15: Biogeochemical Cycles. Climate Change Impacts in the United States: The Third National Climate Assessment, J. M. Melillo, Terese (T.C.) Richmond, and G. W. Yohe, Eds., U.S. Global Change Research Program, 350-368. doi:10.7930/J0X63JT0.]

Green Ninja. 2018. https://greenninja.org/resources [access on 1 May 2020]

Hopeless Production, 2018. Climate Cards https://rotomster.itch.io/climate-cards [access on 4 May 2020]

Iten, N. & Petko, D. 2016. predictor of learning success ?47(1), 151–163. doi:10.1111/bjet.12226

Karn Bianco. 2018. https://karnbianco.itch.io/on-thin-ice [access on 5 May 2020]

Kasedo Games. 2018 https://www.riseofindustry.com/ [access on 5 May 2020]

Klei Entertainment. 2017. https://www.kleientertainment.com/games/oxygen-not-included [access on 7 May 2020]

Meya, J.N. and Eisenack, K. 2018. Climatic Change 149: 319. https://doi-org.ezplib.ukm.my/10.1007/s10584-018-2254-7 [accessed on 17 Feb 2019]

Oliver Franklin-Wallis. 2017. 'Eco' is a survival game with a difference: it wants to save the world https://www.wired.co.uk/article/strange-loop-games-eco-simulation [access on 5 May 2020]

Ouariachi, T., Dolores Olvera-Lobo, M., & Gutiérrez-Pérez, J. 2017. Analyzing Climate Change Communication Through Online Games: Development and Application of Validated Criteria. Science Communication, 39(1), pp.10–44.

Paradox Interactive. 2015. https://www.citiesskylines.com/#about [access on 7 May 2020]

Pidwirny, M, 2006. "The Carbon Cycle". Fundamentals of Physical Geography, 2nd Edition. http://www.physicalgeography.net/fundamentals/9r.html [access on 8 June 2020]

Plethora Project. 2016. https://www.plethora-project.com/blockhood [access on 5 May 2020]

Reckien, D. & Eisenack, K. 2015. Climate Change Gaming on Board and Screen: A Review. doi:10.1177/1046878113480867

Rolle, F. 2018. seawater as a basis for climate change studies. 2018 IEEE International Workshop on Metrology for the Sea; Learning to Measure Sea Health Parameters (MetroSea), 99–103.

Sailer, M., Hense, J. U., Mayr, S. K. & Mandl, H. 2017. SC. Computers in Human Behavior,. doi:10.1016/j.chb.2016.12.033

Sau, N., Weng, C. & Ahamad, R. 2016. Environmental Awareness and Behaviour Index for Malaysia 222(7), 668–675. doi:10.1016/j.sbspro.2016.05.223

Sekhavat, Y. A. 2019. A Rewarding Framework for Multiplayer Serious Games based on Competitive Reinforcement. 2019 IEEE 7th International Conference on Serious Games and Applications for Health (SeGAH), 1–8.

Shahiddan Saidi. 2014. Kesedaran Isu Tenaga Dan Perubahan Iklim Rendah Dalam Kalangan Rakyat, http://www.ukm.my/news/arkib-berita/year-2014/februari-2014/kesedaran-isu-tenaga-dan-perubahan-iklim-rendah-dalam-kalanganrakyat/ [accessed on 17 Feb 2019]

Shahino Mah Abdullah. 2018. https://www.bharian.com.my/rencana/komentar/2018/01/376558/peka-dalam-tanganiperubahaniklim. [accessed on 17 Feb 2019]

Strange Loop Games. 2018. https://www.play.eco/ [access on 5 May 2020]

Videnovik, M., Kionig, L., Vold, T. & Trajkovik, V. 2018. Testing framework for investigating learning outcome from quiz game. 2018 17th International Conference on Information Technology Based Higher Education and Training (ITHET), 1–5.

Videogames, C., Zou, Y. R., Mustafa, N., Memon, N. A. & Eid, M. 2015. ECO ECO : Changing Climate Related Behaviors For.

Walsh, J., D. Wuebbles, K. Hayhoe, J. Kossin, K. Kunkel, G. Stephens, P. Thorne, R. Vose, M. Wehner, J. Willis, D. Anderson, S.Doney, R. Feely, P. Hennon, V. Kharin, T. Knutson, F. Landerer, T. Lenton, J. Kennedy, and R. Somerville, 2014: Ch. 2: Our Changing Climate. Climate Change Impacts in the United States: The Third National Climate Assessment, J. M. Melillo, Terese (T.C.) Richmond, and G. W. Yohe, Eds., U.S. Global Change Research Program, 19-67. doi:10.7930/J0KW5CXT.

Wyrwa, A. 2018. Climate Change Mitigation Game 21–25.

Zufri, T., Sn, S. & Ds, M. 2016. Character Design as Bridging Tools of Ideological Message in Game.

ATLAS CHRONICLE: DEVELOPMENT AND VERIFICATION OF A SYSTEM FOR PROCEDURAL GENERATION OF STORY-DRIVEN GAMES

Elizabeth A. Matthews[1] and Juan E. Gilbert[2]
[1]*Washington and Lee University, USA*
[2]*University of Florida, USA*

ABSTRACT

Procedural Content Generation for Games is the application of computers to generate game content such as landscapes, vegetation, or maps. This paper proposes a system (Atlas Chronicle) for the generation of world maps for games that feature story-driven locations. The system uses a combination of story abstraction, graphs, physics simulation, Perlin noise, interpolation, and climate mapping to generate 2D tile-based maps given a basic story structure. To measure the fitness of the levels generated, a user study was performed using established game enjoyment metrics. The study utilized three different content generation approaches for comparison. Eighteen participants (11 Male, 7 Female), aged between 18 and 24 years old were screened based on their prior gaming experience. Results show that levels generated by Atlas Chronicle resulted in statistically similar responses as for the manually designed and static levels.

KEYWORDS

Procedural Generation, Video Games, Video Game Enjoyment

1. INTRODUCTION

1.1 Motivation

One of the efforts towards creating more enjoyable games involves the generation of content for said games. Traditionally, this content has been generated manually by human game designers and level designers. However, the two major problems with manual content generation for games are the expense (Takatsuki, 2007) and the fact that it does not scale (Iosup, 2011). Procedural Content Generation for Games (PCG-G) is the application of computers to generate game content and select the enjoyable items for use in games (Hendrikx et al., 2013).

Procedural Content Generation (PCG), or Procedural Generation (PG) for short, is the generation of virtual content by computers, typically through a human-defined procedure. As games get larger and more expansive, a cheaper and faster approach to generating the game content is highly desirable. PG has been utilized in games for a long time, starting with one of the earliest games, Rogue (Epyx, 1980).

Games with PG can have a minimal amount of generated content, but the most prevalent and noticeable forms are repeated-play variations. Games like Diablo (Blizzard North, 1996) have the same storyline each time the game is started by a gamer, but the dungeons in which the player progresses through the story are procedurally generated. As a result, each time the game is played, the exploration is different.

Traditionally, story-driven games have had minimal or compartmentalized procedural generation. Due to the innate relationship between the world map layout of locations of interest and the story to be told, the map is difficult to change without taking these story restrictions into account. The system described in this paper proposes a method that keeps the story structure intact but randomizes the directions one must travel to progress in the story. An abstracted story graph is used to implicitly build a map around the story locations.

1.2 Related Work

Procedural Generation has been utilized to create enjoyable games since the early 1980s (Epyx, 1980). The more traditional approach has been to generate a multitude of options independently of the user, while a more recent approach has been to dynamically generate the content based on the user's gameplay.

The procedurally generated content ranges in size and scope in the final game. Most commonly created are "game bits," which are the basic units that compose a game (e.g. textures or sounds), or "game spaces," which are the navigational world/space in which the player exists (Hendrikx et al., 2013). The systems which create the procedural content range from tools and materials for game designers to utilize in their normal workflow to independent designers and domain experts which fully design and evaluate the game (Khaled et al., 2013). The Infinite Mario Competition is frequently cited by some of the PG researchers discussed in this section and has been one of the main motivators for discovering new PG techniques (Shaker et al., 2011).

There are two important approaches in PG techniques: Independent Procedural Content Generation (IPCG) generates content without context from the user, and Experience Driven Procedural Content Generation (EDPCG) generates content based on a user's performance and play style in the game. Independent Procedural Content Generation (IPCG) is the most popular version of PG, despite a recent rise in interest in research in EDPCG. IPCG generates many content variations, given a certain structure, then selects a variation for each play-through. The generation does not take input from the user. IPCG can be used to generate content from quests or puzzles (Pereira et al., 2016; Barros et al., 2016), platformer levels as in Spelunky or Mario (Baghdadi et al., 2015; Shaker et al., 2012; Yu and Hull, 2009), 3D terrain (Beckham and Pal, 2017; Frade et al., 2012), maps or mazes (Moore Jr, 2015; Togelius et al., 2013), creative sandbox games like Minecraft (Patrascu and Risi, 2016; Mojang, 2011), or infinite style games (Saltsman, 2009; Henschke et al., 2012).

2. METHODOLOGY

Story-driven games, often in the category of Role-Playing Games (RPGs), are one of the game categories that PG has barely touched due to the intertwined nature of the game world's map and the game story. We developed a system, Atlas Chronicle, that relies on the nature of RPG stories in which there is a partial order to the locations to visit. Further, the relative distances between story-based locations of interest remain within story-defined constraints of minimum and maximum distance and connectivity.

If a system can calculate a controlled randomization of locations for each location visited in the game that satisfies the minimum and maximum distance between the locations as defined by the story, one can infer the world around these locations to build a full map. The development of Atlas Chronicle finds this set of locations using a physical model of the game graph. Atlas Chronicle was developed in Python (2020) with the use of the PyGame module (PyGame, 2020) for visual and interactive aspects.

2.1 Story Abstraction

In a story-driven RPG there are locations of interest (LOI). These LOI can be a town, cave, castle, or even a non-interactive terrain type, so the journey the player experiences travels through different terrains. An RPG story can be abstracted into LOI and distance restrictions between each LOI. These restrictions are a story-experience restriction of distance: Town A and Cave B must be between 10 and 15 kilometers of each other. Restrictions represent a minimum and maximum value connecting two LOI.

These restrictions can be of two types: traversable or non-traversable. Traversable means that the restriction between LOIs A and B doubles as a rule that A must directly connect to B via traversable terrain. In our example, Town A and Cave B connected by a traversable restriction means that the direct path between A and B must be connected by walk-able terrain. The "traversable" definition for terrain can change (see Section 2.4 for details). Sometimes LOI have restrictions between them, but not a direct traversable path (e.g., the final location must be at least 50 units away from the starting location). These non-traversable 6 restrictions do not need to block the path between LOI but prevent LOI from being too far or too close to each other. Therefore, a non-traversable restriction does not need to be covered by non-traversable terrain; it simply does not require that the path be explicitly traversable terrain. This property is to allow restrictions to connect LOI to restrict their distances without affecting the connectivity of the terrain. Figure 1a shows a simple visualization of three LOI with three restrictions.

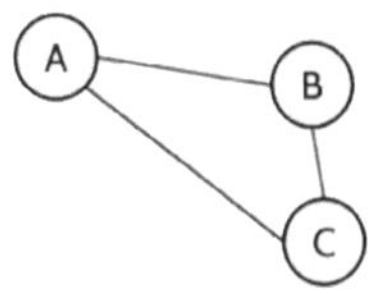

(a) Example of story abstraction with three LOI and three restrictions Green indicates traversable and red indicating not traversable

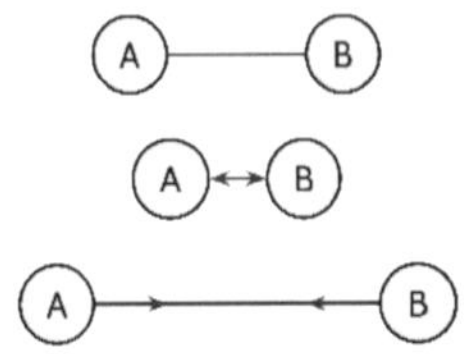

(b) Top to bottom slide spring states: no force applied, increase distance force applied, reduce distance force applied. Green indicates no forces applied and red indicating forces applied away (middle) and towards (bottom)

Figure 1. Story abstractions show LOI as circles and restrictions between LOI as lines

With abstraction, the world can be built around the story. The first step is to find some set of coordinates that satisfy all the restrictions in the connected graph of LOI. The settling of LOI in these satisfactory coordinates used a physics engine.

2.2 Physics Engine

A physics engine (Pymunk, 2019) applies forces on LOI as physical objects to push and pull the LOI into coordinates that satisfy the restrictions. Each LOI was represented as a physical object, and each restriction was made into a slide/spring combination. The connection functions as a free movement sliding joint when within valid distance measurements. If the connection distance/size is less than the minimum value the physical property is changed to a spring-style connection with a resting size of the minimum value. The forces applied will push the two connected LOI objects further away if the distance connecting them is too small. A similar physics interaction happens if the distance is larger than the maximum value with the force applied to bring the two LOI closer to each other. A visualization of this process is in Figure 1b.

With all LOI in the system and connected by slide-spring restrictions (weighted based on the story parameters), each LOI was given a random x,y coordinate and allowed to exist in a physical space. The system was allowed to simulate the forces until all the objects' velocity fell below a small threshold.

The use of a physics engine over other more deterministic algorithms was to account for human error in the story abstraction step. Future applications of the system will be available for game developers and a non-deterministic allowance will allow for imperfect systems to still create solutions.

2.3 Terrain Generation

Once each of the LOI has valid x,y coordinates that satisfy all restrictions to the best of the system's ability, the terrain around the LOI is generated. A randomized floodfill fills in terrain around the LOI. Each LOI was given a seed terrain, with each interact-able/town-based LOI creating four seeds around it of traversable terrain. The edges of the map were filled with void tiles, which are tiles that will be replaced in further iterations.

Figure 2 shows the process visually. Each of the seed tiles and edge void tiles were placed in a list, A, to be used in the floodfill sequence, Figure 2a and 2b. The floodfill algorithm, Figure 2c, was as follows:

1. Select a tile t from the list of available tiles A
2. Populate list T of possible floodfill adjacent tiles from t
    a. Check all cardinal directions North, South, East, West of t
    a. Add tile to T if it is unfilled and viable
3. IF no tiles are in T, remove t from A and return to step 1
4. ELSE select one tile t^1 randomly from T
5. Fill t^1 with the same tile type as t and add t^1 to A
6. Repeat steps until A is empty

Viable means that, in the case of void tiles, attempting to fill the tile cannot cross a boundary along the line of any traversable restriction. Any two LOI connected by traversable restrictions will have a map that connects them via traversable terrain. The final result was a map of traversable ("land"), not traversable ("mountain" or "water"), and void tiles, Figure 2d.

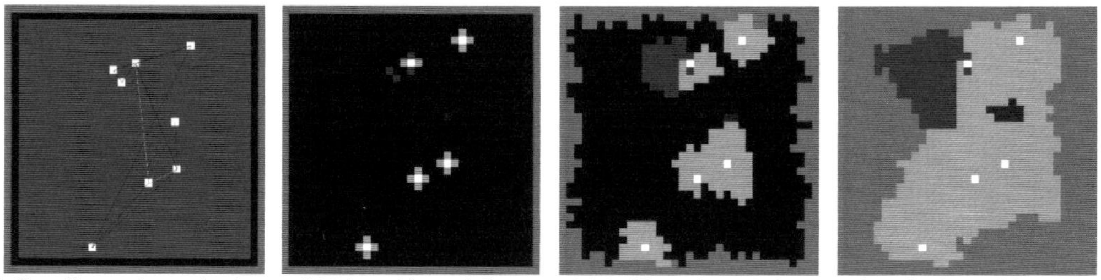

(a) Coordinates determined with physics engine | (b) Map with seed tiles based on LOI definitions | (c) Halfway through the flood-fill process | (d) A final possible map given LOI and restrictions

Figure 2. The process from the coordinates generated by the space manager to 2D map. Void tiles are pink, traversable terrain is green. Non-traversable appears in two formats: mountains (maroon) and water (blue)

2.4 Recursive Process

The next step repeated the process from Section 2.3 recursively. The traversable map generated, Figure 2d, is called a field. A field is a subset of what makes a continent, which is a subset of a world. A field is a set of LOI separated by traversable or not traversable terrain. A continent consists of fields separated by not traversable terrain. A world contains continents separated by water.

The next iteration for creating a continent repeated the process with fields in place of the LOI (Figure 3). The fields were connected by restrictions, placed in a physics engine randomly and allowed to settle (Figure 3a). The floodfill has a similar process with void tiles around the edge, but the floodfill seed tiles were mountains instead of landfill (Figure 3b), to ensure the two or more fields were connected by mountains, thus creating a single continent (Figure 3c and 3d). Figure 3e shows the climate to terrain mapping, covered later in this section.

The final recursive step repeated the process with continents instead of LOI (Figure 4a). Instead of floodfilling a third time, for this study's purposes the map is complete, and the unfilled areas were filled with ocean/water tiles (Figure 4b).

2.5 Terrain Mapping

After the continents were formed, the system mapped terrain types onto the landfill tiles (Matthews and Malloy, 2012). A climate was assigned to each LOI. Climates are made of a value between 0.0 and 1.0 for both temperature and humidity. A climate map was made by first creating seed values from each LOI and an average value was added to the edges (Figure 5a) to enable interpolation (SciPy, 2019) to the edges of the map. Then two interpolation maps were generated to interpolate the climate values in the unassigned tiles between LOI, one for each temperature and humidity, visualized as blue and red respectively in Figure 5b. Noise (noise 1.2.2, 2019) was added for a more natural shape of terrains in Figure 5d. Then the climate was mapped to a corresponding terrain type based on a look-up process called a Terrain Boundary Map (TBM) in Figure 6.

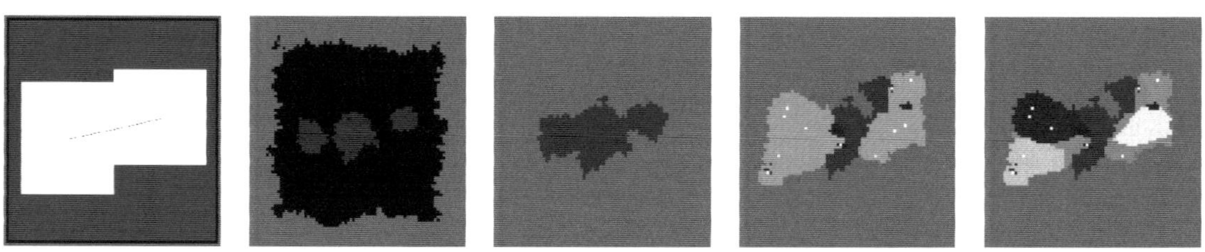

(a) Physics engine with two fields | (b) Halfway through floodfill process | (c) Final mountain shape created | (d) Placement of fields using 3a | Climate mapping (Figure 5) applied

Figure 3. Recursive process for continent ending with one possible continent generated

(a) Physics engine with three continents (b) Final possible world creation

Figure 4. Recursive process for world ending with one possible world generated

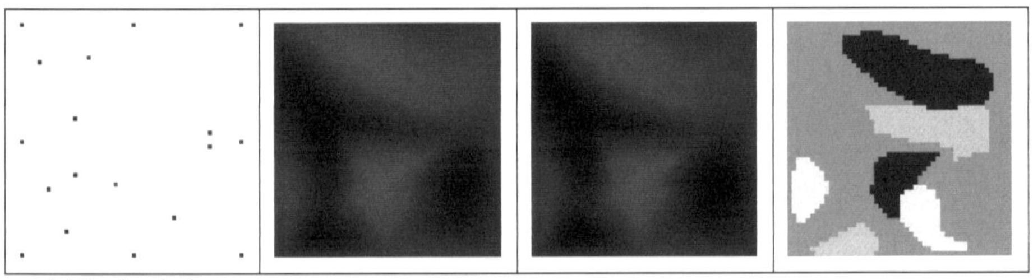

(a) Seed and edge values (b) Interpolation (c) Noise added (d) Terrain mapping

Figure 5. An example of mapping seeded climate values to a full map via interpolation. The final steps translate the two-dimensional climate to a terrain via the Terrain Boundary Map (Figure 6)

The system achieved the climate to terrain mapping by creating a nearest neighbor map to the designer's specifications, the TBM (Matthews and Malloy, 2012). For this study the map seen in Figure 6 was used, but any amount of terrain values can be used. The values for temperature and humidity were used as a x,y coordinate look-up in the nearest neighbor map, which converted the two values into a single terrain type. To create more organic looking separations between terrains from the interpolation step, a small amount of noise was added to the climate map before TBM look-up.

2.6 Testing Game Engine

The intended run-time of a normal RPG is 40+ hours, which was not feasible for a rapid, repeated test in a user study. Instead, for testing the procedural generation in RPGs used a minimal game engine and storyline created for the study. The engine was also programmed in Python/Pygame, seen in Figure 7. The game engine only contained the minimal elements to progress through the story: Overworld movement, locked terrain type travel, text boxes/interactable locations of interest, gating items obtained from locations of interest.

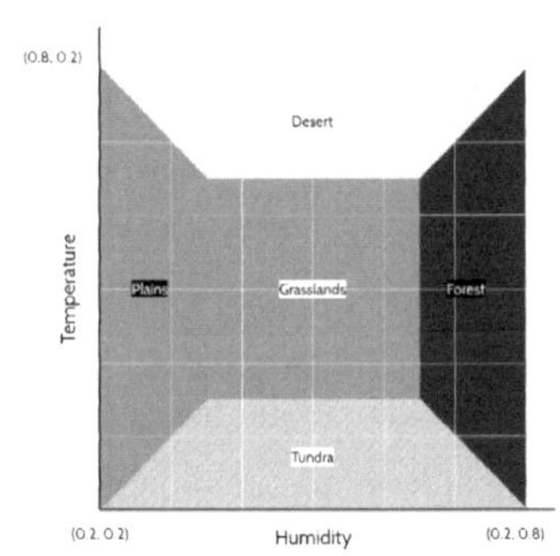

Figure 6. Terrain Boundary Map used in examples for testing game

Figure 7. Example gameplay of the 2D RPG testing engine for Atlas Chronicle

The gating items were given to the player once they interacted with a location containing the item (e.g. The Desert Palace gives the player the Crystal of Courage). Certain locations would not permit further progression until the correct gating item was obtained. These gating items were used to simulate the traditional gating behavior of RPGs, where some challenge is required to "open up" the next exploration area. The map generated by Atlas Chronicle was converted to a two-dimensional game via Python and PyGame. The game engine kept track of the time elapsed in-game and would pause the game automatically at timed intervals to collect the survey information. The game would only be allowed to continue after the participant completed the survey.

2.7 User Study

The terms "replay value" or "replayability" are often used when describing the benefit of procedural generation in games. We define the concept of replay value formally, with respect to the use of this term to describe video game enjoyment, as the rate of enjoyment decline over time spent playing the game. There are established methods for measuring enjoyment in video games using subjective style questionnaires. One frequently used questionnaire, the Game Experience Questionnaire (IJsselsteijn et al., 2008), has been thoroughly tested (Kätsyri et al., 2013; Mekler et al., 2014; Johnson et al., 2015) and is easily applied to measuring enjoyment in PG applications. The Fang et al. Questionnaire was also used because it is reliable way to measure Affect (Fang et al., 2010). Both the GEQ and Fang et al. Questionnaire were used for this study.Participants were selected from applicants with some expressed interest in playing video games and were screened using a brief screening form. The screening form asked for the applicant's self-reported gamer level and to select which types of games they regularly enjoy. Applicants who selected RPGs as a game type they regularly enjoyed were selected to participate. Also selected were applicants who labeled themselves as an expert or frequent gamer. A total of 18 participants (11 Male, 7 Female), aged between 18 and 24 years old (average age of 20), were selected for the study.

The user study included two phases: phase 1 evaluated an infinite runner type game that was generated by a separate procedural generation system (Matthews, 2019). Phase 2, described in this paper, measured enjoyment of static, manual, and PG (Atlas Chronicle) versions of the RPG. The same participants were used for both phases to allow a within-subjects comparison. Due to the length of time necessary for each phase, the two phases were accomplished on separate days, with some participants performing phase 2 before phase 1.

Participants were assigned the three content generation formats in random order: static, manual, or procedural. For the procedural and manual formats, each successive game that was played was different, with the creation of the content created by the computer or human designers, respectively. The static format game was replayed using a single created level for all games played.

Participants completed successive play-throughs of the RPG for half an hour per generation type. Due to the rapid iterative process, the subjective questionnaire enjoyment measurements were recorded exactly five times instead of after each game iteration. The RPG would play for 6 minutes before displaying the questionnaire, repeated for a total of five times per generation type. The time was decided after a pilot test determined the average play time a single game of the simplified RPG would take. The data collection was contained within the computer rather than on paper or at a different digital location to minimize player removal from the game-play experience. After the fifth questionnaire was completed the participant was informed to come find the observer and take their stretch break (a brief walk and restroom access). After the break, the participant was switched to the next content generation type.

2.8 Analysis

The independent variables were the three level generation methods: static, manual, and procedural. The dependent variables were the subjective questionnaire values: The 14 questions from the In-Game GEQ Module and Affect as measured by the 5 questions in the Fang et al. Questionnaire. User responses were recorded periodically during each Game/Generation section. The responses were on a Likert scale from 0 to 4. To detect patterns, a contingency table was built upon varying factors and then the results were tested for statistical significance.

Figure 8. Color key used in the subjective contingency tables

The first test applied on a contingency table was the Chi-Squared test. GEQ03, "I felt bored," was examined by segment number. The p-value was less than 0.01, therefore, the null hypothesis was rejected, and it was concluded that there was a relationship between segment number and response values for GEQ03. The questionnaire data are discrete rather than continuous; therefore, nonparametric tests were needed. Due to repeated significance testing, the chances of a Type I error ("false positive" or rejection of a true null hypothesis) are elevated, and hence significance values for each test must be adjusted to reflect the true probability under the null hypothesis. The Holm-Bonferroni p-value adjustment method was applied to counteract this effect.

For visualization, colors are used to distinguish the different response values, with the color key labeled in Figure 8. Seen in Figure 9a, the numerical totals are represented as a proportion of the total responses per segment. A larger segment indicates a larger percentage of the total. The upper x-axis is used to indicate the segment number and the lower x-axis is used to indicate the pairwise results. The chi-squared p-value is in the upper right and the Wilcoxon results as labels are on the bottom axis.

The results from the chi-squared test and nonparametric pairwise tests indicated that that boredom, as measured by GEQ03, increased significantly from the first segment (Segment 1) to the last segment (Segment 5) during the test.

Given that there appeared to be a general increase in boredom over time, the analysis compared the early and late responses, focusing on the survey responses from segment 1, collected after the participants had played the game for the earlier designated amount of time, and segment 5, which were collected after playing the generation type for the full amount of time (Figure 9b). Generally, the pairwise analysis indicates that segment 1 for the manual designs was "better" than segment 5 of the static and procedural designs regarding negative affect scores. But all other categories were too similar to differentiate. However, one can conclude is that the segment 1 (start) values for all three generation types were similar, and all three segment 5 (end) values were similar. The conclusion is that procedural was no better and no worse than any other generation approach.

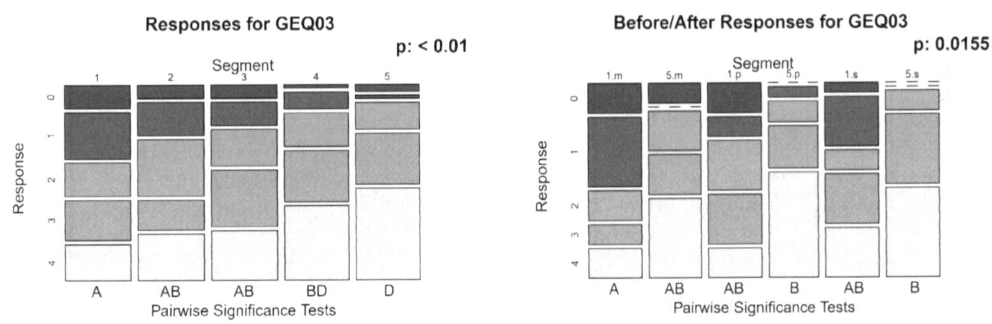

(a) Overall responses for boredom over all five segments

(b) Responses at the start and end of the test, pooled by generation type

Figure 9. Visual contingency tables using the color key from Figure 8 for the GEQ question "I felt bored." Y-axis is the response value from 0 (not at all) to 4 (extremely). X-axis on the top labels the segment for which the response was recorded, with m/p/s for manual/procedural/static. Bottom X-axis labels the pairwise analysis: columns which do not share a letter are significantly different

3. CONCLUSION

Based on the analysis, the boredom question from the GEQ measured a decline in enjoyment, over time. However, when comparing a before and after approach between the generation types, the procedurally generated test set performed the same as the manual and static design sets. This does call into question the claim of procedural generation increasing replay value, but for this research we can conclude that procedural generation is no better and no worse than static or manual generation approaches. According to our results, if a game designer wanted to have multiple, varied levels for their game, Atlas Chronicle would be a viable option because no enjoyment would be lost by using procedural generation, and procedural generation is faster and more cost-effective than manual procedures.

This study contributes to the analysis of procedural generation and enjoyment within video games. As such, the study was designed to minimize any external factors. The game engine utilized in this study was simplified to reduce confounding factors. A next step would perform the test on longer variations of a game utilizing the Atlas Chronicle map generation. Additionally, the story narrative used for testing Atlas Chronicle was simple due to the shorter variation of the game. Another avenue would be to examine the effects with a more compelling storyline. Participants were limited to college-aged individuals and the results may vary given different age ranges. The study measured a decline in enjoyment over time during a single-day session. Future studies should look into multiple-day studies, playing the game once per day. Future work could extend this research by adapting the definition to encompass the desire to replay a game as part of "replay value." Finally, the measurement tools utilized in this study were previously established enjoyment measurement tools, but not specifically tools to measure the type of enjoyment that procedural generation is said to bring to games. Future work must be done to examine how to measure "replay value" as affected by procedural generation in video games.

We revealed statistically relevant conclusions about the procedurally generated maps created by the Atlas Chronicle system. In summary, the maps generated were no different than human-designed maps in terms of retaining enjoyment over time. Participants experienced the same decline in enjoyment over time regardless of the content generation used.

REFERENCES

A. Iosup. Poggi: generating puzzle instances for online games on grid infrastructures. Concurrency and Computation: Practice and Experience, 23(2):158–171, 2011.

A. Saltsman. Canabalt (pc game). Adam Atomic, 2009.

ACM Transactions on Multimedia Computing, Communications, and Applications (TOMM), 9(1):1, 2013.

Blizzard North. Diablo (pc game), 1996.

C. Beckham and C. Pal. A step towards procedural terrain generation with gans. arXiv preprint arXiv:1707.03383, 2017.

C. Patrascu and S. Risi. Artefacts: Minecraft meets collaborative interactive evolution. In Computational Intelligence and Games (CIG), 2016 IEEE Conference on, pages 1–8. IEEE, 2016.

D. Johnson, P. Wyeth, M. Clark, and C. Watling. Cooperative game play with avatars and agents: Differences in brain activity and the experience of play. In Proceedings of the 33rd Annual ACM Conference on Human Factors in Computing Systems, pages 3721–3730. ACM, 2015.

D. Yu and A. Hull. Spelunky (pc game), 2009.

E. A. Matthews and B. A. Malloy. Incorporating coherent terrain types into story-driven procedural maps. In Meaningful Play, 2012: Designing and Studying Games that Matter, 2012.

E. A. Matthews. A Study of Techniques for Measuring Enjoyment in Video Games Containing Procedural Generation. PhD thesis, University of Florida, 7 2019.

E. D. Mekler, J. A. Bopp, A. N. Tuch, and K. Opwis. A systematic review of quantitative studies on the enjoyment of digital entertainment games. In Proceedings of the SIGCHI Conference on Human Factors in Computing Systems, pages 927–936. ACM, 2014.

Epyx. Rogue. Game [PC], 1980.

G. A. Barros, A. Liapis, and J. Togelius. Playing with data: Procedural generation of adventures from open data. In DiGRA/FDG, 2016.

J. Kätsyri, R. Hari, N. Ravaja, L. Nummenmaa, et al. Just watching the game ain't enough: striatal fmri reward responses to successes and failures in a video game during active and vicarious playing, 2013.

J. Togelius, M. Preuss, N. Beume, S. Wessing, J. Hagelbäck, G. N. Yannakakis, and C. Grappiolo. Controllable procedural map generation via multiobjective evolution. Genetic Programming and Evolvable Machines, 14 (2):245–277, 2013.

L. T. Pereira, C. Toledo, L. N. Ferreira, and L. H. Lelis. Learning to speed up evolutionary content generation in physics-based puzzle games. In Tools with Artificial Intelligence (ICTAI), 2016 IEEE 28th International Conference on, pages 901–907. IEEE, 2016.

M. Frade, F. F. de Vega, and C. Cotta. Automatic evolution of programs for procedural generation of terrains for video games. Soft Computing, 16(11):1893–1914, 2012.

M. Hendrikx, S. Meijer, J. Van Der Velden, and A. Iosup. Procedural content generation for games: A survey.

M. Henschke, D. Hobbs, and B. Wilkinson. Developing serious games for children with cerebral palsy: case study and pilot trial. In Proceedings of the 24th Australian Computer-Human Interaction Conference, pages 212–221. ACM, 2012.

Mojang. Minecraft (pc game), 2011.

N. Shaker, J. Togelius, G. N. Yannakakis, B. Weber, T. Shimizu, T. Hashiyama, N. Sorenson, P. Pasquier, P. Mawhorter, G. Takahashi, et al. The 2010 mario ai championship: Level generation track. IEEE Transactions on Computational Intelligence and AI in Games, 3(4):332–347, 2011.

N. Shaker, M. Nicolau, G. N. Yannakakis, J. Togelius, and M. O'neill. Evolving levels for super mario bros using grammatical evolution. In Computational Intelligence and Games (CIG), 2012 IEEE Conference on, pages 304–311. IEEE, 2012.

noise 1.2.2. noise 1.2.2. Website, 2019. URL https://pypi.org/project/noise/.

O. K. Moore Jr. Procedural content generation: Using ai to generate playable content. 2015.

PyGame. Pygame 1.9.6. Website, 2020. URL https://www.pygame.org/.

Pymunk. Pymunk 5.5.0. Website, 2019. URL http://www.pymunk.org/en/latest/.

Python. Python 3.7. Website, 2020. URL https://www.python.org/.

R. Khaled, M. J. Nelson, and P. Barr. Design metaphors for procedural content generation in games. In Proceedings of the SIGCHI Conference on Human Factors in Computing Systems, pages 1509–1518. ACM, 2013.

SciPy. Scipy 1.3.0. Website, 2019. URL https://www.scipy.org/.

W. Baghdadi, F. S. Eddin, R. Al-Omari, Z. Alhalawani, M. Shaker, and N. Shaker. A procedural method for automatic generation of spelunky levels. In European Conference on the Applications of Evolutionary Computation, pages 305–317. Springer, 2015.

W. IJsselsteijn, Y. de Kort, and K. Poels. The game experience questionnaire. Manuscript in preparation, 2008.

X. Fang, S. Chan, J. Brzezinski, and C. Nair. Development of an instrument to measure enjoyment of computer game play. Intl. Journal of Human–Computer Interaction, 26(9):868–886, 2010.

Y. Takatsuki. Cost headache for game developers. Website, 2007. URL news.bbc.co.uk/2/hi/business/ 7151961.stm.

BALANCING INTRANSITIVE RELATIONSHIPS IN MOBA GAMES USING DEEP REINFORCEMENT LEARNING

Conor Stephens and Chris Exton[1]
Lero – The Science Foundation Ireland Research Centre for Software,
Computer Science & Information Systems (CSIS), University Of Limerick, Ireland
[1]Dr

ABSTRACT

Balanced intransitive relationships are critical to the depth of strategy and player retention within esports games. Intransitive relationships comprise the metagame, a collection of strategies and play styles that are viable, each providing counterplay for other viable strategies. This work presents a framework for testing the balance of massive online battle arena (MOBA) games using deep reinforcement learning to identify the synergies between characters by measuring their effectiveness against the other compositions within the games character roster. This research is designed for game designers and developers to show how multi-agent reinforcement learning (MARL) can accelerate the balancing process and highlight potential game-balance issues during the development process. Our findings conclude that accurate measurements of game balance can be found with under 10 hours of simulation and show imbalances that traditional cost curve analysis approaches failed to capture. Furthermore, we discovered that this approach reduced imbalance in each character's win rate by 20% in our example project a key measurement that would be impossible to measure without collecting data from hundreds of human-controlled games previously. The project's source code is publicly available at https://github.com/Taikatou/top-down-shooter.

KEYWORDS

Deep Reinforcement Learning, Game Balance, Design

1. INTRODUCTION

The game balancing process aims to improve a game's aesthetic quality's and ensure the consistency and fairness of the game's systems and mechanics. Traditionally this process was achieved through a combination of data collected from playtesting analytical tools such as measuring the risk-reward ration of an item. This process is getting progressively more time consuming with rising levels of complexity in the game's design. To the constant updates that result in shifts in the game's balance. Game Designers have looked for options when testing the balance of games with reinforcement learning being a strong contender for the new solution. Reinforcement learning could potentially evaluate the quality of the game every evening when the developers are asleep, accelerating the project's timeline and giving designers more confidence when carrying out playtesting with participants. The sample problem this paper is focused on is an example project based on the popular MOBA game genre an asymmetric multiplayer game that is played in a square arena with a top-down perspective. We will evaluate the effectiveness of reinforcement learning when evaluating the balance of the game by measuring the effectiveness of different team compositions using accelerated simulated play controlled by deep reinforcement learning agents.

2. GAME DESIGN

The hope of any game's design that is optimising the rules and content of a game to further progress it towards its aesthetic goals (Hunicke, Leblanc and Zubek, 2004). Common goals of Game balance is to ensure entertaining and fair games for the players (Adams, 2009). This can take the form of understanding various metrics about game mechanics and comparing them with other content in the game's systems. An example of the game balance proccess would be to balance a revolver gun; the designer could record the mean, median and standard deviation of the damage of the gun and compare it to the other weapons. This damage by itself may not highlight the revolver as being too strong; the gun may carry a cost to compensate for the damage it is doing, e.g. the player's speed is reduced by half. Understanding the benefit of the weapon vs the cost is the principle of a cost curve in a game, cost curves are a type of cost-curve. One of the best-known examples of cost-curve analysis is the Mana Curve in *Magic: The Gathering* (Flores, 2006) which can be described as the relationship the card game has with mana as input and power as the output. Where the best gameplay options are. As a player, you will choose these options and disregard options that are not as good, as a designer, you should pay attention to where new weapons and cards sit on this curve.

2.1 Game Balance

Game balance can be described as the numeric properties of a game that makes players perceive the play as fair and remain enjoyable and challenging. Game Balance has traditionally been an analytical process of understanding data collected from play or using character stats to understand more transient game properties such as minimum time to kill within a game to the session length. Esports titles feature and tune multiple types of balance using a variety of tools and approaches; Situational Balance is the how different strategies are more favourable depending on the map or against the opponent's strategies.

2.2 Intransitive Relationships

Intransitive Relationships consist of game rules involving the type of mechanic used. The most often used example is *Rock, Paper, Scissors* where the intransitive relationship consists of which class beats which other class (Adams, 2009). Traditional approaches to balancing games with intransitive relationships are to use the probability of how likely the character in question is to beat other characters; *Rock Paper Scissors* has a ratio of 1:1:1. This is simple with equal scoring, but games have an intransitive relationship with unequal scoring. These computations are traditionally calculated using rulesets but are not possible in MOBA games as the relationships are defined by playstyle and the different effectiveness of weapons and abilities. Currently, designers rely on player statistics and playtesting to compute the win rates and probabilities of these characters. Cost curve analysis is also an option; however, it is designed for single-character interactions and does not account for the situational balance of the game.

2.3 Metagames

Early research on the topic of metagames coined the term metagame, paragame and orthogame (Carter, Gibbs and Harrop, 2012). The metagame is how players use outside influences to gain an advantage in the metagame; this is possible due to an externally sourced strategy and an understanding of some of the hidden information within the orthogame. Metagaming has different meanings regarding the different genres and games it can be featured in examples include playing the game differently that how your character would be able to play in tabletop role-playing games such as *Dungeons and Dragons*, where metagaming can give the player an advantage but breaks the aesthetic of the experience.

3. RELATED WORK

The most relevant research in this area was carried out by *King* and evaluated the possibility of using Deep Learning to achieve Human performance playtesting on their match 4 *"Crush Saga"* games (Stefan Freyr Gudmundsson, 2018). This research showed the power of deep learning to simulate play, especially within such a high profile game; our research differs from this for two main reasons. Firstly it is a multiplayer game the outcomes of the next state are dependent on all four agents in the environment. Secondly, this research focuses on testing the game's level design we will be focusing on mechanics an area of the game that is defined much earlier on in development.

Exploratory research for evaluating game balance in an adversarial game has been shown as possible using optimal agents (Jaffe et al., 2012). This research pioneered simulating games to evaluate the balance of card games. The research identified the power differences between the intransitive relationship in the game, this being between (Green, Red and Blue). This research was carried out in symmetric perfect information game different from MOBA titles such as *League of Legends* and *Dota II*.

New research into balancing decks of cards within the collectable card game *Hearthstone* (Silva, 2019) showed how genetic algorithms alongside simulated play could show how many viable options there are for players and to identify key compositions and decks that would be used if a card within the deck changes. This research shows how genetic algorithms can create fair games by changing the available mechanics given to both players within a very dense strategy space (over 2000 cards to evaluate). This was achieved by using an evolutionary algorithm to search for a combination of changes to achieve balance within the strategy space. This was measured by optimising the decks to have as close to a 50% win rate over a variety of conditions such as balancing the game with as few possible changes to each deck.

4. CHARACTER DESIGN

The characters were designed as a simple intransitive relationship similar to other MOBA games; we have DPS (Damage-per-second), Tanks and Healers all bringing their unique utility. The DPS does the most damage and has greater mobility, the tanks are slower but have more sustain in the form of additional health, and the healers provide utility to themselves and other DPS roles. Each character has strengths and weaknesses Tanks cannot outrun DPS, DPS cannot survive by themselves for long periods due to a lack of sustain and healers cannot out damage the other roles. The design ambition of an asymmetric multiplayer game involves character roles complement each other. Players must work together as a team to overcome their opponents by choosing the most applicable characters in the current situation. Each character has an assigned weapon and different stats and abilities, as shown below.

4.1 Weapons

Guns: Standard projectile weapon can fire every second, can hold ten bullets as ammo and takes 1 second to reload. Each bullet fires at 500 units per second and does ten damage on collision. Can only collide with walls and members of the opposite team. Each projectile has a random spray effect.

Healing Gun: The Same implementation as the standard gun but only can collide with members of the same team, does seven damage to enemy teams and does seven healing per shot to teammates.

Sword: Melee combo style weapon designed by *More Mountains* has three attacks in combo each attack has an active hitbox that lasts 0.2 seconds and does 10 damage on hit. When hit enemies are invincible for 0.5 seconds after successful hit.

4.2 Character Descriptions

DPS

- Weapon: Gun
- 40% Faster movement speed

Sprint

- Weapon: Sword
- Dash Ability: boosts character in the direction of movement by six units of distance.

Healer

- Weapon: Healing Gun

HealerAOE

- Weapon: Gun
- Area of Effect healing for 0.75 heals per second around a 12 (Unity Unit) diameter area.

Tank

- Weapon: Sword
- Breather Ability heals ten hp over 3 seconds, cannot use weapons during this time has a cooldown period of 6 seconds.

4.3 Cost Curve Analysis

When initially balancing the characters, we set about defining the value of each character in terms of its health. This is a cost curve analysis where the value of the character is compared against its costs. This is achievable by evaluating all the other properties of the character Damage, Heals etc. In terms of health. Some properties were harder to define in terms of health, such as characters size. Our conversion for health was based on the increased likelihood to get hit due to the larger hitbox multiplied by the maximum damage of a projectile attack. The results of this analysis shown are in Table 1 below.

Table 1. Character Cost Curve Analysis

	Health	Damage	Heal	Speed	Ability	Size	Value
DPS	30	9	0	4	0	0	47
Sprint	30	17	0	0	3	0	50
Healer	30	7	7	-1	0	0	45
AOE	30	9	0	0	9	0	48
Tank	40	17	0	0	5	-10	52

5. METHODS

This research is attempting to balance an example game using deep reinforcement learning techniques by understanding the different win rate of characters within an asymmetric multiplayer team vs team game. The game is a small top-down battle MOBA game with five playable characters each possessing different gameplay options and stats. The differences character classes support the intransitive relationships within the game that will affect the meta that players would hopefully adopt after learning to play the game. A two-layer neural network plays each character with 512 neurons in hidden layers layer, Each agent's neural network has different input and output. We train this neural network using Proximal Policy Optimization (PPO) algorithm alongside a curiosity learning signal to offset the effect of the sparse rewards in the environments. Each iteration of an agent's policy is updated using gradient descent with a batch size of 1024 and 2 epochs of the experience buffer. The experience buffer contains 10240 of the most recent experiences due to PPO's on-policy nature. The experience buffer represents a list of observations and rewards at each decision interval.

5.1 Tools

This research and the learning environment that supports it is comprised of a variety of tools and software. The game engine we are using is Unity 3D. The machine learning framework that connects Unity games and our models are called (Machine Learning) ML-Agents (Juliani et al., 2018) an open-source plugin developed by Unity 3D that allows developers to train reinforcement learning agents within Unity 3D. The learning environment and the character abilities are based on the multiplayer example project found within *MoreMountains* Top Down Engine plugin for Unity. We choose to base the game in Unity due to its popularity within the game development community, in 2018 John Riccitiello the CEO of Unity claimed at *TechCrunch Disrupt SF* that half the worlds games are made in Unity. All these decisions come together to show developers they can use the tools they are familiar and bake reinforcement learning into existing games.

6. TRAINING

Before the experiments are carried out, agents are trained together within a learning environment; this is a multi-agent reinforcement learning environment. Each agent has a variety of input and output signals to both control the character and understands the world this is necessary to train the agent with the PPO algorithm that controls the agents (Schulman, 2017). The environment reward is given at the end of a game with agents are rewarded for winning the game with a reward of +1 and punished for losing with a negative reward of –0.25. Due to the sparse nature of the learning-environment curiosity, learning is applied to help the agent both explore and understand its environment. Curiosity Learning allows the agent to learn how its actions change the next state of the world and how it gains intrinsic rewards by exploring the different options within the environment. (Juliani et al., 2018) Due to the multi-agent nature of our experiment, curiosity learning is less accurate due to how the next state of the environment has high dependencies on all the actions of the agents.

6.1 Representation of Input and Output

6.1.1 Input Signals

The games physical environment is perceived by the agents using one-hot encoded raycasts. The agent fires 24 ray casts in a circle with equal distance between them of 15 degrees. Each ray cast is 25 units in length, and they can collide with projectiles and the physical walls of the battle arena. If the ray hits something, it returns a fraction of the distance it travelled vs 25 units. Each ray gets an id to determine what it hits with the default 0 being no-hit,1 being walls and 2 being projectiles. The agents' abilities and stats all implement the ISense interface that records any necessary information that would be shown to the player in the way of an animation or user interface component. This was done so that the agent would have the same level of knowledge of the world that prospective players would have. Each agent knows the whereabouts and health of the other agents as well as each agents team affiliation. This is to mimic the effect of being able to see the other players screen and UI when compared to the local multiplayer version of this game.

The first signal type is the ray casts; agents shoot raycasts through the environment every 15 degrees surrounding the agent as shown below. The raycast scans for two different collision types the first is obstacles such as walls, the second are for projectiles and where they are on the map. This implementation hoped to simulate the same understanding players would have of the game without having to run lengthy computation of the pixels on the screen. The second group of input signals are the player stats; these include the player's position, the direction the players' weapon is facing both encoded as a 2D vector, the players' health and the current animation of the sword. Abilities have their senses so that the AI understands the state of the ability and its cooldowns and properties that would traditionally be shown to the player through UI or animations/SFX.

6.1.2 Output Signals

Each agent has a separate model with the action space continuous with output values being floats ranging from –1 to 1. Models have 6 or 7 outputs depending on if the character has a special ability. The first two outputs are the movement values for the x and y-axis of the character; the second 2 outputs are the aiming axis for x and y. The next three values are the shoot button, reload button and ability button. Button values are converted to Boolean values by checking if they are greater than 0.4.

7. EXPERIMENT

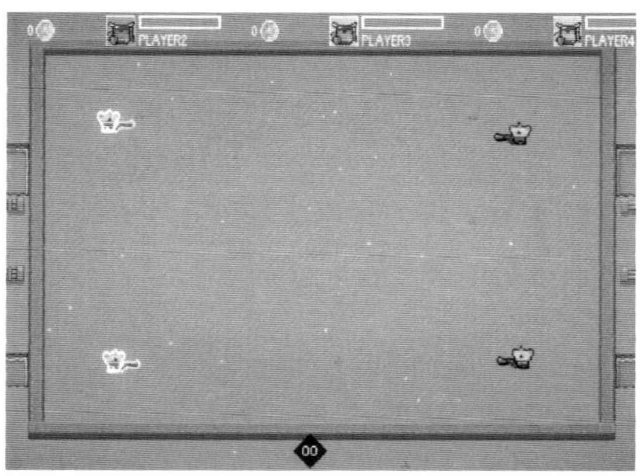

Figure 1. Learning Environment – (teams highlighted using colour)

The experiment is as follows; each round is played within a 2D arena with four spawn-points in each corner. Characters for each team are selected at random and spawned in the four corners of the map the agents have their current models. Each round is complete if the victory condition of being the last team alive is achieved or the time for the game runs out, at the end of the game agents may receive a reward for the game and the episode within the experience buffer is ended. The time for the game starts at 160 seconds longer than what the designers of the game *(MoreMountains)* recommendation of 60. Throughout the training, this time is changed as part of the curriculum for the agents learning (Narvekar, 2017). This change happens corresponding to the agent's step count versus the max step count of the learning environment. A more popular approach is to base the curriculum off the reward the agents have received. Still, due to the zero-sum nature of this learning environment, no progress would be made using this solution; this is described below. The MARL learning environment also creates an auto-curriculum effect where characters understand how to play against each other with progressive difficulty due to the advancement of the learning environment. The agents are trained at 50 times speed and selected at random.

Each team of two is comprised of two random characters at the beginning of the round. The victory condition is to be the last team standing if the timer runs out the team with the most kills wins. We measure the win-rate of the various characters and their combinations. The hope of this is to see synergies between characters and the intransitive relationships they provide within the META game. Successful completion of the 5 AI models over 10 hours of training using on an Nvidia RTX 2070 GPU using TensorFlow within a single learning environment. The game was played again at the same 50 times speed with the AI's using inference from the models. After the completion of the game Wins and Losses were recorded for each team composition.

8. PRELIMINARY RESULTS

Figure 2. Win rate of different team compositions (550 games)

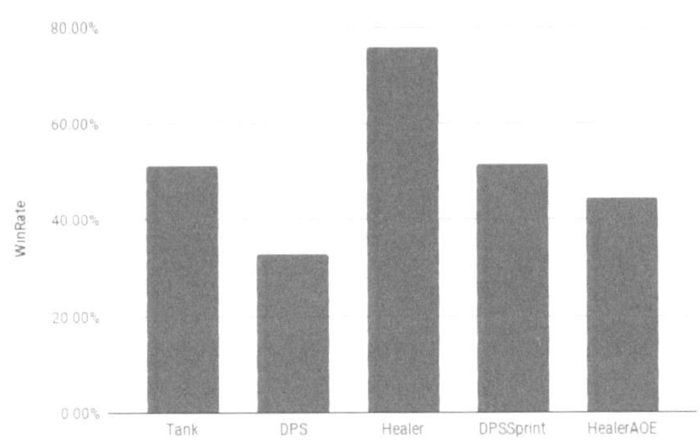

Figure 3. Win rate of individual characters (100 games)

After running the AI models using inference, we collected data from 551 games that ended in wins and losses As shown in Figure 2 the results for this game's balance was quite shocking with healer combos being by far the strongest and DPS combos being by far the weakest. This can be seen as a symptom that healing and damage together are too strong. We reran the simulation for 104 games and collected the character's win-rate as shown in Figure 3 this shows that the Healer character is by far the best character to play due to its versatility during the game. This achieves our conclusion due to how organising a playtesting session for this game would reveal the same result; however, take significantly more time to organise and execute.

The META game with this games' current balance shows that doubling character types strengths them and increases your likelihood to win the game. This could be seen as a strength or a weakness of the game's design. This research shows the difficulty of balancing a team game without playtesting due to the discrepancies between the simulated results and the cost-benefit analysis we carried out before the experiment as shown in Table I. After careful consideration of the balance of the game; we decided to' nerf' the healer characters and 'buff' the DPS characters. After careful consideration of the logs and watching the playback of the game, the healers' ability to heal was reduced. The Heal Gun's healing was reduced to five, and the AOE Healers damage was also reduced to five to be less than the DPS characters. We felt tanks were fairest in the initial results with dual tanks having a win rate of 50%. However, their synergy with the other roles was lacking the implemented solution was the shield mechanic. A way of making their team member invulnerable for 5 seconds. This ability takes the place of the breather ability and has a cooldown of 25 seconds.

9. SECONDARY RESULTS

This research has shown that reinforcement learning can prevent early playtesting session for multiplayer games, allowing sole developers to work on team-based games that were not previously possible. Using AI to test games is an exciting topic, this paper shows the effect of Reinforcement Learning when during the early balancing process or asymmetric games. Applications of this research could be used to test the level difficulty of Players Vs. AI games such as World of Warcraft and other level difficulty problems. After running the same simulation for another 200 simulations, we arrived at the following results, as shown in Figure 4. These results are far more promising with each character achieving a potential win rate of above 60% if paired with a healer or a tank. The biggest weakness in the current balance is that DPS Tanks are not currently a strong combination due to the lack of sustain this could be a good thing to encourage players to play tanks or a negative aesthetic due to the restricted gameplay possibilities this presents.

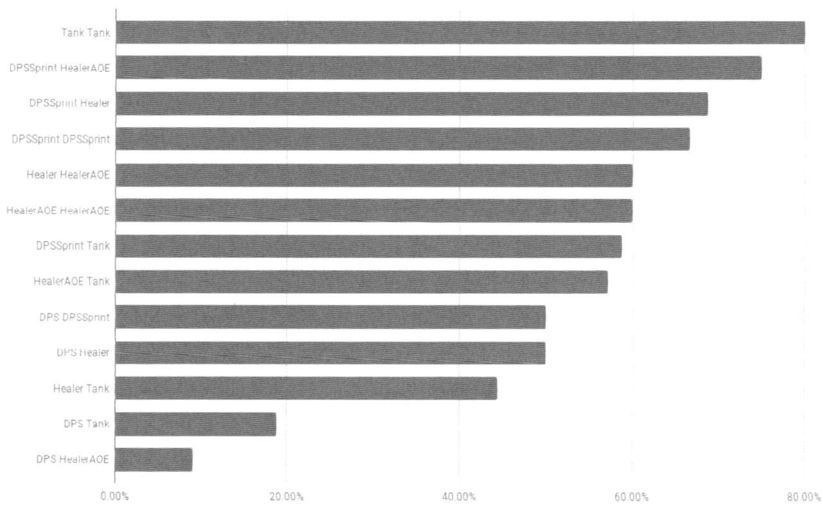

Figure 4. Win rate of team compositions

The character-specific win-rates also changed drastically with the DPS Sprint being the best character at the cost of the traditional DPS role, as shown in Figure 5. Three characters currently have win-rates of approximately 50%. The standard deviation also changed from the two experiments from the original experiments, as shown in Figure 6. This change in the standard deviation is our most significant result it is approximately 20% reduction of the level of imbalance of the game's characters. This is a significant figure and would allow developers to measure the change in the fairness of the games over time in a significantly more credible way than the previously used perceived balance found in other competitive games.

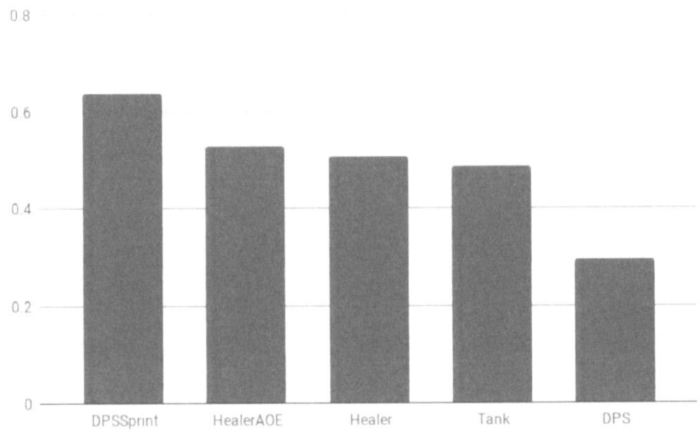

Figure 5. Win rate of individual characters

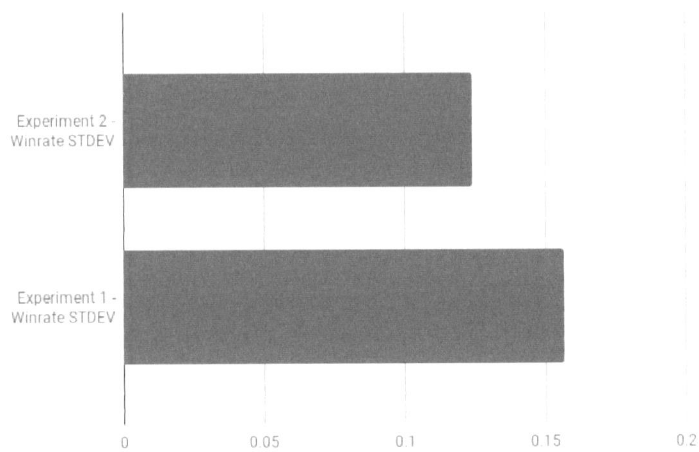

Figure 6. The standard deviation of win-rate - Experiment 1 vs Experiment 2

10. DISCUSSION

This research has shown that reinforcement learning can measure the imbalance within a multiplayer game. Furthermore, this solution can aid games designers when identifying specific mechanics or systems, causing an imbalance. This utility and speed provided by the learning agents can empower designers to rebalance their game to pursue their aesthetic ambitions further. We expect other developers and researchers to push the boundaries of what is possible with simulated play, especially concerning the design of the game's systems. The next area of research we hope to look at is multiplayer Player vs Event games and to evaluate the difficulty of level design in a cooperative multiplayer setting. This could either review the effects of learning signals on agent cooperation or measuring the deviation of procedurally generated content.

This research also poses several critical questions about the structure and purpose of reinforcement learning in game design. The questions that we believe to be of particular importance in this area of research include:

- Can we self-balance a game using Adversarial Learning, (Where one learning agent is responsible for the game balance and can change character stats?
- Can we identify character relationships in existing esports games that have open API's (Application Interface) such as *Hearthstone or DOTA II*
- How accurate are AI agents decisions when compared to human players, and by extension is imitation learning a more accurate behaviour.

Thus it is clear that this research has both expanded reinforcement learning into a new area of applicability and paved the way for an essential discussion on its future applications.

The authors would recommend several improvements that would accelerate the training time of this research and make it more accessible within the games industry. The first is multiple parallel learning environments; this would expedite the collection of data for the policy update and could allow the experience buffer to contain more diverse experience each iteration. We would including Self-Play (Silver et al., 2018) with the learning environment, a learning environment design paradigm where the current policy plays against previous policies, this can show an increase over time and allows the reward estimates to be upwards instead of zero-sum. Self-Play would facilitate more stable training and allow the agents to adapt to different playstyles with the same characters.

ACKNOWLEDGEMENT

This research was supported by University of Limericks Computer Science and Information Systems department and *Lero*, The Science Foundation Ireland Research Centre for Software.

REFERENCES

Adams, E. (2009). Fundamentals of Game Design. New Riders Publishing, p.329.

Carter, M., Gibbs, M. and Harrop, M. (2012). Metagames, Paragames and Orthogames: A New Vocabulary. In: FDG '12. [online] Association for Computing Machinery, p.1117. Available at: https://doi.org/10.1145/2282338.2282346.

Debus, M. (2017). Metagames: On the Ontology of Games Outside of Games. In: FDG '17. [online] Association for Computing Machinery. Available at: https://doi.org/10.1145/3102071.3102097.

Hunicke, R., Leblanc, M. and Zubek, R. (2004). MDA: A Formal Approach to Game Design and Game Research. AAAI Workshop - Technical Report, 1.

Jaffe, A., Miller, A., Andersen, E., Liu, Y., Karlin, A. and Popoviundefined, Z. (2012). Evaluating Competitive Game Balance with Restricted Play. In: AIIDE'12. AAAI Press, p.2631.

Juliani, A., Berges, V., Vckay, E., Gao, Y., Henry, H., Mattar, M. and Lange, D. (2018). Unity: A General Platform for Intelligent Agents. CoRR, [online] abs/1809.02627. Available at: http://arxiv.org/abs/1809.02627.

Narvekar, S. (2017). Curriculum Learning in Reinforcement Learning. [online] pp.5195--5196. Available at: https://doi.org/10.24963/ijcai.2017/757.

Pathak, D. (2017). Curiosity-driven Exploration.

Salen, K. and Zimmerman, E. (2003). Rules of Play: Game Design Fundamentals. The MIT Press.

Schulman, J. (2017). Proximal Policy Optimization Algorithms. CoRR, [online] abs/1707.06347. Available at: http://arxiv.org/abs/1707.06347.

Silva, F. (2019). Evolving the Hearthstone Meta. CoRR, [online] abs/1907.01623. Available at: http://arxiv.org/abs/1907.01623.

Silver, D., Hubert, T., Schrittwieser, J., Antonoglou, I., Lai, M., & Guez, A. et al. (2018). A general reinforcement learning algorithm that masters chess, shogi, and Go through self-play. Science, 362(6419), 1140-1144. doi: 10.1126/science.aar6404.

Stefan Freyr Gudmundsson, L. (2018). Human-Like Playtesting with Deep Learning. pp.1-8.

LOCALIZATION AND REGIONAL ASPECTS OF GAME PRODUCTION – A RESEARCH OVERVIEW

Marcus Toftedahl
*University of Skövde, Division of Game Development,
Högskolevägen 2, Skövde, Sweden*

ABSTRACT

This paper focus on how localization is addressed in research on game development processes. The research aim is to get an understanding of how localization, game localization and its subsets of content and cultural issues, linguistic issues and technical issues are addressed and discussed in game development research. This has been done through a literature study, where 488 papers regarding game development processes have been scrutinized in order to identify game localization related research. The results shows that localization is rarely addressed in game development research, but regional aspects and relevant concepts related to game localization can be found.

KEYWORDS

Localization, Game Development, Regional Aspects, Game Development, Creative Industries, Software Development

1. INTRODUCTION

Localization is the "process of modifying products or services to account for differences in a distinct market", a definition provided by the (now defunct) Localization Industry Standards Association (LISA) (Fry & Lommel, 2003, p. 13). Further, localization is often divided into three categories that the process of localization needs to address; linguistic issues, content and cultural issues and technical issues. In software development the need of localization has its origins with the advent of office software such as word processors and spreadsheet software in the late 1970's (O'Hagan & Mangiron, 2013). When the software was distributed outside the market of origin, alterations needed to be made according to differences in language, but also in other areas such as formatting conventions including the format of dates, numbering and currency. O'Hagan and Mangiron (2013) describe this as a major shift in mindset when producing software for a global market, where the software developers began to not only localize a specific product but change development practices towards a more localization friendly development cycle. A product that is produced in one part of the world can immediately be available for purchase in another. This is a challenge for all product development, making localization an important factor of the production process.

In a previously conducted literature review containing 488 research articles on game development and management of creativity, it was identified that the vast majority of articles relating to game development took little to no consideration of regional aspects in their research approaches (Engström, Marklund, Backlund, & Toftedahl, 2018). Further, 84% of the articles from the study did not mention regional aspects, and only 2.6% had regional aspects as main focus. It should be noted that regional aspects in this case refers to a broad area of aspects, including practices, data from specific regions, location of companies etc. – i.e. not strictly localization related content.

This paper is written with the aim to survey how (if?) localization is addressed in research on game development processes. The research aim is to get an understanding of how localization, game localization and its subsets of content and cultural issues, linguistic issues and technical issues are addressed and discussed in game development research.

2. PREVIOUS WORK

This research has been conducted within the overarching research project Game Hub Scandinavia (GHS), focusing on exploring the current state of game development practice from an academic and industry perspective. Examples of other topics explored within GHS, thus in some ways related to this paper, are: localization in indie game development studios (Toftedahl, Backlund, & Engström, 2018); game engines and production tools (Toftedahl & Engström, 2019); and the two literature studies described below (Engström et al., 2018; Marklund, Engström, Hellkvist, & Backlund, 2019).

While the aim of this article is to explore how game localization is addressed in research articles regarding the craft and processes of game development, this research is based on methods, data and results from the larger literature study conducted by Engström et al. (2018). In the study, a large number of research articles regarding game development and creative industries were identified and scrutinized, focusing on how contemporary research takes the duality of video game development from a software development and creative production perspective into account. In the initial literature review 2278 publications were included, subsequently reduced to a set of 488 papers. The selection process involved identifying only papers written in English and published between 2006 and 2016. To briefly summarize the literature selection process, a series of keywords related to game development or creative- and cultural industries in conjunction with development processes were used in several wide-reaching databases (Scopus, Springer, ACM, and DiGRA digital archive) to generate the initial set of 2278 publications. Through title and abstract analysis, this set was then reduced to 488 papers that were reviewed and coded. During the coding process three particular parameters relevant for the study were included: research quality evaluation; identification whether a paper was based on empirical data from the games industry; and, if regional aspects were addressed. The details of the fundamental method of the study are described in detail in Engström et al. (2018).

A continuation of the literature review project was conducted by Marklund et al. (2019), going more in-depth on one of the research questions used in the initial literature review. Using the 488 papers from the initial literature review, the paper by Marklund et al. (2019) focuses solely on papers with empirically grounded research based on data informed by game developers or game development studios. In this paper, a subset of 48 of the initial 488 papers was used. All included papers were fulfilling the following criteria: they contain empirical data from industry practitioners (i.e. not development conducted in an academic setting); they display a high quality of research (i.e. having a clearly stated research question, method description and results); and, they are relevant to our understanding to the practices of game development.

3. METHOD

In order to understand how game localization and regional aspects of game development have been discussed in previous literature a review using the papers identified in Engström et al. (2018) and Marklund et al. (2019) has been carried out. Since the previous studies using the dataset have had different aims, an approach to include as many of the previously identified papers has been made. To accomplish this, two passes of review have been made.

Firstly, a simple full text search of the total of 488 papers included in the original literature review by Engström et al. (2018) was conducted. To catch papers relevant for this study (i.e. game localization) a word search for "locali*" and "translat*" was made on the set of papers to include variations of localization and translation (i.e. different spellings, capitalization etc.). With the specific key word search, articles mentioning localization and related concepts should appear search query. The query resulted in 61 articles in total. Upon closer inspection only 16 articles were about the practice of localization, the other mentioned localization in other contexts and meanings such where the majority was about physical locations and re-localization and localization economies versus urbanization economies as a part of emerging "creative cities and regions". The same trend was seen in relation to the "translat*" search, where the term translation in relation to mathematics was found.

Since the corpus of 488 papers included research from software engineering and creative software development in general as well as game development, a reading of titles and abstracts was conducted to find the papers that had a specific focus on game development. Five papers were removed in this pass, not mentioning game development. In the end 11 papers regarding game development was found to cover some aspects of localization.

Secondly, a thematic analysis of the 48 papers from the study by Marklund et al. (2019) and the papers identified in the previously described localization keyword search was conducted. Thematic analysis is described by Braun and Clarke (2006, p. 6) as:

> *"[...] a method for identifying, analyzing, and reporting patterns (themes) within data. It minimally organizes and describes your data set in (rich) detail. However, it also often goes further than this, and interprets various aspects of the research topic"*

One paper identified in the keyword search was already included in the set of 48 papers, thus 10 additional papers were added to a specific group to be able to separate the two groups of papers. The papers included from the study by Marklund et al. (2019) are also a subset of the corpus of papers used in Engström et al. (2018), with a focus on game development with data from game developers and game development studios. This subset of papers do therefore already have a specific scope regarding game development, thus making a more thorough analysis regarding localization is plausible to catch game localization descriptions where other phrasings (than localization) are being used.

As this review aims to identify game localization related topics in a corpus of articles previously identified to describe game development, a continuation of the thematic analysis done by Marklund et al. (2019) has been carried out. The coding process was conducted using the MAXQDA qualitative analysis software program allowing both thematic coding and free text commenting of large data sets. The MAXQDA software can after the coding present compilations of the coded segments and comments for easier analyses. The thematic analysis process was divided into three main phases; a preparation phase, a content processing and coding phase, and an analysis phase. In more detail, the first phase involved familiarization with the corpus of papers and identifying relevant codes related to the aim of this paper. The coding categories from the study by Marklund et al. (2019) was kept intact in order to be able to cross-reference game localization aspects with the previously identified game development related information. One code from the previous analysis was left unaltered and to be included in the game localization coding; the identification of "Region of business" (i.e. data gathered from a game developer in a specific country). The codes chosen for the localization related material was mainly based on aspects derived from the three categories of localization (i.e. linguistic, cultural and technical issues) (O'Hagan & Mangiron, 2013) and the Global product development cycle (Fry & Lommel, 2003). The final codes used for the localization related aspects of game development were:

- **Regional aspects** – over-arching category, divided into following sub-categories:
    - **Data from specific region/s** – results based on data from a specific, named region/country.
    - **Development and localization** – development processes with direct relation to localization.
    - **Localization** – paper mentions localization specifically.
        - **Technical issues** – data or results related to technical issues of localization.
        - **Linguistic issues** – data or results related to linguistic issues of localization.
        - **Cultural issues** – data or results related to cultural issues of localization.
    - **Business strategies** – specific business strategies related to different regions.
    - **Globalness of the game industry** – statements related to the global nature of the game industry.

The content processing and coding phase involved scrutinizing the papers and using MAXQDA to apply the corresponding codes to the papers. The complete set of papers was analyzed by reading through them and marking text segments with codes from the established code categories. The third and final phase, the analysis phase, involved searching for themes in the compiled and coded material for analysis. The themes and trends found in the coded material were then grouped to make the themes easy to describe and present.

4. RESULTS

The literature study shows that from a corpus of 488 papers regarding game development and management of creativity very few are addressing game localization aspects of game development. The keyword search conducted on the 488 papers only gave 16 results regarding localization, and 11 of them were papers focusing on game development in one way or another. Using the dataset from the study Marklund et al. (2019) containing 48 papers, 27 papers mentions regional aspects in general.

The set of papers specific for this study hence consisted of 37 papers in total. The 37 papers are combination of the 11 papers from the keyword search and the 27 papers mentioning regional aspects from the study by Marklund et al. (2019), with one paper overlapping the two sets. Table 1 shows a quantitative overview of the occurrences of the codes, where number of documents containing the specific code category is shown as well as the total number of occurrences.

Table 1. Quantitative overview of the coded documents

Code category (sub-categories of Regional aspects)	Number of documents containing code	Total number of occurrences
Data from specific region	23	23
Globalness of game industry	17	24
Localization	11	25
Business strategies	7	14
Development and localization	7	12
Cultural (aspects of loc.)	4	8
Technical (aspects of loc.)	2	2
Linguistic (aspects of loc.)	2	2

The most frequent element of regional aspects found in the papers is research based on data from a specific region. This is where it is explicitly stated in the paper that the data is gathered from a specific region, i.e. often found in the method description of the paper. The most common region regarding this aspect is Finland, with 9 papers based on data from Finnish game developers. The second most frequent region of data collection is USA with 3 papers, followed by Canada with 2 papers. Table 2 shows a breakdown of the data from specific regions in more detail.

Table 2. Papers with data from specific regions

Paper/Country	Finland	USA	Canada	China	Turkey	Korea	Singapore	UK	Poland	France	Germany	Sweden	Nether-lands
Hagen (2004)												x	
Lee, Lee, Cho, Song, and Rhew (2006)						x							
Myllärniemi, Raatikainen, and Männistö (2006)	x												
Tschang and Szczypula (2006)		x											
van de Weerd, de Weerd, and Brinkkemper (2007)													x
Stacey and Nandhakumar (2008)							x						
Kultima (2010)	x												
Binark and Bayraktutan (2012)					x								
Legault and Ouellet (2012)			x										
Wimmer and Sitnikova (2012)											x		
Chung and Fung (2013)				x									
Hodgson and Briand (2013)			x										
Kasurinen, Laine, and Smolander (2013)	x												
Kasurinen, Strandén, and Smolander (2013)	x												
Koutonen and Leppänen (2013)	x												
Lê, Massé, and Paris (2013)										x			
Kasurinen, Maglyas, and Smolander (2014)	x												
Kasurinen and Smolander (2014)	x												
Murphy-Hill, Zimmermann, and Nagappan (2014)		x											
Musial, Kauppinen, and Puhakka (2016)	x							x	x				
Nelson and Palumbo (2014)		x											
Vanhala and Kasurinen (2014)	x												

Regarding the globalness of the game industry, 17 papers mentioning the global nature of the game industry were found. This is a wide category, where both remarks of how the game industry is a global business and more in-depth analyses regarding this are made. This category often has a business perspective, thus cross-coded with the business strategy code. One example of this is from Tschang (2009):

"Hollywood movies have a world-wide following, no less in Asia than in other regions. The US-made online game World of Warcraft (WOW) has become a worldwide phenomenon, with a large proportion of its revenues coming from China."

Chung and Fung (2013, p. 248) presents another perspective, regarding how the globalness of the game industry is reflected in business decisions, focusing on local and regional business practices:

"The Chinese online gaming companies have reached a stage where locally developed games can compete with quality foreign games from Korea and the United States. Some Chinese game companies now export their products to nearby Asian countries, competing with regional markets traditionally dominated by Korean game companies. While the state-market framework has protected local game companies within the Chinese market, the real competition and arena for expansion takes place outside the country, in the world market."

While both Hollywood movies and big blockbuster games such as *World of Warcraft* are often used as examples of the global game industry, there are examples where small-scale companies/developers and their perspectives are considered as well. With a Finnish perspective, Vanhala and Kasurinen (2014, p. 84) mention the importance of having a global strategy for small companies:

"We studied six computer game start-ups in Finland. This means that the sample size was small and homogeneous. However, all the companies were aiming at the international markets with their products, the companies covered different release platforms and genres, and were developing games as their main source of income, so the companies did have variance and were representative organizations of the games industry."

Even though overarching business strategies in the global game industry is an important topic, there are few articles mentioning how to handle the global nature of the game industry from a development perspective. Only 7 articles have been identified to discuss the development aspect of localization in one way or another. In an article by van de Weerd et al. (2007) with the approach to construct a reference method for game production, localization is lifted as a specific task in game production. The reference method for game production is derived from four game production methods, constructing one super method containing activities and concepts from the four included production methods. van de Weerd et al. (2007) use three methods described in the following three game production books: *Game Development and Production* (Bethke, 2003); *Introduction to Game Development* (Rabin, 2005); and, *The Game Production Handbook* (Chandler, 2009). The forth method in the study is a proprietary method used at a game development company. van de Weerd et al. (2007, p. 316) present one version of a game production process, quoting Chandler (2009):

"Chandler describes in 'The Game Production Handbook' four main processes in the game production cycle. These are Pre-Production, Production, Testing and Post-Production. The pre-production phase encompasses the definition of the game concept, the definition of the game requirements and the definition of the game plan. After pre-production there is production, in which builds of the game are created and localized."

Further, van de Weerd et al. (2007, p. 319) gives an overview of the proprietary game production method included in the study, based on the processes of a game development company called Zylom:

"The game production process as it is carried out at Zylom is divided into four phases, namely Design, Development, Quality assurance and Localization. The method process consists of 11 activities, 59 activities, and 60 concepts."

Regarding localization in production, van de Weerd et al. (2007) emphasizes the lack of in-depth descriptions of the localization process. In the development process descriptions from *Introduction to Game Development* (Rabin, 2005) it is noted by van de Weerd et al. (2007, p. 322) that detailed descriptions of hiring staff members and performing market and sales related activities is included, but localization is not described using the same detail:

"The ITGD method is the only one to address in detail the hiring of staff members as part of the game production process and performing marketing and sales related activities. Activities are not only management specific; also the actual game development process is covered in quite some detail. However, the localization of finished games is described very briefly and is therefore too basic to be really useful."

As a contrast to the brief description in Introduction to Game Development, van de Weerd et al. (2007) notes that The Game Production Handbook has a very detailed description of the localization process:

"The TGPH method excels when it comes to the localization process and the finalization of the game production project. The localization steps and the definition and creation of closing kits are thoroughly discussed. Finally, the part of the project in which code is released is also well explained in TGPH compared to other methods."

As a conclusion, van de Weerd et al. (2007) have included localization in their amalgam of the four game development processes. Localization is in their proposed reference method placed in the post-production phase, in conjunction with quality assurance. The conclusion that localization is an activity carried out in the later stages of development are mirrored in other papers as well; Bernhaupt (2015) mentions localization as a part of the later development stage, Zoeller (2013) identifies that quality assurance managers and localization producers wants to know where in the game foreign language testers encounters problem, and Deuze, Martin, and Allen (2007) explicitly mention localization as an outsourcing activity.

Regarding localization and its components of cultural, technical and linguistic issues, few papers mention any of the specifics. Regarding technical issues, Chung and Fung (2013) mention the development of broadband access in Asian countries and connects this to the possibility of growing e-services. Alves, Ramalho, and Damasceno (2007, p. 276) connect growing technical infrastructures as a possibility to expand into new markets:

"On the one side, the game must be available in several languages, adhere to particular regional requirements and developers have to orchestrate complex distribution channels. On the other side, the increasing number of mobile phone subscribers, especially in developing countries, represents a huge unexplored consumer market."

The quote from Alves et al. (2007, p. 276) above is also one of few articles mentioning linguistic issues, even briefly. Linguistic issues, regarding that the game must be available in a language that the player can understand is not a topic discussed in detail in any of the articles included in this study.

Cultural issues are mentioned in some articles from two main perspectives: local regulations and knowledge of local references. Both Chung and Fung (2013) and Bernhaupt (2015) mentions how the knowledge of local rules and regulations must be taken into account. Bernhaupt (2015, p. 5) means that localization is an important phase for games where adaptations to the game content must be made:

"Localization: an important phase for games that will be delivered to different markets (countries) is the localization phase. In this phase game-play can be adjusted to suit the tastes of the market, to allow language translation and modifications due to local regulatory authorities."

Chung and Fung (2013) gives an example where the complex nature of the local Chinese regulations and censorship of games are described. The description gives an overview of the relations between a number of Chinese governmental agencies handling the authorization and censorship of games in China. In general, one agency has the power allow or ban any media publication and another agency reviews the content of games based on certain regulations involving protecting minors from disturbing content etc. Thus, the approval process is long and complicated and Chung and Fung (2013, p. 240) concludes:

"Our talks with these government agencies and game companies revealed that, before a foreign game is released in the Chinese market, game companies have to receive dual approval from these two agencies."

Callele, Neufeld, and Schneider (2006, p. 44) mention cultural conditioning in localized products as an area important to take into consideration:

"Emotional requirements can require localization efforts. International audiences (and members of international teams) might interpret the same symbols and events differently. Test your scenarios on your target markets to ensure that they don't elicit inadvertent interpretations. Perhaps the most cited example is the color red, which in North America means danger, whereas in China, red means good fortune."

Also, local traditional stories, myths and legends that are common in one region but incomprehensible in another is an aspect that needs to be addressed. Tschang (2009, p. 38) gives one example of this:

One especially popular theme has been the Three Kingdoms period of Chinese history where states were at war. On the other hand, while Chinese culture may sell well in countries that neighbour China (e.g. Chinese online games being popular in Vietnam and Taiwan), this does not necessarily carry over to the global market."

5. CONCLUSIONS

Game localization from a development perspective has been identified as an area where more research is needed. It was identified already in the previous studies (Engström et al., 2018; Marklund et al., 2019) that the vast majority of articles relating to game development have taken little or no consideration of regional aspects in their research approaches and regional aspects that might affect game development are seldom discussed. The main conclusion from this literature review is building further upon that statement. Localization is rarely discussed in game development research, and if it is discussed it is briefly mentioned.

Even though the set of articles used in this paper can be questioned – localization or regional aspects was not an inclusion criteria in the original data collection phase – it is rather peculiar that the process of localization is only mentioned briefly. The set of papers this study is based on includes papers published until 2016, an obvious flaw in a fast moving field. A quick search in the databases used in the original literature review (i.e. Scopus, Springer, ACM, and DiGRA digital archive) using combinations of game, development and localization published between 2017-2020 in the search query, revealed only one article focusing on the specific topic of this paper; the aforementioned article on indie game localization by Toftedahl et al. (2018) also from the GHS project.

One aspect of the lack of research of localization with a production perspective is the difficulty of obtaining access to developers and development material. Bernal-Merino (2014) and O'Hagan and Mangiron (2013) have identified this, where confidentiality issues and non-disclosure agreements makes it difficult to get access to production settings. Even though research on localization is limited, there are research done highly relevant for the understanding of localization as a process in game development. Going beyond the localization terminology, aspects related to the process can be found. For example, the localization subcategories of cultural-, technical-, and linguistic issues can be found if looked for as the results from this paper shows. Thanks to the broad scope of the papers included in the dataset, these more specific areas could be found when scrutinized. One example is the paper by Chung and Fung (2013) where the commercialization of Chinese online gaming is the main topic, but both technical and cultural aspects of this are addressed. While not framed explicitly as a localization paper, it covers aspects very relevant for the understanding of how work within the Chinese market.

As a contrast to this literature study, where localization is scrutinized from a game development research perspective, a literature study by Mangiron (2017) has conducted a translation studies perspective of game localization. Mangiron presents a historical overview of the state of game localization research, identifying a number of common research topics and methods. Most research from this perspective are conducted as descriptive studies within translation, mainly with qualitative approaches. Mangiron (2017) also highlights the interdisciplinary nature of the topic, where research angles from translation studies, game studies, media studies and culture studies have been identified. Research on game localization have had a strong focus on cases involving console games, and virtually no attempts has been identified regarding the growing field of mobile games. A strong dominance of Japanese games has also been identified. From a development perspective Mangiron (2017) highlights a study by O'Hagan and Chandler (2016) where it is stated that:

"Game localization has been largely ignored in game studies and constitutes a relatively new area of research in translation studies".

Even though more research on game localization is needed, from several perspectives, the approaches made contains vital information for future research approaches. The approach taken by van de Weerd et al. (2007) where a number of game development process descriptions have been combined into a super process could easily be adapted to a game localization process description, taking information from both game development and translation studies. Further, to scrutinize general game development process descriptions from both academic and industry sources could be a way of identifying questions (and answers) regarding the complexities of game localization and its connection to current game development practices.

ACKNOWLEDGEMENT

This research is funded by the EU Interreg ÖKS project Game Hub Scandinavia 2.0.

REFERENCES

Alves, C., Ramalho, G., & Damasceno, A. (2007). *Challenges in requirements engineering for mobile games development: The meantime case study.* Paper presented at the 15th IEEE International Requirements Engineering Conference (RE 2007).

Bernal-Merino, M. Á. (2014). *Translation and localisation in video games: making entertainment software global*: Routledge.

Bernhaupt, R. (2015). User experience evaluation methods in the games development life cycle *Game user experience evaluation* (pp. 1-8): Springer.

Bethke, E. (2003). *Game development and production*: Wordware Publishing, Inc.

Binark, M., & Bayraktutan, G. (2012). A Critical Interpretation of a New "Creative Industry" in Turkey: Game Studios and the Production of a Value Chain *Computer games and new media cultures* (pp. 371-391): Springer.

Braun, V., & Clarke, V. (2006). Using thematic analysis in psychology. *Qualitative research in psychology, 3*(2), 77-101.

Callele, D., Neufeld, E., & Schneider, K. (2006). *Emotional requirements in video games.* Paper presented at the 14th IEEE International Requirements Engineering Conference (RE'06).

Chandler, H. M. (2009). *The game production handbook*: Jones & Bartlett Publishers.

Chung, P., & Fung, A. (2013). Internet development and the commercialization of online gaming in China *Gaming Globally* (pp. 233-250): Springer.

Deuze, M., Martin, C. B., & Allen, C. (2007). The professional identity of gameworkers. *Convergence, 13*(4), 335-353.

Engström, H., Marklund, B. B., Backlund, P., & Toftedahl, M. (2018). Game development from a software and creative product perspective: A quantitative literature review approach. Entertainment Computing, 27, 10-22.

Fry, D., & Lommel, A. (2003). *The localization industry primer.*

Hagen, U. (2004). Where do game design ideas come from? Innovation and recycling in games developed in Sweden. *World, 24*, 2007.

Hodgson, D., & Briand, L. (2013). Controlling the uncontrollable:'Agile'teams and illusions of autonomy in creative work. *Work, employment and society, 27*(2), 308-325.

Kasurinen, J., Laine, R., & Smolander, K. (2013). *How Applicable Is ISO/IEC 29110 in Game Software Development?*, Berlin, Heidelberg.

Kasurinen, J., Maglyas, A., & Smolander, K. (2014). *Is requirements engineering useless in game development?* Paper presented at the International Working Conference on Requirements Engineering: Foundation for Software Quality.

Kasurinen, J., & Smolander, K. (2014). *What do game developers test in their products?* Paper presented at the Proceedings of the 8th ACM/IEEE International Symposium on Empirical Software Engineering and Measurement.

Kasurinen, J., Strandén, J.-P., & Smolander, K. (2013). *What do game developers expect from development and design tools?* Paper presented at the Proceedings of the 17th International Conference on Evaluation and Assessment in Software Engineering.

Koutonen, J., & Leppänen, M. (2013). *How are agile methods and practices deployed in video game development? A survey into Finnish game studios.* Paper presented at the International Conference on Agile Software Development.

Kultima, A. (2010). *The organic nature of game ideation: game ideas arise from solitude and mature by bouncing.* Paper presented at the Proceedings of the International Academic Conference on the Future of Game Design and Technology.

Lê, P. L., Massé, D., & Paris, T. (2013). Technological Change at the Heart of the Creative Process: Insights From the Videogame Industry. *International journal of arts management, 15*(2).

Lee, S. H., Lee, G. H., Cho, H. H., Song, D. H., & Rhew, S. Y. (2006). *An empirical model of the game software development processes.* Paper presented at the Fourth International Conference on Software Engineering Research, Management and Applications (SERA'06).

Legault, M.-J., & Ouellet, K. (2012). So Into It They Forget What Time It Is?: Video Game Designers and Unpaid Overtime *Managing dynamic technology-oriented businesses: High-tech organizations and workplaces* (pp. 82-102): IGI Global.

Mangiron, C. (2017). Research in game localisation. *The Journal of Internationalization and Localization, 4*(2), 74-99.

Marklund, B. B., Engström, H., Hellkvist, M., & Backlund, P. (2019). What Empirically Based Research Tells Us About Game Development. The Computer Games Journal, 8(3-4), 179-198.

Murphy-Hill, E., Zimmermann, T., & Nagappan, N. (2014). *Cowboys, ankle sprains, and keepers of quality: How is video game development different from software development?* Paper presented at the Proceedings of the 36th International Conference on Software Engineering.

Musial, M., Kauppinen, A., & Puhakka, V. (2016). Recognised Creativity: The Influence of Process, Social Needs, and the Third Drive on Creative Individuals' Work through Social Media *Social media and networking: Concepts, methodologies, tools, and applications* (pp. 1249-1280): IGI Global.

Myllärniemi, V., Raatikainen, M., & Männistö, T. (2006). *Inter-organisational approach in rapid software product family development—a case study.* Paper presented at the International Conference on Software Reuse.

Nelson, W. A., & Palumbo, D. B. (2014). When design meets Hollywood: Instructional design in a production studio environment *Design in Educational Technology* (pp. 75-88): Springer.

O'Hagan, M., & Mangiron, C. (2013). *Game Localization: Translating for the global digital entertainment industry* (Vol. 106): John Benjamins Publishing.

O'Hagan, M., & Chandler, H. (2016). Game localization research and translation studies. *Border crossings: Translation studies and other disciplines, 126*, 309.

Rabin, S. (2005). *Introduction to game development*: Charles River Media Boston.

Stacey, P., & Nandhakumar, J. (2008). Opening up to agile games development. *Communications of the ACM, 51*(12), 143-146.

Toftedahl, M., Backlund, P., & Engström, H. (2018). *Localization from an Indie Game Production Perspective: Why, When and How?* Paper presented at the DiGRA '18 - Proceedings of the 2018 DiGRA International Conference: The Game is the Message, Torino, Italy.

Toftedahl, M., & Engström, H. (2019). *A Taxonomy of Game Engines and the Tools that Drive the Industry.* Paper presented at the DIGRA INTERNATIONAL CONFERENCE 2019: GAME, PLAY AND THE EMERGING LUDO-MIX.

Tschang, F. T. (2009). Creative industries across cultural borders: The case of video games in Asia *Creative economies, creative cities* (pp. 25-42): Springer.

Tschang, F. T., & Szczypula, J. (2006). Idea creation, constructivism and evolution as key characteristics in the videogame artifact design process. *European management journal, 24*(4), 270-287.

van de Weerd, I., de Weerd, S., & Brinkkemper, S. (2007). *Developing a reference method for game production by method comparison.* Paper presented at the Working Conference on Method Engineering.

Vanhala, E., & Kasurinen, J. (2014). *The role of business model and its elements in computer game start-ups.* Paper presented at the International Conference of Software Business.

Wimmer, J., & Sitnikova, T. (2012). The professional identity of gameworkers revisited. A qualitative inquiry on the case study of German professionals. *Eludamos. Journal for Computer Game Culture, 6*(1), 153-169.

Zoeller, G. (2013). Game development telemetry in production *Game analytics* (pp. 111-135): Springer.

DEVELOPING A DIGITAL GAME WITH HIGH-ABILITY/GIFTED STUDENTS IN A LOW-INCOME PUBLIC SCHOOL: A BRAZILIAN EXPERIENCE

Paula Mastroberti
Federal University of Rio Grande do Sul, Brazil

ABSTRACT

This paper is about a digital game educational project developed with a group of high-ability/gifted students of the Room-Pole for Inclusion and Resources – High-ability and Giftedness (RPIR-HA/G). This Pole is located in a low-income district in Porto Alegre, Brazil. The project was one of the actions performed by the Extension Program *Ludopoetics,* which is, in turn, under the *Sequential Graphic Arts on Media Culture for Children and Young*: Education, Production, and Reading Research. I coordinate both as a teacher at the Visual Arts Department of Federal University of Rio Grande do Sul. The project was developed in 2019 and counted with a team composed of three undergraduate students. The Coordinator of the Pole, Aline Russo, has also supported this project; The Room-Pole IR-HA/G shelters about 25 students, most of them teenagers from 11 to 17 years old, coming from eighteen municipal public schools of the district. The project team planned and ministered a series of workshops about game creation from the basics: conception and design, art, animation, and computer programming. We applied a ludic methodology in order to engage the participants, and only open-source apps were used during the activities. Finally, the group of high-ability/gifted (HA/G) students were divided into two teams and developed two game projects. Our main objectives were to approach games as a serious subject of education and art education; to develop methodologies in art education using games as a strategy and as a result at the same time; and finally, to teach the high-ability/gifted students what is a game, how to do it and what are the required skills to make it. To support our proposals, we took Johann Huizinga, Ian Bogost, Scott Rogers, among other authors.

KEYWORDS

Game and Art Education, Game Creation, Game and Poetics, High-Ability and Gifted Students' Education

1. LEVEL ONE: CONTEXTS

I start this paper mentioning a Research Project, which I coordinate, titled *Sequential Graphic Arts on Media Culture for Children and Young*: Education, Production, and Reading. It began in 2017, and its ending date is scheduled to 2021. As the title says, the main objective is to investigate how children and young students from different schools (private and public, high and low income) learn visual aesthetics values through media culture. From that, we investigate what we can do, as trainers of Visual Art undergraduate students and future teachers, to approach their culture and to promote a more critical thinking and an aesthetic consciousness about it. In 2019, we decided to take games (digital, board, card, or mixed) as the central cultural phenomenon of investigation. Our surveys indicated that games, especially digital ones, are the most popular entertainment among the researched children and teenagers: about 80% of them would rather play with smartphones or consoles than read comics or books. As entertainment, playing games usually comes first even if compared to watching animation movies or live-action series, especially for boys. The social-economic factor does not seem to interfere with their preferences: the responses were quite similar. To low-income ones, a smartphone is an essential tool for everything: working, studying, communicating and having fun. The only difference between low-income and high-income groups was that the latter had better gadgets and better Internet access; high-income students also had to balance their leisure time with other activities in obedience to their parents. Kids of all social-economic levels mention their toy tablets.

The surveys were applied on two public and two private schools at Porto Alegre. We used a qualitative methodology. The research was made in order to verify media culture habits and preferences of those students in which the sponsored undergraduate students were going to apply their work plans, in order to link visual arts teaching and media culture. To support our actions, we studied names such as Fernando Hernandez (2000) and Richard Shusterman (1998). I also created the Extension Program *Ludopoetics* to enlarge our possibilities of acting inside de game's field, and to deepen the studies about games, especially digital ones. I called it "ludopoetics" because my primary interest was to link playfulness to poetics. In other words, alongside with other philosophers' authors such as Huizinga (2010), I understand the game as an art and as a possibility to enlarge human aesthetics and ethical experience through the game's fictional interactive environments.

I worked with three undergraduate students and, on 2019, we were invited by Aline Russo, coordinator of the Room-Pole to Inclusion and Resources – High-Ability and Giftedness (RPIR – HA/G), to act with a group of high-ability[1]. We organized and offered them a workshop plan composed of seven parts on how to develop a digital game, which was enthusiastically approved. The project was ministered to 11 high-ability/gifted students whose ages varied between 13 and 16 years-old, boys and girls, all of them belonging to unstructured low-income families, with problems of self-esteem, depression, and others.

What follows next is a description of the operations in the Room-Pole IR – HA/G. Section 2 is based on the reports of the undergratuated students, Aline Russo, and Aline Letícia Machado's undergraduate thesis. I am very grateful for the commitment of this team and the Coordinator of the Room-Pole, who welcomed us. This paper would not be possible without their accurate descriptions and the pictures and videos they carefully took. I would also like to extend my gratitude to all HA/G boys and girls that engaged so enthusiastically in our proposals. After reporting this experience, I will make some final considerations.

2. LEVEL TWO: THE WORKSHOPS

2.1 The Plan

The team of monitors was composed of three undergraduate students: Emmanuel Rambo dos Santos, Iris Matiele Ozuna, and Aline Letícia Machado. Their planning involved seven steps (or stages), applied as if they were levels of a game structure. The participants could not pass to the next level without accomplishing the previous one. The steps were as follows:

Step 1 – Presentation of the project and the undergraduate's team; presentation of the HA/G students; interviews;

Step 2 – Introduction workshop: what is a game, how to make a game, relationship between game and art; organization of development teams;

Step 3 – Workshop about how to plan a game: argument and game design;

Step 4 – Digital art and graphic design workshop: characters concepts, scenarios, and animation using the open-sources apps Krita and Autodesk Sketchbook;

Step 5 – Programming workshop using the open-source game creator GDevelop;

Step 6 – Excursion to University of Vale do Rio dos Sinos (UNISINOS), to visit the Digital Game Course and to meet the team of the Atomic Rocket Entertainment Project supervised by Rossana Baptista Queiroz;

Step 7 – Completion of the projects and collective evaluation.

We planned weekly workshops, always on Thursday, from 9h to 12h AM, as they should occur on the inverse turn of their school classes, inside the Room-Pole. We did not force all the HA/G students to engage and 11 participants enrolled, being three girls and eight boys. Their ages ranged from 11 to 16 years old. Many other students wanted to participate, but they could not, because their schedules did not match to the workshops'. We based the methodology plan on Scott Rogers's roles and production categories (Rogers, 2014).

[1]A person is considered with high-ability or giftedness when he or she presents a high-level skill. Sometimes the HA/G person gets very involved with a task, seeking to deepen his or her abilities and gifts. He or she can also be very creative, using his or her knowledge to innovate in his or her area of interest (Renzulli & Reis, 2004). The RPIR – HA/G is a city hall organ and operates from inside a municipal school. It serves eighteen municipal schools in Porto Alegre, all of them located in low-income districts. Aline Russo coordinates this Room-Pole since 2014.

2.2 Acting

2.2.1 Interviewing

Before starting the workshops, the team held a meeting to introduce themselves and to explain the project to the group of high-ability students. They also interviewed them in order to know their opinions and preferences about games. We used Google Form to register their answers. Under the question "What are you used to hear about digital games from your parents?", they answered that their parents used to say that games might provoke addiction, or they were just a silly hobby, not useful at all. Under the question "Do you think digital games can cause you any harm?" many of them were in doubt, and about one third answered "yes" mentioning "addiction" as the first harm, and then "vision problems" or "tendonitis." Nevertheless, at the same time, they also pointed out that games are an entertaining way to learn other languages or to develop reasoning. It is important to notice that not even one of them quoted games as a possibility to experience fiction narratives or to interact with different environments, even virtual (they may hardly have access to augmented reality). A game as Pokémon Go, for example, demands powerful devices, and a broad internet band. The next question was: "Do you think games can be a work of art?" The answers were very diverse. They highlighted the visual graphics as a fundamental characteristic to influence expression and emotional feelings. The visual aspects of a game are also valued as a condition to recognize a game as a good one. According to them, the visual arts movements and animation are essential to guarantee a more emotional immersion. Most of them prefer Role Playing Games (RPG), but they declare to appreciate shooting, strategies, or construction games too. Against our expectations, the HA/G youngsters did not mention any puzzles or logic games. They quoted League of Legends, Paladins, Grand Theft Auto (GTA), Minecraft, Roblox, The Sims, Fortnite among their favorites. Cell phones and computers tied as the most used devices. The console came in second place.

It is imperative to mention that the absolute majority had never thought of creating a game of their own. So, one of the reasons they agreed to engage in our project could be that they were very curious about what was going to happen.

2.2.2 What is a Game? How to Create it?

In the first workshop, the monitors presented the steps of making a game, emphasizing its more essential aspects. The students should pay attention to rule planning, concept arts, game design, character animation, soundtrack, and programming. Then, they asked the participants to divide in two groups, choosing what kind of function each one would like to perform the most, according to Rogers' categories: artist or animator, level or game designer, programmer, sound maker, tester, or leader-writer. The monitors worked on making them bring up their primary skills and subjects of interest; then, they helped the students fit them in Roger's categories as best as possible or according to their preferences. The girls' abilities leaned toward arts (drawing and painting) and one of them proved to be a perfect leader. The boys were more inclined to creative writing (poetry, stories), programming, animation, leadership, and digital design. The girls preferred to stay together. As they were eleven in total, two of the boys took the initiative and went to the girls' team. This way, there were three girls and two boys on one team, and six boys on the other. From now on, I will name the girls-and-boys team, Team A, and the o-boys team, Team B. The next propositions included a quick layout to what kind of game both groups would like to create and sketches of a protagonist character.

2.2.3 Practice 1: Plot, Rules, and Game Design

In the second workshop, the monitors were happy when they realized that both teams brought many ideas to work on their games. The students seemed very excited and looked forward to the beginning. So, the undergraduates just supervised the tasks and roles that each team member was going to perform. They also helped them organizing the main game concepts. In this workshop, the teams took the time to define main game characteristics: the story, the basic rules, and the general visual concepts. They also developed and presented a game's map, drawing it on the blackboard.

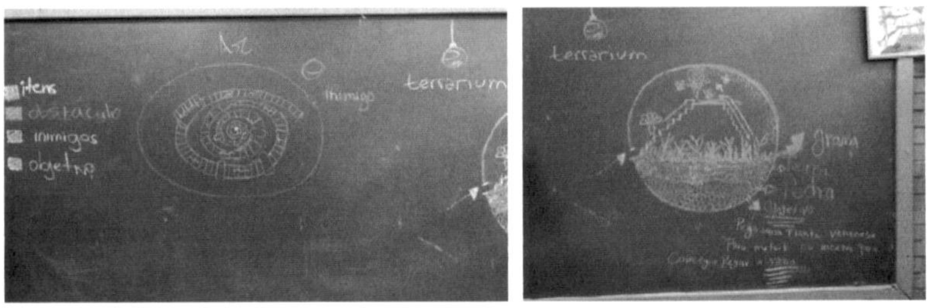

(a) (b)

Figure 1 (a, b). The game map of Team A. Program's archive

Figure 2. A game map of Team B. Program's archive

2.2.4 Practice 2: Games' Development (Script, Characters' Design, and Level Design)

In this stage, the Team A stood out. They seemed better organized, and they executed the tasks more efficiently. Consequently, the monitors gave more support to Team B and just observed the other one. In his report, Emmanuel wrote that both sides are very talented and had excellent ideas for their projects. Team B, in particular, looked very nervous and took a little more time to start it, maybe because they were very self-critical. Nevertheless, Iris Ozuna reported us problems: some of the boys had have difficulties to be present at the workshops, due to family problems or adverse economic situation (for example, one of them at times had not even had a coat to wear). Communication by cellphone was also trickier.

The Team A plot was about an astronaut who needed to save the Earth searching for resources in his peregrination through the universe while many alien enemies challenged him. The Team B plot was about a ghost (a guy who died in an accident) who should overcome his fears, level by level until he reached the eternal peace. Their choices reinforced the qualities we desired to emulate in our workshop project: a poetic charge reflected on consistent playful stories, building with aesthetical and ethical values.

2.2.5 Practice 3: Games' Development (Art Design and Edition, Sound Design)

For this workshop, we got some tablets from the LIFE (Interdisciplinary Laboratory to Educational Training), a Program of our university for educational needs. The artists on each team learned how to work on free apps like Autodesk Sketchbook to draw and paint characters, elements, and sceneries, and the Krita app to animate them. However, due to technical reasons and the few numbers of devices, Iris Ozuna used analogic techniques to make them understand how animation frames work, such as drawing over tracing paper or paper cutouts to produce stop motion. To those of them who were not interested in developing artistic abilities, the monitors taught how to create sound effects by using cellphones in order to register musical instruments and school noises around. I must point out that all participants, after finishing their specific tasks, used to help those who did not finish theirs yet. This pro-activity generated an atmosphere of unprecedented cooperation among them, as they had never produced anything together, even though they had met before in other meetings in the Room-Pole.

Figure 3. The HA/G students work on collages. This exercise aimed to deconstruct the characters' bodies in order to stimulate non-conventional forms. Aline Letícia Machado, in white cloth, supervises a student on the right. Aline Russo, using glasses, appears in front of her. Program's archive

Figure 4. The students practiced analogic and digital technics to develop arts and animation. Below, while a student draws over vegetal papers, his fellow is animating using a tablet. They digitalized all analogic rafts later. Program's archive

Figure 5. A girl draws a scenario element using a tablet. Unfortunately, many of the artwork could not be used in the final prototype, because they did not have enough time to finish the animation in order to use them. Program's archive

Figure 6. Iris Ozuna is teaching a boy how to animate using Krita's tools. Program's archive

Figure 7. A student with musical skills is trying to create sound effects playing his guitar. Program's archive

2.2.6 Practice 4: Game's Development (Programming)

The monitors introduced an open-source cross-platform app called G-Develop. They installed it on Aline Russo's notebook, and the students could learn some basic notions. None of the monitors were experts in programming, so we called a teacher from the Digital Games Course of the University of Vale do Rio dos Sinos, João Ricardo de Bittencourt Menezes, to train them first. We chose G-Develop not just because it is an open-source and free platform, but because it is easy to manipulate, and people of all ages can learn how to operate it. A thirteen-year-old boy was delighted. He had never tried programming before, but he got so fond of it that he exclaimed to have finally discovered what he wanted to do for a living.

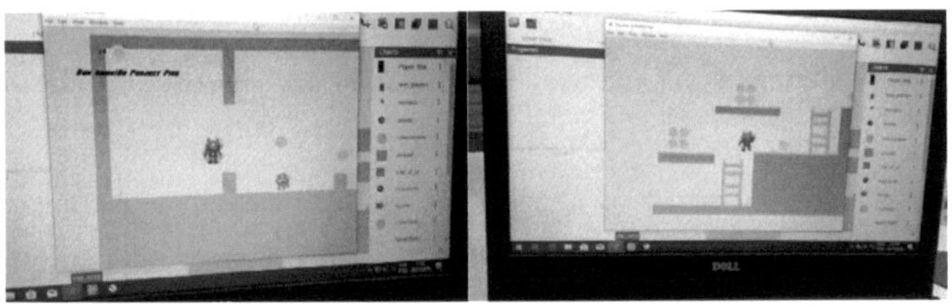

(a) (b)

Figure 8 (a, b). Video frames of the game's build programmed by the thirteen-year-old boy. Program's archive

2.2.7 Final Meeting: Presentation and Collective Evaluation of the Teams' Projects

Both sides had to present their game projects. They should explain what the game goals were, and what would be necessary to conclude them. Team A finished their prototype with a complete phase, but they have to put aside the girl's arts and substitute them by templates. Team B did not finish theirs, partly because their design was more complicated, partly because of the problems already mentioned in Section 2.2.4. After it, monitors, students, and the coordinator discussed and reflected on the experience. They commented on their main difficulties and the positive learning they had. The students claimed for more workshops to conclude their games. The monitors complimented both teams' goals and their collectiveness spirit, they also highlighted that the most crucial workshops were to introduce the required steps to develop a game, to stimulate some skills and the collaborative spirit necessary to do that.

Figure 9. The Team A's presentation. We can see Aline Leticia and Emmanuel at the center, behind the participants. Program's archive

2.3 Planned and Non-Planned Activities: Outspreads

We intended to do the excursion to UNISINOS before the final meeting, but the group only visited the University almost a week later. Aline Russo, the Room-Pole Coordinator, went along with them. This visiting was essential for many reasons: first, they did not know that a degree course to train professional game developers existed; second, they had never been to any university campus before. We chose this university because ours does not have a similar degree course. Besides, UNISINOS is a partner in *Ludopoetic* Program. They visited the Atomic Rocket Entertainment Project Laboratory, and they talked to the undergraduate students and their coordinator, Rossana Baptista Queiroz. The students could test some games that were being developed by the Atomic team.

(a) (b)

Figure 10 (a, b). The visit to Atomic Rocket Entertainment Project. Program archive

After that, the monitors and Aline prepared a farewell party for everybody. Emmanuel, Iris, and Aline Leticia commented later on how they loved the experience and how they still miss the students very much. The participants proposed to continue the meetings to finish their games, once they did not have enough time, and so Emmanuel and Iris continued to go there for a while to assist their work. Both presented the results of this project twice in 2019: first, at the Extension Hall of our university, and another to the Visual Arts Education Degree Course freshman. At that time, Aline Leticia was busy producing her undergraduate thesis, which is about this project (Machado, 2019), and could not go back to Room-Pole anymore. She graduated in 2019. Aline Russo related that the students got so involved with this project that they took every time they could to continue working on their games, even after the project's closure. By messenger, she particularly mentioned that thirteen-year-old boy who decided to be a programmer, she said he went beyond what he was taught, reaching the third level in high-ability/giftedness, according to Joseph S. Renzulli and Sally M. Reis (2004). He got completely obsessed with deepening his skills and started to create a new game totally by himself.

Figure 11. Image of the boy's new game sent later through Whatsapp by Aline Russo. Program archive

In her report, she also praised the monitors' performance. In essence, they knew how to teach without taking away the autonomy of the participants, and they were supporting, purposeful, and active as teachers, keeping the students engaged. But, what about the HA/G students? What they had to say about the experience? We collected some testimonials by Whatsapp, which I translated from Portuguese:

> "I think it was an outstanding experience and I hope it happens again. I found the learning to be very good, but [...] the experience could be more dynamic, because I was a little bored" (a 11-year-old boy);

> "I learned about game development, and to make them in groups showed us the importance of an internal organization, this was the major difficulty we faced during the project execution" (a 14-year-old boy);
>
> "I [...] liked the teachers (Iris and Emmanuel) because they were funny, but when it was needed [...] they called out our attention. I didn't like that it was too short, it was so cool [...] I didn't miss anything, they taught us all we need to know. I liked practically everything, theory and practice classes, I liked the excursion, and I think nothing should be different." (another 11-year-old boy).

We understood the first 11-year-old boy comment as a warning to be more careful about our dynamics and actions, trying to give attention to each participant's rhythm and maturity.

Having reported on the workshop, I now turn to my own considerations.

3. FINAL LEVEL: WINNERS

The first lesson we can take from this report is that it is not easy to create a game. I am not just talking about financial resources, cutting-edge technologies, or high skills. I am talking about ethical qualities such as perseverance, patience, mutual respect and collaboration. To be a game developer requires the same competences as to be a game player: when one plays, it supposes one has agreed with the rules. The players must have mutual understanding, and the interaction with a fictional play's ambiance implies accepting whatever happens inside, or they will not emulate playfulness. Above all, playfulness must bring joy and pleasure feelings to every player, even when he or she loses. The playfulness sensation is what matters, Ian Bogost (2010) called it *engagement.* He says the engagement qualities of a game depend on the sophisticated rhetoric of its system, like visual and sound effects, level design, and others. However, I prefer to enlarge this conception, including the player forms of interaction (actions, choices, interpretations) and the emotions involved when he or she emulates a game ambiance.

As I considered in a highlighted paper published in 2019, in the Brazilian Game Society Symposium at Rio de Janeiro (Mastroberti, 2019), we need to amplify game's studies towards a more humanistic view, joining human themes to technological training. It implies to understand what the *ludopoetics* concept means: a ludic experience emulating a poetical ambiance, understanding *poetics* as a combination of aesthetic and ethical values, as according to Aristoteles (2016). We can apply *ludopoetics* ideas to all knowledge fields and professions. In order to be better artists or educators, we need to perform playfully. We need to potentialize our classes and schools, our studios, and poetic works to a ludic, defiant, and engaged experience, capable of raising our curiosity, our desire of knowledge. Likewise, if we want to make a game, we have to approach it as any creative and challenging humanistic work.

The HA/G students proved to be very enthusiastic about the idea of a game's creation. They did learn basic notions about it, such as how to make digital art, how to structure a level game design, how to animate, how to program, all of that using open-source technology. On the other side, the instructors also challenged them to develop qualities as cooperation, mutual agreement, patience, and resignation when it was necessary to abandon a path or to remake things that did not work out. Those were fundamental skills to develop, mainly because people frequently highlight their giftedness at the expense of their emotions. We cannot forget they are in a social-economic disadvantaged condition as well. They have to deal with the most adverse situations, and we need to strengthen them to overcome what may. So, during the process of making their games, the participants had to give up many things: some artworks ended up not being used, some more complex ideas were left out. Moreover, they got disappointed when they realized they would not complete their games on time. However, as the monitors and the Coordinator of the Room-Pole perceived and let them know, they achieved crucial goals, some of them not being planned.

The monitors and the students transformed the Room-Pole in a playful place to be. The high-ability students had never developed a project together and had to look after each other in order to learn problem resolution, deepening their relationships. The undergraduate monitors' age was an advantage and a problem at the same time. Due to the age factor they established an excellent communication with the school students, they had similar cultural preferences, and they built a friendly atmosphere. However, at times, the Coordinator had to interfere when they lost control. That happened not only because the monitors were young, but also because the experience of teaching was new for them. Their age and lack of experience defied them to balance camaraderie and educational attitude without losing spontaneous affectiveness. Finally, during the period they were together, they created and played a real game indeed, even without notice: an educational and poetic one. I am sure it was an unforgettable and playful experience for all sides, monitors, and students.

When the project ended, Aline Russo asked for more projects like this one. At this moment, I have a new sponsored student working at the Room-Pole developing an animation movie project. Another digital game project may happen there soon, as part of an interdisciplinary project of our university, under the coordination of the Physical Institute. So, the game is not over.

REFERENCES

Aristoteles, 2016. *Poetica.* 34, São Paulo, BR.

Bogost, I., 2010. *Persuasive games: the expressive power of videogames.* MIT Press, Massachusetts, USA.

Hernandez, F., 2000. *Cultura visual, mudança educativa e projeto de trabalho.* Penso, Porto Alegre, BR.

Huizinga, J., 2010. *Homo ludens.* Perspectiva, São Paulo, BR.

Machado, A. L., 2019. *A arte e a educação em jogo: colaboratividade na produção de um jogo digital*. Undergraduate thesis. Lume Digital Repository, UFRGS, BR. Link access: https://lume.ufrgs.br/handle/10183/206259

Mastroberti, P., 2019, Ludopoéticas: Relações possíveis entre jogo, arte e educação a partir de ações de pesquisa. *Proceedings of SB Games – Education Track*. Rio de Janeiro, Brazil, no page numbers. Link access: https://www.sbgames.org/sbgames2019/files/papers/EducacaoFull/195670.pdf.

Renzulli, J. S. and Reis, S. M., 2004. *Identification of students for gifted and talented programs.* Corwin, Thousand Oaks, CA.

Rogers S., 2014. *Level up: the guide to great video game design.* Wiley, Hoboken, USA.

Shusterman, R., 1998. *Vivendo a arte: o pensamento pragmatista e a estética popular.* 34, São Paulo, BR.

ANALYSIS OF ANXIETY AND IMMERSIVE PROCESS IN DIGITAL GAMES USING HTC VIVE

Gabriel Batista Caldeira and Rosilane Ribeiro da Mota
Hochschule Furtwangen University, Germany
Pontifícia Universidade Católica de Minas Gerais, Brazil

ABSTRACT

This work aimed to evaluate the anxiety level and the level of immersion of a player when using the virtual reality HTC Vive to interact with a digital game. With this objective in mind, a digital game was developed that is of runner genre. Assessing the level of anxiety was carried out using the SUDS and IDATE questionnaires. The immersion evaluation process was conducted through the IPQ questionnaire. Two contexts are proposed to assess user anxiety and the immersive process. In the first, the player interacted with the game using the keyboard/mouse, answering the questionnaires at the end. In the second context, the same player interacted with the game through HTC Vive, also answering questionnaires. It was observed that the level of anxiety of the participants did not increase significantly and that the level of immersion had a significant increase, demonstrating that it is justified to use the HTC Vive to obtain a better immersive process. This was also the first study to indicate that games can have a positive influence in times of great anxiety and stress, such as exams for university students.

KEYWORDS

Virtual Reality, HTC Vive, Immersive Process, Anxiety

1. INTRODUCTION

Interaction with digital games is a practice that is increasing in popularity, in the Entertainment Software Association (2015) it is reported that 72% of the general population and 97% of adolescents, interact with digital games regularly (McMahan, Parberry, Parsons 2015). For this reason, it is necessary to carry out the analysis of the productive process of games and it is also important to study the benefits that digital games can bring, as Granic, Lobel e Engels (2014) mention in their work studies on the cognitive aspect in this area are very scarce and so there is a need for deeper analyzes on these processes.

In the study carried out by Granic, Lobel e Engels (2014), it is stated that it is in the theory of uses of gratuities which lies one of the main reasons why individuals use media: manage the state of their mood and emotional state. With that, it is possible to affirm that digital games are among the most effective and efficient way to generate positive feelings in children and young people. Some studies claim that there is a relationship between interacting with digital games and improving or increasing the flow of positive emotion (Russoniello, O'Brien and Parks 2009)(Ryan, Rigby and Prybylski 2006). Studies suggest that puzzle games, short-term commitments games and games that have a high degree of accessibility (e.g. Angry Birds, Bejewled II) - can improve the mood of the players, promoting relaxation and decreasing anxiety (Russoniello, O'Brien and Parks 2009).

Anxiety consists of an unpleasant emotion that can be divided into state and trace (Spielberger, Gorsuch, Lushene 1970). Anxiety-state is different in intensity according to time, that is, it refers to acute situations that correspond to momentary episodes. Trait anxiety refers to the differences that each individual presents for behavioral responses (Spielberger, Gorsuch, Lushene 1970). This makes it possible to assess the state of anxiety in a person in different situations, such as for example after a person interacted with a digital game.

In the study by Alsina-Jurnet and Gutiérrez-Maldonado (2010), it can be seen one of the main characteristics in the treatment of psychological disorders through the use of virtual reality is the sensation of presence or feeling of being present. One of the most important aspects of the illusion is that the virtual environment evokes approximately the reactions and emotions as an experience in the physical world. This means that the sense of presence is essential and can be used as a metric to assess the player immersion. We are using the term immersive process as the sense of presence in this paper.

With the topics presented previously, the general objective of this work was the evaluation of a player's anxiety and immersive process when he/she is using a virtual reality device. For this purpose, a game was developed that was used for the evaluation of anxiety and immersion when a player was using virtual reality glasses, HTC Vive.

2. RELATED WORKS

In Alsina-Jurnet and Gutiérrez-Maldonado (2010) a study was carried out in which five user characteristics were evaluated: anxiety, spatial intelligence, verbal intelligence, personality and experience with computers, all of which could influence the feeling of being present. This was the first study that researched the relationship between spatial intelligence with the feeling of being present in a virtual environment. In this work, it was identified that the greater the user's anxiety the greater it was his feeling of being present.

In the work of Perandré and Haydu (2018), an analytical-behavioral therapeutic intervention was performed for participants with social anxiety disorder. For this, virtual reality was used as a therapeutic resource. This job concluded that intervention with virtual reality caused a therapeutic effect and better confrontation in the face of social interactions.

In the work of Granic, Lobel and Engels (2014), a research was made on the effects of positive aspects of interacting with digital games, focusing on four main domains: cognitive, motivational, emotional and social. Considering these potential benefits is important, in part, because the nature of these games has changed drastically over the past decade, becoming increasingly complex, diverse, realistic and social in nature. The goal of this work was to provide sufficiently strong evidence and theoretical reasoning to inspire new education programs and research on mental health benefits, little explored in digital games.

In Alsina-Jurnet and Gutiérrez-Maldonado (2010), we could see a research aiming to understand personal characteristics and the feeling of being present in a virtual environment. The study of Perandré and Haydu, (2018) that uses virtual reality as a therapeutic resource . The research of Granic, Lobel and Engels, (2014), shows how games are dramatically changing. But in none of these researches it is studied how virtual reality interferes with the immersion and anxiety of a player. That is why the study proposed by this paper is important.

3. METHODOLOGY

In this section, the development of the digital game will be addressed, the questionnaires used to assess anxiety and immersion, carrying out the related experiments.

3.1 Hardware

For processing the digital game with suitability for virtual reality a notebook was used with the brand Asus and ROG Strix GL702ZC model. This notebook has the Windows 10 operating system, 64bit, 8GB RAM, 1TB Hard Disk, AMD Ryzen 5 1600, 3.2 GHz processor 6 core, 12 threads and an AMD Radeon graphics card RX 580, (Laptop) 4096MG GDDR5 1077Mhz core clock. In the experiments, the user used the notebook and played using keyboard and mouse, viewing the game directly on the notebook screen. As for playing in virtual reality, the players used HTC Vive connected directly to the notebook.

3.2 Questionnaires

Two questionnaires were used to carry out the evaluation of anxiety, the SUDS (subjective units of discomfort scale), which provides a subjective anxiety scale and the STAI (strait-trait anxiety inventory), which provides trait and state of anxiety. The immersive process was evaluated through the IPQ questionnaire (Igroup presence questionnaire).

The IPQ questionnaire (Igroup presence questionnaire) is a self-report type of questionnaire, it was initially created by Schubert, Friedmann and Regenbrecht (2001). In its first version, as well as in the Portuguese version used in this work, it was intended to measure the following variables: spatial presence, involvement, experienced realism and global presence. To measure these variables, there are 14 questions proposed in a five-point Likert scale format, using different anchors. In this work, the Portuguese version of the questionnaire IPQ was used. This version was translated and validated by Vasconcelos-Raposo et al, (2016).

The spatial presence variable refers to the feeling of being physically inserted in the virtual environment, since the involvement refers to the attention that the person gives to the virtual environment and the involvement experienced by it. Another aspect is the experienced realism it represents the subjective experience of realism in the environment virtually. The global presence variable is the feeling of being present in the virtual environment (Vasconcelos-Raposo et al, 2016).

In the SUDS questionnaire (Subjective Units of Discomfort scale), participants indicate the level of their perceived anxiety on a scale ranging from 0 (not at all anxious) to 10 (very anxious) (Wolpe, 1969). With this questionnaire it is possible to obtain the subjective level of anxiety of an individual, and this test was used in conjunction with the STAI test to assess the anxiety of the players. To assess the anxiety obtained by this questionnaire, a comparison was made of the values obtained after the interaction with keyboard/mouse with those obtained after interacting with HTC Vive.

The STAI questionnaire (Strait-trait Anxiety Inventory) is of the self-report type, evaluating the state and a person's anxiety trait. For this work, only the anxiety state scale was used due to established objectives. The questionnaire consists of 20 items that are scored in an interval of 1 (not significant) to 4 (very significant). The Portuguese version of the Strait-trait anxiety inventory (STAI) was used, called Inventário de ansiedade traço-estado (IDATE)(Spielberger, Gorsuch and Lushene, 1970),(Biaggio, 1990).

Each question has a corresponding score according to the answer of the player. However, for questions with a positive type, the score is reversed (for example, if the patient responded 4 for these questions, an inverted score is given, a value is assigned 1 in coding) (Biaggio, 1990). The assessment is made by adding all the scores found in the questionnaire, respecting the rule for positive and negative issues. This value, therefore, varies between 20 to 80 and the higher the value, the greater will be considered the person's anxiety.

3.3 Game Development

In order to explore the level of anxiety of a player, a controlled environment was needed. A digital game was created with this goal in mind. For game development the Unreal Engine 4 (UE4) and the Blueprint programming language were used. Among the reference games, at the time of the experiments, there was none that met the requirements among them that presented the same gameplay for PC and VR. Thus it was decided to develop a simpler game, placing the gameplay on both platforms as constant to assess the difference in anxiety and immersion in the two platforms.

It was decided to use the Unreal Engine for the development of the game, because it generates final results with more professional quality (Dickson, Block and Echevarria, 2017).

A digital game of the runner genre was developed, consisting of a race where the player controls a character and must dodge various obstacles. To control the character by dodging obstacles and to move around in the virtual world, the player uses the following commands: forward, back, right, left and jump. If the player is hit by an obstacle, the map is restarted and the player must restart the course.

For a better experience of the player this game has three levels of difficulty. These difficulties were designed so that both experienced players and inexperienced ones could be challenged. Through the initial menu the player can choose the desired difficulty, and this difficulty can also be changed during the game via a menu break.

The game has 4 stages, each of which has obstacles with different elements. In the first stage, the obstacles are composed of spheres and rivers of lava, representing the element of fire. In the second stage, obstacles are composed of spheres and rivers of water. In the third stage, there are two types of obstacles, spheres of smoke and blue rays, and at this stage the player also walks over white smoke, and each of those elements represents air. In the last stage, the obstacles are blocks of stone that represent the element from the earth. These elements were designed to characterize a better narrative related to the game scenario.

When the user finishes the game, a victory screen appears for the player, in which the player could choose between restarting the game or quitting.

Figures 1 and 2 show the first and last stage of the digital game developed. In the left part of these figures it is possible to see the initial phase of the game in which the player has to avoid some lava objects and on the right you can see the final part where the participant has to dodge some earth cubes.

Figure 1. The first stage of the game on the left and last stage on the right. Source: Designed by the author

Figure 2. The first stage of the game on the left and last stage on the right. Source: Designed by the author

The corridor to the left of Figure 1 provides access to the corridor in the left part of Figure 2, this part being considered the first part of the game. That part has 4 obstacles: the first deals with an immobile sphere with a part of lava down; the second obstacle is a sphere that keeps moving along the corridor and it also has a part of lava under it; the third is 4 spheres that rotate in counterclockwise direction, and the fourth is a tree trunk that needs to be crossed.

It is possible to see the second stage of the game in Figure 3, and the third stage was indicated in Figure 4. For the composition of the scenario, there is a village in the second stage and some trees and, as obstacles, there are spheres of water and the player must avoid falling into the river. In the third stage, the player walks through a region with white smoke and must dodge from rays and blue spheres.

3.4 Design of Experiments

Based on the work done by Alsina-Jurnet and Gutiérrez-Maldonado (2010), a study was proposed that assessed a player's anxiety when interacting with a digital game using HTC Vive.

An experiment was carried out with thirty university students. The students belonged to a private institution, 24 of them male and 6 female. It was defined that the participants would meet the same criteria, namely: they would not be under the effect of any form of controlled medication; they did not have any psychological disorder; they were not receiving any form of psychological therapy; did not have any kind of medical problems, like heart disease or epilepsy; they had Portuguese as their native language.

These criteria are important because if any of the players suffer from any psychological disorder or if they are receiving any type of therapy, these people could influence the result of the level of anxiety and the data would not be reliable.

Figure 3. The second stage of the game. Source: Designed by the author

Figure 4. The third stage of the game. Source: Designed by the author

At the beginning of the tests it was presented to the participants how the whole process would work, and if the participants had any questions. Those would be clarified. Soon after, the participants filled in their personal information in a questionnaire that was available online on Google Forms.

The experiment had an average duration of 20 minutes for each participant, of which, 6 minutes were to interact with the game via HTC Vive device, 6 minutes to play via keyboard/mouse and 8 minutes to filling in the questionnaires. Interaction with the game via keyboard/mouse or with virtual reality glasses was defined by the time of six minutes or if the user could complete the game. In other words, the game was finished and the players answered the questionnaire, if the player played for 6 minutes without success in finishing it or if he managed to finish the game before the time. The players were not aware of the 6 minutes time and were just playing. This kind of measure was taken to avoid affecting the level of anxiety of the players.

The experiment was divided into 2 stages. In the first stage the players interacted with the game through keyboard/mouse, answering the SUDS, IDATE and IPQ questionnaires when finished. The data obtained in that first stage were defined as reference data for the comparison with the data that were obtained in the second stage. For the second stage the players used HTC Vive for interacting with the digital game, responding to the same questionnaires once completed. The answer to the questionnaires was available online and if the participants desired, a copy was sent by email to the participant.

With the completion of the experiments, then the data from the experiment were analyzed. The change in anxiety was assessed through the questionnaires SUDS and IDATE. The change in the immersive process was accessed through the IPQ questionnaire. An analysis was made of the score obtained in the first and second part of the experiments to identify the change in anxiety and immersive process obtained with the use of HTC Vive.

4. RESULTS

Due to the fact that the game was proposed and developed by the researcher, an initial test was performed with a participant to find out if any game modification were necessary. This test was performed in the same way as the other tests, except for the time, which in this case lasted 40 minutes. With the completion of this test, it was identified that the difficulties of the game were in levels much higher than expected. With that in mind, obstacle speeds have been reduced to facilitate dodging of the same by the players.

Another problem was identified in this pilot test, it was related to one of the particle systems used that caused a malfunction in the game. This particle system was located in the first stage of the game and simulated fire. The problem was that this system caused an FPS drop in this area. An error was also identified that did not allow the menus to be displayed for HTC Vive. The correction of this error was made by assigning hotkeys to different difficulties of the game, making it possible to activate different levels without menu access.

In the end, the results of this Alpha test were not considered with the values of the general tests, as they are dealt with different experiences for the player.

Approximately 33.3% of participants completed the game via keyboard/mouse. With HTC Vive, only 13.3% of the participants managed to complete the game. It was reported by users a greater difficulty in interacting with the game in virtual reality.

With the SUDS questionnaire it was possible to identify that if you play with HTC Vive the subjective anxiety level of a player had an average increase of 10.3%. This was the first questionnaire for the evaluation. With the values that are shown in Table 1 for the SUDS questionnaire, it is possible to verify that users reported having a little greater anxiety when playing with the virtual reality glasses. This can be a result of strangeness in the first use of the device for most of the participants.

As seen in Spielberger, Gorsuch and Lushene (1970) and Biaggio (1990), the questionnaire score STAI consists of a value from 20 to 80. On this scale, there is no definite cut due to the fact that the level of anxiety may vary according to the individual characteristics and sampling. This score is a summation with all the questions present in the questionnaire taking into account that the negative and positive questions have different values in the score. In the work of Biaggio (1990) it is possible to see that in neutral conditions the average for the STAI-state is 39.63. This value will be considered as a reference for this work. The values obtained through the IDATE are shown in Table 1.

With the results of the IDATE-state questionnaire, it is possible to see that the average increase in the anxiety of players when using HTC Vive was 2.6 points. The increase in anxiety was not statistically significant, if compared to the total of 80 questionnaire points or taking note that each question is worth 4 points. However, about 9 people experienced a significant increase in anxiety, this may be due to the fact that the HTC Vive is relatively new and it might be of difficult access for the general public. This significant increase should be considered if any work is being done with the user, as in Perandré and Haydu (2018), as there is a possibility that the user feels greater anxiety for interacting with the virtual reality glasses and this must be considered.

It was observed that about 10% of the population presented dizziness when using HTC Vive. For this reason, these people's anxiety scores were higher than normal. The relative increase in anxiety was about 3 points in SUDS and 8 points in the IDATE questionnaire. When participants reported dizziness, the test was stopped until these participants felt better, and then the questionnaires were applied. It was reported by participants that this dizziness was only momentary and did not present any major risk. It was mentioned by participants who suffered this type of adversity, they were extremely tired, and the tiredness may have contributed to the feeling of dizziness with the use of virtual reality glasses. To do this type of connection of tiredness and dizziness presented with reality glasses, a new study is needed that seeks to understand the correlation between the two.

The evaluation of the immersive process was carried out through variables presented in the IPQ questionnaire that are shown in Table 1. With the results obtained through this instrument, it was possible to see that all variables portrayed higher values for using HTC Vive regarding keyboard/mouse use. In that way, it can be inferred that the device confers a higher level immersion for players.

Table 1. Data of the questionnaires SUDS, IDATE and IPQ

SUDS	IDATE	IPQ
Average mouse/keyboard: 4.63 (SD: 2.14)	Average mouse/ keyboard: 37.46 (SD: 7.25)	Increased in spatial presence: 0.58
HTC Vive average: 5.66 (SD: 2.78)	HTC Vive average: 40.06 (SD: 9.40)	Increase in involvement: 0.635
17 people had an increase	13 people had an increase	Increased in realism experienced: 0.55
6 people had a decrease	14 people had a decrease	Increased in global presence: 0.59

As seen in Granic, Lobel and Engels (2014), games can promote relaxation and decreased anxiety. In this work it was possible to confirm this statement due to the fact that the anxiety levels found by the IDATE questionnaires and SUDS are below average for the keyboard/mouse interaction and slightly above average for the interaction with the HTC Vive. With the increase of immersion, it is possible then that the players experience these positive effects that games bring in a more intense way. As the player has a greater feeling of being present in the virtual environment due to the HTC Vive, any kind of experience he has will be amplified.

The average anxiety in the IDATE-state for students in the exam period of the subjects was 45.71, as seen in Biaggio (2010). In this work, the average was 37.46 using keyboard/mouse. And considering that the tests of this work were applied during a final exam period of university students, which is a period that students show a significant increase in the state of anxiety and stress, the result of this experiment can be indicative that the game developed for this work can have offered a slight reduction in the state of anxiety of students. Even with the highest score obtained by the IDATE-state of 40.06 by the participants playing with virtual reality glasses, there was a decrease. If the value when the game was played via a keyboard/mouse 37,46, this decrease further reinforce the previous statement.

5. CONCLUSION

The objective of this work was to evaluate anxiety and the immersive process for the HTC Vive using a developed game for this research of the runner genre. This work was based on the research of Alsina-Jurnet and Gutiérrez-Maldonado (2010). The choice of the runner genre indicated the necessity of new evaluations, by the observation that this genre may not be adequate for VR. In the future new researches will be made involving other genres, with that we are going to be able to understand the difference between levels of anxiety and immersion for games VR and non VR in different games genres. In the developed game for this research 10% of the total players had motion sickness while playing in VR. In future works new elements in the interface and gameplay could be tested to reduce this sensation.

As was discussed in the results subsection, through the application of the SUDS and IDATE questionnaire, there was no significant increase in the average anxiety of users. However, some users have experienced a significant increase in anxiety and in these specific cases, it is suggested that HTC Vive should be used more carefully. At the work of Perandré and Haydu (2018), virtual reality was used as a therapeutic resource, but it was not considered that users could have greater anxiety when wearing glasses of virtual reality. Due to these factors, it is advisable that introductory exercises are done with the devices so that these users will have a more pleasant experience.

This work indicated the positive aspects that games can promote during periods of stress and anxiety, for example, during exams for college students. As previously seen, there is a factor that may indicate that the game has reduced students anxiety while they were playing. It is proposed as a future work a study that analyzes this indication and can confirm or refute the findings found in this work. It would also be interesting to develop another line of research aimed at studying the development of games to decrease anxiety in individuals who are in a state of extreme anxiety. It could also be proposed the same experiment encompassing more questionnaires and devices. Another future research that could be proposed is to use a commercial VR game and do the same measurements proposed in this research, after that we can compare with the results found in this work using the VR game developed by the researcher.

REFERENCES

A. Biaggio, 1990. *A decade of research on state-trait in brazil.* in Cross-cultural anxiety, C. Spielberger and R. Diaz-Guerrero, Eds. New York: Taylor Francis, pp. 157–167.

C. Russoniello, K. O'Brien, and J. M Parks, 2009. *Eeg, hrv and psychological correlates while playing bejeweled ii: A randomized controlled study*. vol. 144, pp. 189–92, 02 2009.

C. Spielberger, R. Gorsuch, and R. Lushene, 1970. *Manual for the state-trait anxiety inventory*. Consulting Psychologists Press.

Entertainment Software Association, 2015. *Essential facts about the computer and video game industry: Sales, demographic, and usage data*. Available at: <http://www.theesa.com/wp-content/uploads/2015/04/ESAEssential-Facts-2015.pdf>. Accessed: 30 May 2017.

I. Alsina-Jurnet and J. Gutiérrez-Maldonado, 2010. *Influence of personality and individual abilities on the sense of presence experienced in anxiety triggering virtual environments*. International Journal of Human-Computer Studies, vol. 68, no. 10, pp. 788 – 801. [Online] Available: https://doi.org/10.1016/j.ijhcs.2010.07.001

I. Granic, A. Lobel, and R. C. M. E. Engels, 2014. *The benefits of playing video games*. American Psychologist, vol. 69, no. 1, pp. 66–78. [Online]. Available at: doi:10.1037/a0034857

J. Vasconcelos-Raposo, M. Bessa, M. Melo, L. Barbosa, R. Rodrigues, C. M. Teixeira, L. Cabral, A. A. Sousa, 2016. *Adaptation and validation of the igroup presence questionnaire (ipq) in a portuguese sample*. Presence, vol. 25, no. 3, pp. 191–203.

J. Wolpe, 1969. *The practice of behavior therapy*. New York, NY: Pergamon Press.

P. E. Dickson, J. E. Block, G. N. Echevarria, and K. C. Keenan, 2017. *An experience-based comparison of unity and unreal for a stand-alone 3d game development course*. pp. 70–75, 2017. [Online] Available at: http://doi.acm.org/10.1145/3059009.3059013

R. M. Ryan, C. S. Rigby, and A. Przybylski, 2006. *The motivational pull of video games: A self-determination theory approach*. American Psychologist, vol. 30, no. 4, pp. 347–363. [Online] Available at: doi:10.1007/s11031-006-9051-8

T. McMahan, I. Parberry, and T. D. Parsons, 2015. *Modality specific assessment of video game player's experience using the emotiv, Entertainment Computing*. vol. 7, pp. 1 – 6, 2015. [Online] Available at: https://doi.org/10.1016/j.entcom.2015.03.001

T. Schubert, F. Friedmann, and H. Regenbrecht, 2001. *The experience of presence: Factor analytic insights*. Presence: Teleoperators and Virtual Environments, vol. 10, no. 3, pp. 266–281. [Online] Available at: https://doi.org/10.1162/105474601300343603

Y. H. T. Perandré and V. B. Haydu, 2018. *Um programa de intervenção para transtorno de ansiedade social com o uso da realidade virtual*, Temas em Psicologia, vol. 26, pp. 851 – 866, 06.

ANALYSING THE EFFECTIVENESS OF ONLINE GAMIFIED LEARNING METHODS AS OPPOSED TO TRADITIONAL LEARNING METHODS FOR TEACHING COMPUTER PROGRAMMING

Owen Sacco
Malta College of Arts, Science and Technology, Malta

ABSTRACT

Traditional teaching methods for teaching computer programming suffer from keeping students engaged and motivated to learn how to code. On the other hand, video games have a very high successful rate of keeping players motivated and engaged for hours without loss of focus to solve a set of tasks without feeling fatigued or frustrated. In this regard, in this research we analyse the effectiveness of gamified learning methods compared to traditional learning methods for teaching computer programming by conducting a study where students are taught computer programming using both teaching methods. The results from our user study are presented in this paper.

KEYWORDS

Traditional-Based Learning, Gamified-Based Learning, Computer Programming Education

1. INTRODUCTION

The main research study of this work is to examine the effectiveness of online gamified learning as opposed to traditional taught methods when teaching computer programming. Currently, students struggle to learn computer programming and find the topic hard to grasp (Olsson, et al., 2015; Lahtinen, et al., 2005). The main problem consists of students are not motivated and engaged in the subject, which results in students not practicing computer coding enough in order for them to learn the subject. Moreover, traditional taught methods are not feasible at keeping students motivated and engaged for learning computer programming. In this regard, other methods such as online gamified learning methods need to be employed to motivate students to code more and be more immersed in the subject. Video games are very successful in keeping players immersed, motivated and engaged for hours without loss of focus to accomplish tasks set out in the game (Green & Bavelier, 2006). Moreover, in games, players solve complex tasks within virtual environments without feeling fatigued or frustrated, compared to traditional taught learning methods where students struggle to solve computer programming tasks. Gamified learning methods therefore consist of integrating game elements in teaching methods in order to increase students' motivation and engagement whilst learning computer programming. Through this research, an analysis will be conducted to study the effectiveness of employing online gamified methods to examine whether students' motivation, engagement, attention and retention are improved through play.

Several online gamified platforms, such as CodinGame[1], provide users to learn coding through fun by completing tasks similar to tasks in games. Mainly, users are requested to solve specific game-like problems through code and are rewarded accordingly after completing successfully the task.

This research consists of first analysing students' behaviour through traditional methods - the students were taught specific coding concepts using traditional methods and afterwards were given coding tasks to complete. Once the coding tasks were complete, the students were asked to fill-in a survey about their learning experience using traditional methods. The research then analysed the students' behaviour through online gamified methods

[1] CodinGame - https://www.codingame.com/

- the students were then introduced to online gamified platforms and were asked to complete tasks on this platform. Once the students completed the gamified tasks, the students were asked to fill-in a survey about their learning experience using the online gamified platform. Ultimately, the survey results from both methods were compared to analyse which teaching methods students preferred and also to analyse whether students' motivation, engagement, attention and retention improved using online gamified methods. The results of such study are provided in this work. The remainder of this paper is as follows: Section 2 offers core information about gamification and reviews current work in this area. Section 3 provides an explanation of the different teaching methods used for our analysis in this work and Section 4 presents in detail our results from our user study. Section 5 concludes the paper by providing an overall discussion and the future steps of this work.

2. RELATED WORK

Teaching computer programming requires abstract thinking and problem-solving skills apart from learning the computer programming lanague, which constantly poses a challenge for educators to teach such a subject (Piteira, et al., 2018). Normally, when students are presented with complex tasks to solve using computer programming, studennts are overwhelmed and since they do not receive any immediate saisfaction or short term wins, they end up feeling unengaged, unmotivated and thus, loose attention in class (Fotaris, et al., 2016). However, when players are presented with complex tasks to solve in video games, players are kept at a high level of attention, last for many hours and strive until they solve the tasks and win (Green & Bavelier, 2006). In this regard, several studies have been proposed to incorporate game-elements in educational context, in particular in teaching computer programming (Costa, et al., 2017; Ibanez, et al., 2014), in order to increase students' attention, engagement, motivation and retention.

Gamification involves adding game elements to non-game context (Deterding, et al., 2011). Game-elements in a non-game setting consist of the use of points, medals, levels, progress bars, leader-boards, amongst others (Deterding, et al., 2011). Gamification in educational environments can provide an increase to students' engagement in learning whilst providing instant feedback by indicating the player whether s/he won or not (Seaborn & Fels, 2015). In a gamified environment, students can learn by completing activities and also learn through error which are represented as achievements, medals, honour board, etc. (Richards, et al., 2014). Gamification provides an environment where learning is rewarded and allows students to assess their skills and abilities. Moreover, through gamification, students may see failure as a learning opportunity (Piteira, et al., 2018) and it encourages them to redo the task until the students grasps the concepts and ultimately manage to solve the task. In (Borys & Laskowski, 2013) the authors identified 36 learning principles that video games could benefit as a learning tool in education, which included immediate feedback, self-learning, information on demand, collaborative learning amongst others. Thus, current literature illustrates the imortance of applying gamification to teaching methods since it could motivate and engage students to learn more. Although several research have studied the use of gamification in education, a more in-depth research is required to study the effectiveness of incorporating gamification in teaching methods (Dicheva, et al., 2015). In this regard, this motivated the research study area of this paper.

The most closest study to the research presented in this paper is the work in (Fotaris, et al., 2016). In this work, the authors study the effects of gamification using the following applications: Kahoot![2], an open-source adaptation of Who Wants to be a Millionaire, and Codecademy. Although these methods provide gamified environments, students are not provided with game-like tasks when writing code. Therefore, in our research study, we opted to use a platform that provides game-like tasks to analyse the engagement and motivation of students whilst solving tasks through writing code since as mentioned above, video games should incrase students' attention, motivation, and should encourage them to strive until they solve the tasks and win (Green & Bavelier, 2006). In this regard, CodinGame is chosen as the platform to conduct the study in this paper to assess students' engagement, motivation, attention and retention in learning computer programming through solving game-like tasks.

[2] Kahoot! - https://kahoot.com/

3. METHODOLOGY

The user study was conducted on a 16-week 2nd year undergraduate study unit in which students learn how to program using the *C#* programming language. The total amount of students following this unit is around 70 students. In this unit, lectures cover fundamental programming concepts ranging from data types and variables, selection, arrays and loops, methods, classes and objects (object-oriented paradigm), encapsulation and abstraction, polymorphism, inheritance, interfaces, exception handling, graphical user interfaces and databases. As part of the user study, two main teaching methods were used to introduce different programming concepts in order to analyse which method was most effective and which method students preferred. The two main teaching methods are the traditional teaching methods and the gamified teaching methods. First, the traditional teaching methods was used and afterwards the students were asked to fill-in a survey about their learning experience using traditional methods. Subsequently, gamified teaching methods were used and students were asked to fill in a survey to gain insights about their learning experience using gamified methods.

This section provides an explanation of the different teaching methods used in our user study for analysing the effectiveness of online gamified teaching methods for teaching computer programming in class.

3.1 Traditional Teaching Methods

Traditional teaching methods are the most common type of teaching methods used in class for teaching computer programming courses. Traditional teaching methods for teaching computer programming consist of *lecture-type* methods, *live-coding* type methods and *task-based* type methods.

Lecture-type teaching methods consist of the lecturer presenting computer programming concepts using slides with minimum amount of programming in class. Students must attentively listen to what the lecturer is explaining, and try to formulate an understanding of how such concepts are applied in computer programs. The students ask questions based on the concepts presented in class rather than on any queries which they might encounter whilst applying these concepts when coding. At the end of the lecture, students are given review tasks based on the concepts presented in class to work out of class. Students work individually on these tasks out of class and have to solve the tasks based on what they have learnt during the lecture without having the lecturer present to answer any of their queries which they might encounter whilst coding.

Live-coding type methods consist of the lecturer presents computer programming concepts by live-coding examples in class and the students follow the lecturer by coding (i.e. copying) what the lecturer has just coded. With this method, the students are not only learning the concepts but can visualize better how these concepts can be applied in computer programs. With this method the students have the opportunity to ask questions not only about the concepts presented but also any other queries which the students encounter whilst programming. At the end of the lecture, the students are given review tasks to work out outside of class. Yet again, students must work these tasks individually out of class and have to solve the tasks without having the lecturer present to answer any of their queries which they might encounter whilst working out these tasks

Task-based type methods consist of hands-on practical sessions whereby most of the lectures consist of the students being given practical tasks to work out in class and they learn programming concepts as they solve the tasks and progress from one task to another. The lecturer in this type of teaching method is more of a facilitator whereby the lecturer is only present to answer any queries and ensures that the students are progressing from one task to another. Thus, in this type of teaching method, the students learn by coding themselves in class.

3.2 Gamified Teaching Methods

Gamified teaching methods consist of teaching computer programming concepts with game-elements in order to engage and motivate the students to learn programming concepts through fun and play. An online gamified platform called CodinGame[3] is used during these sessions whereby students are given practical tasks to solve which are related to the programming concept being taught. These are presented in the form of a quest or task in a game. The students are provided with the goal which they have to reach and are also given rules about the

[3] CodinGame - https://www.codingame.com/

game. The students must then program their task based on the rules provided in order to reach the goal. In the end, they could test their code and see their solution being animated. The platform indicates whether they have managed to solve the task by reaching the goal and it also indicates in which part the students failed. When students complete the task successfully, they unlock achievements, gain experience points and are provided with their score. Moreover, students could compete against each other in a leader board which shows the scores of each player sorted from highest to lowest. In this way, students are incentivised similar in games to be better and beat their "opponents" (opponents being their classmates) in the leader board.

4. EVALUATION – USER STUDY

This section presents the results of our user study. The responses follow a five point Likert scale: 1 – Strongly Disagree, 2 – Disagree, 3 – Undecided, 4 – Agree, and 5 – Strongly Agree.

The survey first asked the participant's gender and we observe that 80% are male, 15% are female and 5% prefer not to say.

The survey then asked the participants what is their frequency at playing video games. This is to determine their level at playing digital games. We observe that 42% play video games frequently, 16% play video games often, 16% sometimes play video games, 21% play video games occasionally and only 5% never play video games. These results depict that most of the participants know how to play video games.

4.1 Traditional Teaching Methods

This section presents the results from the participants' experience when learning computer programming through traditional teaching methods. The traditional teaching methods include lecture-type teaching methods, live-coding type teaching methods and task-based type teaching methods as explained in section 3.

Q1 – Motivates Learning: participants were asked whether traditional teaching methods motivate them to learn computer programming. Figure **1** depicts that most of the participants are unsure whether traditional teaching methods motivate them in learning computer programming whereas only a few strongly agree that these methods motivate them.

Q2 – Fun and Engaging: participants were asked whether traditional teaching methods are fun and engaging. Figure **2** depicts that most participants disagree that traditional teaching methods are fun and engaging and only a few strongly agree that these methods are in fact fun and engaging.

Q3 – Sufficient Material: participants were asked whether traditional teaching methods provide enough material for the students to learn computer programming. Figure **3** illustrates that most participants agree that these methods indeed provide sufficient material for the students to learn computer programming.

Q4 – Assignment / Exam Preparation: participants were asked whether traditional teaching methods prepares them well enough for an assignment and/or exam. Figure **4** depicts that most participants agree that through these methods they feel that they are prepared enough for an assignment and/or exam, and only a few do not feel prepared well enough for an assignment and/or exam.

Q5 – Motivates Research: participants were asked whether traditional teaching methods encourages them to research more about the computer concepts explained in class. Figure **5** illustrates that most participants do not feel encouraged to research more about programing concepts whereas 35% feel motivated to research more.

Q6 – Motivate Attention in Class: participants were asked whether traditional teaching methods motivates them to be more attentive during class. Figure **6** illustrates that the traditional teaching methods do not motivate students to be attentive in class. This could be linked with *Q2* above since they do not find traditional teaching methods as fun and engaging.

Q7 – Motivates Class Attendance: participants were asked whether traditional teaching methods motivates them to attend class. Figure **7** illustrates that students are not motivated to attend class when computer programming is taught through traditional teaching methods. Similar to *Q6*, this could be correlated with the students not finding traditional teaching method as fun and engaging as noted in *Q2*.

Q8 – Motivates Computer Programming Career: participants were asked whether traditional teaching methods motivates them to choose a computer programming career. Figure **8** illustrates that the majority of students are undecided, whilst 20% of students agree and another 20% of students strongly agree that traditional teaching methods motivates them to choose a computer programming career in the future.

4.2 Gamified Teaching Methods

This section presents the results from the participants' experience when learning computer programming through gamified teaching methods. The gamified teaching methods consist of teaching computer programming concepts with game-like tasks using the online gamified platform called CodinGame[4] as explained in section 3.

Q1 – Motivates Learning: participants were asked whether gamified teaching methods motivate them to learn computer programming. Figure **1** depicts that most of the students agree and strongly agree that they are motivated in learning computer programming through gamified teaching methods whereas only a few disagreed.

Q2 – Fun and Engaging: participants were asked whether gamified teaching methods are fun and engaging. Figure **2** depicts that the majority of the participants find gamified teaching methods as fun and engaging and only a few do not find gamified teaching methods as fun and engaging.

Q3 – Sufficient Material: participants were asked whether gamified teaching methods provide enough material for the students to learn computer programming. Figure **3** illustrates that the majority of students agree and strongly agree that these methods indeed provide sufficient material for the students to learn computer programming. The online gamified platform provides a learn section which contains many pages with learning content that explains most of the computer programming concepts. The platform provides learning content for a substantial amount of different programming languages. This means that students may not only learn the *C#* programming language, but may also learn other programming languages through this platform.

Q4 – Assignment / Exam Preparation: participants were asked whether gamified teaching methods prepares them well enough for an assignment and/or exam. Figure **4** depicts that most participants are undecided whether gamified teaching methods prepares them well for assessments. The reason for this could be since the gamified teaching methods is still new for the students and this user study was conducted prior to students attempting any assessment. Therefore, the students could not judge whether through gamified learning methods they are well prepared or not for assessments.

Q5 – Motivates Research: participants were asked whether gamified teaching methods encourages them to research more about the computer concepts explained in class. Figure **5** illustrates that 30% of the students strongly agree and 20% of the students agree that they feel encouraged to research more about programing concepts whereas 35% are undecided whether this method encourages them to research more about the computer programming concepts covered in class.

Q6 – Motivate Attention in Class: participants were asked whether gamified teaching methods motivates them to be more attentive during class. Figure **6** illustrates that the majority of the students feel motivated to remain attentive during class. This could be correlated with *Q2* above since they find gamified teaching methods as fun and engaging.

Q7 – Motivates Class Attendance: participants were asked whether gamified teaching methods motivates them to attend class. Figure **7** illustrates that gamified teaching methods motivates the majority of students to attend. Similar to *Q6*, this could be correlated with *Q2* above whereby students find gamified teaching methods as fun and engaging.

Q8 – Motivates Computer Programming Career: participants were asked whether gamified teaching methods motivates them to choose a computer programming career. Figure **8** illustrates that most of the students agree and strongly agree that gamified teaching methods motivates them to choose a computer programming career in the future.

4.3 Comparison of Results

This section presents the comparison of results by comparing the results from the traditional teaching methods and the results from the gamified teaching methods, as illustrated in Table **1**. In Table **1**, for interpretation purposes, the strongly agree and the agree percentages have been added together to form a positive result, the undecided percentages remain unchanged and are represented by a neutral result, and the disagree and strongly disagree percentages have been added together to form a negative result.

---

[4] Codin Game - https://www.codingame.com/

Table 1. Comparison of Results

Question	Traditional Teaching Methods			Gamified Teaching Methods		
	Positive	**Neutral**	**Negative**	**Positive**	**Neutral**	**Negative**
Q1 – Motivates Learning	35%	45%	20%	**65%**	15%	20%
Q2 – Fun and Engaging	20%	35%	45%	**70%**	15%	15%
Q3 – Sufficient Material	**55%**	25%	20%	**55%**	30%	15%
Q4 – Assignment / Exam Preparation	**50%**	30%	20%	30%	**50%**	20%
Q5 – Motivates Research	35%	5%	60%	**50%**	35%	15%
Q6 – Motivate Attention in Class	30%	25%	45%	**60%**	25%	15%
Q7 – Motivates Class Attendance	30%	15%	55%	**60%**	30%	10%
Q8 – Motivates Computer Programming Career	40%	40%	20%	**60%**	30%	10%
Mean	37%	28%	36%	**56%**	29%	15%

Overall, it can be noted that students prefer more gamified teaching methods over traditional teaching methods with a mean positive feeling of 56% for gamified teaching methods as opposed to 37% positive feeling for traditional teaching methods. Moreover, gamified teaching methods gained a higher positive feeling in most of the results, except for the assignment and exam preparation. The students preferred more traditional teaching methods when it came to assignment and exam preparation but were neutral for gamified teaching methods. As explained in the above sections, this could be due to the fact that the survey was conducted before any assignment and/or exam was given to the students and therefore they could not judge whether gamified teaching methods prepare them well enough for any type of assessment. With regards to which teaching methods provide sufficient material, it can be noted that both the traditional teaching methods and the gamified methods provide sufficient material for the students to learn computer programming.

In the end, the survey concluded by asking the participants to select which teaching methods they preferred in certain scenarios. This occurred to reinforce the results which the students have selected for each teaching methods above. The following are the results of the students' preferences.

C1 – Preferred Teaching Methods in General: participants were asked which teaching methods they preferred in general in class and 60% preferred gamified teaching methods as opposed to 40% who preferred traditional teaching methods instead. These results are close to the mean positive results compared above – 56% for gamified teaching methods and 37% for traditional teaching methods.

C2 – Preferred Teaching Methods for Learning Computer Programming: participants were asked which teaching methods they preferred the most to learn computer programming and 65% preferred gamified teaching methods and 35% preferred traditional teaching methods. These results are also close to the mean positive results compared above.

C3 – Preferred Teaching Methods that makes Learning Computer Programming Easier: participants were asked which teaching methods makes learning computer programming easier and 70% have selected gamified teaching methods whereas 30% have selected traditional teaching methods.

C4 – Teaching Methods Most Fun and Engaging: participants were asked which teaching methods made learning computer programming fun and engaging, and 90% have selected gamified teaching methods as the most fun and engaging whereas only 10% have selected traditional teaching methods as fun and engaging. These results are in fact more than the overall positive results compared above where it was recorded that 70% are positive about gamified teaching methods being more fun and engaging as opposed to 20% being positive about traditional teaching methods being more fun and engaging.

C5 – Preferred Teaching Methods to Achieve Better Grades: participants were asked which teaching methods help them to achieve better grades - 60% have selected traditional training methods as the preferred teaching method that helps them to achieve better grades whereas 40% selected gamified teaching methods.

In conclusion, from this study, gamified teaching methods have obtained overall the most positive responses, which are also in-line with the results obtained in (Fotaris, et al., 2016) that use different gamification elements. However, from our results, 60% still feel that with traditional teaching methods they could achieve better grades and thus, one cannot adopt gamified only teaching methods in class but a blended approach should be adopted. In this regard, more research should be studied to explore new methods where gamified teaching methods would be the basis of course delivery for teaching computer programming but it should also incorporate traditional teaching methods in order to prepare students for their assessments.

Therefore, a gamified traditional teaching method is required to improve student motivation, attention, information retention and learning development for learning computer programming.

5. CONCLUSION

In this work we have conducted a user study to analyse the effectiveness of gamified teaching methods through game-like coding tasks compared to traditional teaching methods, and from our findings we have concluded that overall, students prefer having gamified teaching methods. However, the results show that having a gamified only teaching method is not enough but a mixed teaching approach of traditional teaching methods combined with gamified teaching methods is required in order to prepare students in their assessments. In this regard, as future work, we will first analyse the impact gamified teaching methods using game-like problem solving coding tasks have to prepare students in their assessments, compared to when traditional teaching methods are adopted to prepare students in their assessments. Secondly, we will develop and incorporate a gamified teaching methods platform plugin, consisting of game-like problem solving coding tasks (similar to the CodinGame platform), within the Moodle virtual lecturing environment (VLE) as to our knowledge no such plugin containing gamified game-like coding tasks exist for Moodle. Ultimately, we will assess the effectiveness of incorporating such features into the VLE coupled with the course material that is shared with the students within this system by analysing whether students' motivation, engagement, learning development and retention increases.

REFERENCES

Borys, M. & Laskowski, M., 2013. *Implementing game elements into didactic process: A case study.* s.l., Management, knowledge and learning international conference.

Costa, C. J., Aparicio, M., Aparicio, S. & Aparicio, J. T., 2017. *Gamification usage ecology.* s.l., ACM International Conference on the Design of Communication.

Deterding, S., Dixon, D., Khaled, R. & Nacke, L., 2011. From game design elements to gamefulness: defining" gamification. *Proceedings of the 15th international academic MindTrek conference: Envisioning future media environments,* pp. 9-15.

Dicheva, D., Dichev, C., Agre, G. & Angelova, G., 2015. Gamification in education: A systematic mapping study. *Journal of Educational Technology & Society,* 18(3).

Fotaris, P., Mastoras, T., Leinfellner, R. & Rosunally, Y., 2016. Climbing up the Leaderboard: An Empirical Study of Applying Gamification Techniques to a Computer Programming Class. *Electronic Journal of e-learning,* 14(2), pp. 94-110.

Green, C. S. & Bavelier, D., 2006. Effect of action video games on the spatial distribution of visuospatial attention.. *Journal of experimental psychology: Human perception and performance,* 32(6), pp. 1465-1478.

Ibanez, M.-B., Di-Serio, A. & Delgado-Kloos, C., 2014. Gamification for engaging computer science students in learning activities: A case study. *IEEE Transactions on learning technologies,* 7(3), pp. 291-301.

Lahtinen, E., Ala-Mutka, K. & Järvinen, H.-M., 2005. A study of the difficulties of novice programmers. *Proceedings of the 10th Annual SIGCSE Conference on Innovation and Technology in Computer Science Education,* 37(3), p. 14–18.

Olsson, M., Mozelius, P. & Collin, J., 2015. Visualisation and Gamification of e-Learning and Programming Education.. *Electronic journal of e-learning,* 13(6), pp. 441-454.

Piteira, M., Costa, C. J. & Aparicio, M., 2018. Computer programming learning: how to apply gamification on online courses?. *Journal of Information Systems Engineering & Management,* 3(2).

Richards, C., Thompson, C. W. & Graham, N., 2014. *Beyond designing for motivation: the importance of context in gamification.* s.l., Proceedings of the first ACM SIGCHI annual symposium on Computer-human interaction in play.

Ryan, R. M. & Deci, E. L., 200. Intrinsic and extrinsic motivations: Classic definitions and new directions. *Contemporary educational psychology,* 25(1), pp. 54-67.

Seaborn, K. & Fels, D. I., 2015. Gamification in theory and action: A survey. *International Journal of human-computer studies,* Volume 74, pp. 14-31.

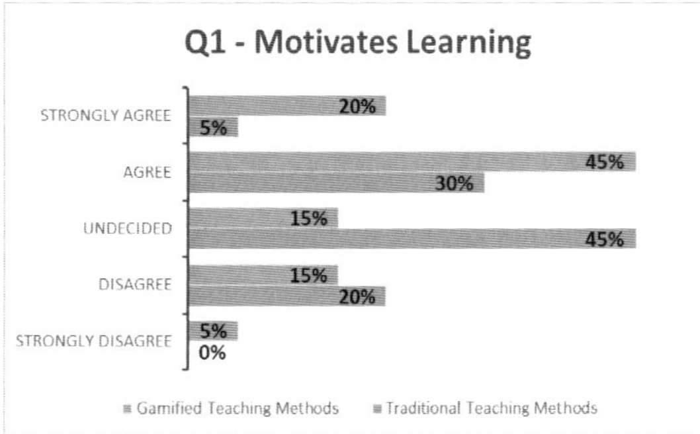

Figure 1. Q1 - Learning

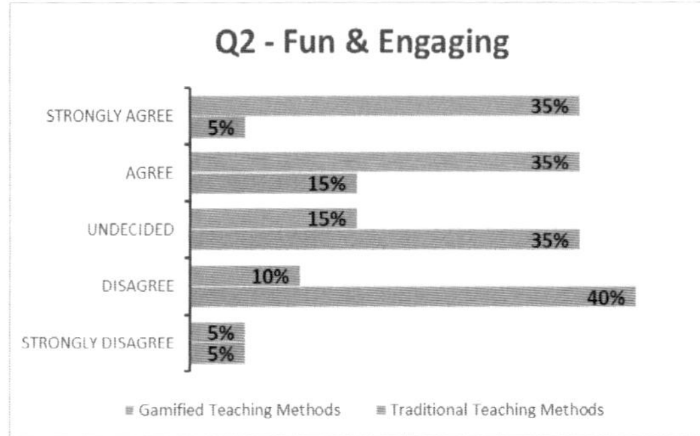

Figure 2. Q2 - Fun & Engaging

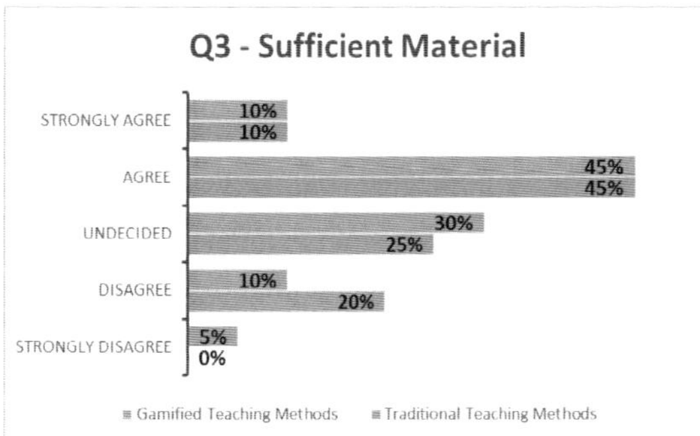

Figure 3. Q3 - Sufficient Material

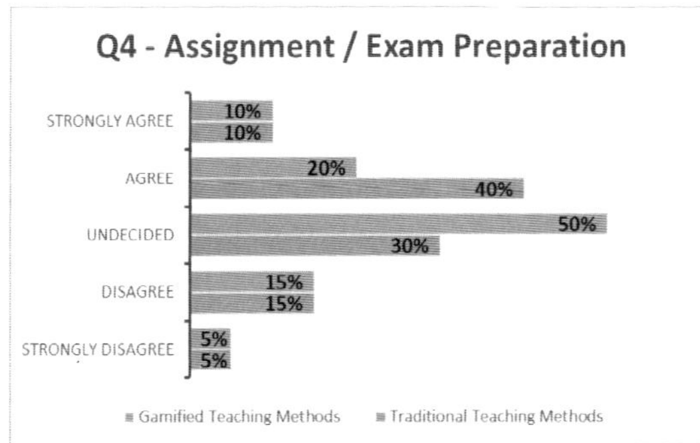

Figure 4. Q4 - Assignment / Exam Preparation

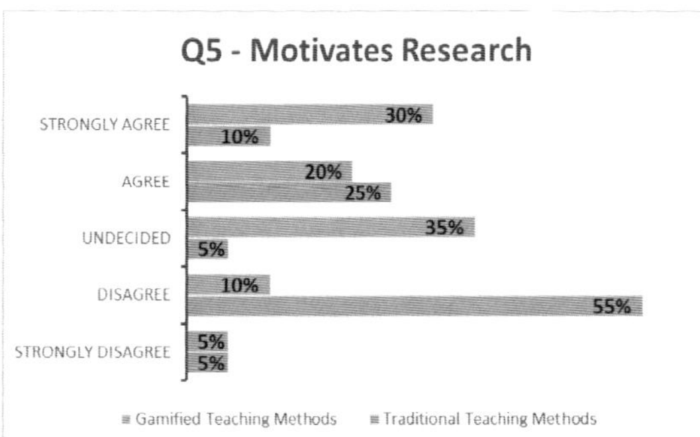

Figure 5. Q5 - Research

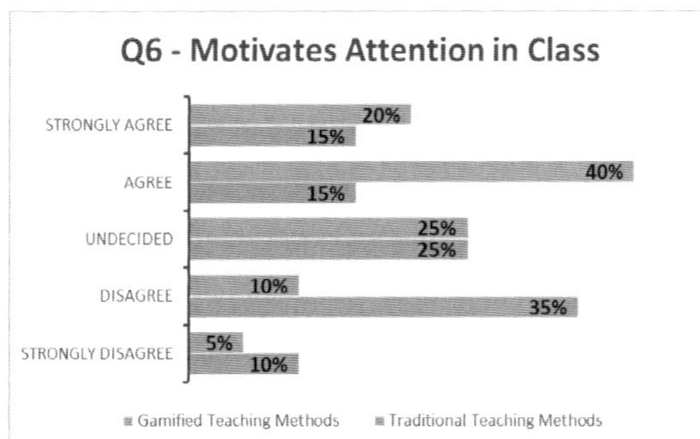

Figure 6. Q6 - Attention in Class

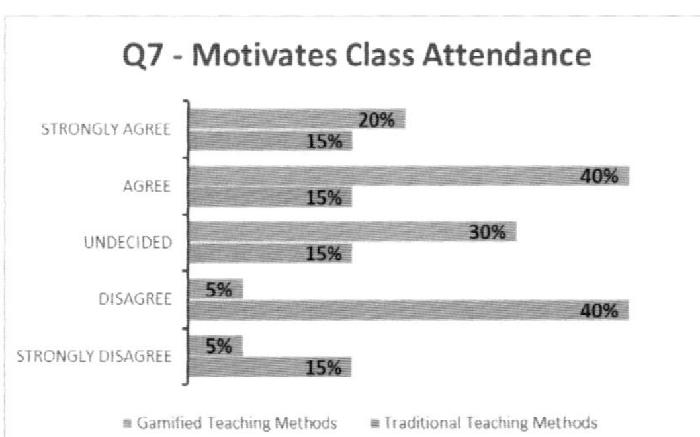

Figure 7. Q7 - Class Attendance

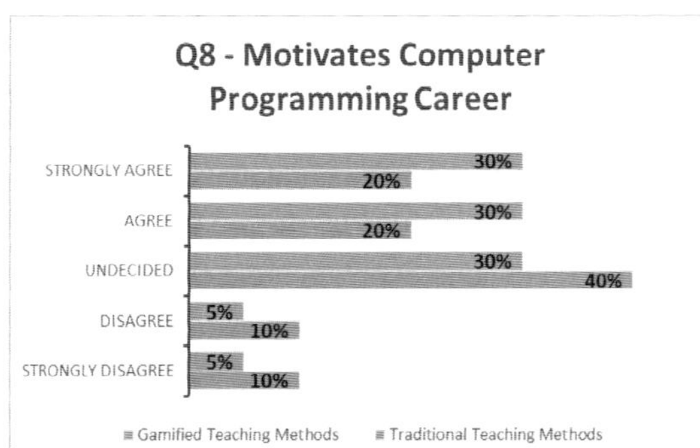

Figure 8. Q8 - Computer Programming Career

A FIRST USABILITY STUDY OF INTERNOVA E-LEARNING PLATFORM AS A TECHNOLOGICAL RESOURCE FOR AGRI-FOOD BUSINESSES

Pedro Miguel Faria, Isabel Araújo, José Evaristo Lima, David Rodrigues and João Nuno Azevedo
Instituto Politécnico de Viana do Castelo, Viana do Castelo, Portugal

ABSTRACT

With the development of the knowledge society and the growth of the increasingly competitive global economy, businesses face new challenges. In this context, the INTERNOVAMARKET-FOOD project arises with the general objective of contributing to the internationalization, technological innovation and marketing of companies of the agri-food sector in the Euro-Region of Northern Portugal and Spain. In this context, online training courses have been developed. This article presents a first usability study about the INTERNOVA E-Learning Platform. In order to analyze the online training, a questionnaire was applied to 4 volunteers, 2 acting as trainees and 2 as trainers. The questionnaire was applied after they used and executed some tasks requested in the platform. The results obtained suggest that the platform has a potential for good usability, is intuitive and dynamic.

KEYWORDS

LMS, Open edX, Usability, E-learning Digital Platform, Lifelong Learning, Training in Companies

1. INTRODUCTION

As the global economy grows, companies face new challenges. In this context, the INTERNOVAMARKET-FOOD project was born with the general objective of contributing to solid and sustainable businesses in the Euro-Region of Northern Portugal, with an optimum level of productivity, capable of generating a sufficient level of employment and having more and better companies that can sell products and services of higher quality, with higher added value, in the national and international market. For this purpose, the need for training in agri-food companies was detected. However, these are geographically dispersed and the time available for training is scarce. Therefore, the development of online training for companies was considered, having chosen to develop an e-learning platform, facilitating the access of workers from any place and at any time, as long as they have access to the Internet. This article introduces the e-learning in the context of the project, presents the INTERNOVA platform focused in its structure design and content production, followed by the description of an usability study and the results obtained.

2. THE E-LEARNING CONTEXT IN THE PROJECT

Driven by globalization, we live in a society that is increasingly competitive at a global level, also characterized by a network society (Moreno, 2015) and consequently the need for continuous training and permanent qualification throughout life (Alheit & Dausien, 2006). It should be noted that in the last two decades there has been an evident growth in the need felt and/or personal interest in the search for personal qualification (Field, 2000), generally due to the acceleration of technological change and the rapid devaluation that affects professional knowledge. Training and qualification are no longer restricted to the "preparation" phase of active life but are a permanent factor in accompanying the professional journey (Alheit & Dausien, 2006). In addition, organizations are currently required to invest and value their intellectual capital. It should be noted that the need for qualification of a company's employees fosters learning for the development of skills that should be recognized by the company itself, as well as by society itself. However, the availability of the target audience, active agents in the business world, to attend training sessions in person is limited, so online training is an alternative. In addition, the field of education has never been indifferent to new technologies and, eventually, to the opportunities offered by the Internet. Technology-supported learning encompasses, in principle, the use of digital technologies to support education. In this context, e-learning and online course development platform models assume a central role in continuous training in businesses (Barros & Neves, 2017). These systems allow the creation of learning facilitator environments, generally providing means for the distribution of interactive multimedia content, while providing online communication channels and means of collaboration, in addition to the multiple functionalities associated with evaluation, both for training and summative purposes (McGill & Klobas, 2009). These platforms make it possible to foster the learning process in a large number of people in a decentralised way (Balaouras et al, 2018).

3. INTERNOVA E-LEARNING PLATFORM

Instigated by today's constantly evolving world, whose competitiveness is increasing, the need arises for training throughout professional activity, including agri-food companies. However, the availability of active agents in the food business world is limited. Therefore, it was considered pertinent to provide training in e-learning format. In this context, it was considered adequate to present the contents in different formats, including the possibility of video, so that the training could be more diversified, and the contents explained more clearly and understandably. Thus, some free access LMS were analysed, which support training with video resources, in addition to the possibility of preparing tests, conducting evaluations, statistics on trainees' school results, monitoring the trainees' learning path, managing users by training, controlling the visibility of content and automatically issuing certificates after completion of training. The LMS that was chosen was the Open edX LMS[1], because besides being a free system, it has some unique characteristics that distinguish it from other LMS (Ch & Popuri, 2013): it provides several courses in various areas of education, and can be enrolled only in those that are intended to be held; the platform can be accessed anywhere and on any mobile device; it provides open forums 24/7, giving trainees a tool to discuss, interact and collaborate with each other; it provides a free digital certificate to the trainee if he has successfully completed the course, verifying and proving the authenticity of a particular course. Thus, a platform based on the Open edX technology was developed and called INTERNOVA. The target public and user of the INTERNOVA platform are the employees of companies in the agri-food industry, from the North of Portugal and Spain, associated with the INTERNOVAMARKET-FOOD project, who have heterogeneous backgrounds. Therefore, as regards training for employees of companies in the agri-food industry, in this article we refer to teacher/student as trainer/trainee. The e-learning platform was developed having interesting characteristics for the intended training, aimed at companies that are partners in the aforementioned project. This technology is a great tool for trainers and trainees. On the one hand, it facilitates the work of adding and editing media contents (texts, images, videos, among others), provide access to statistics on the completion of training and progress of trainees, evaluation of training and the consequent issue of a certificate of successful training completion. On the other hand, it allows the trainees to enrol in the desired training courses, allowing the trainee to attend a training course anywhere and at any time, according to their availability, respecting their own pace of learning. After identifying the training courses and their characteristics, as well the LMS that support it, the INTERNOVA platform was developed, initially through the design of its structure, based on the philosophy of the training courses that were intended to be made available, followed by the production of educational multimedia content.

4. INTERNOVA PLATFORM USABILITY

Usability can be considered by itself a methodology to support the design process, as Nielsen (2012) states "the word usability can also be referred to as a method to improve ease of use during the design process". Krug (2006) states that in a usability test, the process should take place with one user at a time. In that test, an user interface is presented to a user, e.g. a prototype of a website or an application for mobile devices, etc. and

---

[1] https://open.edx.org/

questions are asked in order to find out whether that user can perform the proposed tasks. In the testing process, Krug (2006) states that the ideal number should be around three or four users, and the objectives of the test, as well the questions/tasks to be asked to the users should be established in advance. It was then decided to test the platform in order to try to validate its usability. The platform was tested by a group of four volunteers (two acting as trainees and the other two as trainers) aged between 25 and 39 years old who, after using it, answered a questionnaire in order to validate the platform from the perspective of the trainee as well as from the perspective of the trainer.

4.1 Method

In order to validate the platform developed, users were asked to register and interact with the platform according to their profile (trainee or trainer). The trainees were asked to perform a training. To do so, they would have to start and complete it until they obtained their certificate. The trainers were asked to create a training course with all its components (description, image and moments of evaluation). Subsequently, in order to analyse the difficulties encountered, a questionnaire was applied with a series of questions related to the experience of using the platform, both from the point of view of the trainee and the trainer, in order to evaluate the difficulty presented in solving the proposed tasks. Two questionnaires were prepared, one for trainees (having 12 questions) and the other for trainers (having 11 questions). The questions in the first questionnaire were related to the tasks possible to be carried out by the trainees and the second one questions were related to the tasks possible to be carried out by the trainers. In this way, an attempt was made to test the whole range of tasks that the platform supports. The evaluation was carried out according to a Likert scale, scored with five levels – level 1 ("Difficult") to level 5 ("Easy").

4.2 Results Analysis

From the analysis of the questionnaires to the trainees it was found that they evaluated 10 of the 12 tasks with level 5 (maximum positive level of the scale used). Therefore, the results obtained show that the trainees did not experience difficulties in performing the vast majority of the tasks proposed (Table 1).

Table 1

Tasks	Trainee 1	Trainee 2
1. Access the studio: http://internova.ipvc.pt	5	5
2. Login: "aluno@ipvc.pt" psw: "testealuno"	5	5
3. Search all available training course	5	5
4. Register for the "International Featured Standards & British Retail Consortium" training course	5	5
5. Check which training courses you are enrolled in	5	5
6. See training course	5	5
7. Check how long you have until the end of the training course	5	4
8. Accessing the videos	5	5
9. Complete the first moment of evaluation	5	5
10. Conclude the second moment of evaluation	5	5
11. Access the "INTERNOVAMARKET-FOOD" website through the platform	4	3
12. Ending session	5	5

There was, however, a dispersion of opinions regarding two issues: verification of the time until completion of the training course and access to the "INTERNOVAMARKET-FOOD" project website. Regarding the first question, one of the trainees rated with level 4 "Check how long you have until the end of the training", which was different from the previous items that rated with level 5, while the other maintained the level 5 rating. As for the second question, one of the trainees classified as level 4 and the other as level 3. It was found that this difficulty was due to the fact that the trainee was being asked to verify information whose visibility would not be the most obvious. From the analysis of the trainers' questionnaires (Table 2), a greater divergence of opinions was observed. In 5 of the 11 questions the trainers answered, in consensus, with the maximum positive level of 5. This agreement is relative to the activities of access to the platform, creation of a training course, elimination of content and end of session.

Table 2

Tasks	Trainer 1	Trainer 2
1. Access the studio: http://internova.ipvc.pt:18010	5	5
2. Login: "professor@ipvc.pt" psw: "teste2019"	5	5
3. Create a new training course	5	5
4. Upload a photo to better identify the training course	1	2
5. Edit the description of the training presentation page	1	2
6. Add two sections, each section should contain one unit	3	5
7. In the first section, in the respective unit, create a statement for a multiple-choice question, with 3 options, related to the statement	4	4
8. In the second section, on the respective unit, add a video and also a multiple-choice question related to the video	4	5
9. Publish these contents	1	5
10. Delete one of the sections created	5	5
11. Ending session	5	5

It was found that there was a divergence of opinions on 5 tasks, with 3 of them the trainers responding with level 1 ("Difficult"). In these tasks it was proposed to upload a photo identifying the training course created, edit the description of that training course and publish content. It was found that, for achieving these objectives, the access to them was not so direct and/or intuitive, which motivated some difficulty on the part of the trainers, since for the remaining topics under analysis, the process of resolution was, for the most part, at the distance of a click and in some of them (for example: create a new training, add a section or unit) are of immediate access on the page of the training course. After some time using the platform, the trainers ended up getting acquainted with the tools and access to them, with a very fluid use. Regarding the remaining points of divergence, Trainer 1 experienced some difficulties in adding units, sections and contents to the training. Trainer 2 was able, without any problems, to perform the same proposed tasks, by assessing with the maximum positive level (5).

After the analysis of the results, it can be seen that the trainers did not experienced difficulties in performing the tasks initially proposed in the questionnaire, which leads us to conclude that the care that was taken throughout the development of the project resulted in a platform with a very good usability, intuitive and dynamic. All the tasks from the beginning of the session, through the registration, until the conclusion of the session was accomplished without any problems.

5. CONCLUSION

In a constantly evolving and increasingly competitive society, access to lifelong learning is urgently needed. These training courses, taking into account the target audience that is in the active life, should be in the e-learning modality. This article presents an e-learning platform – INTERNOVA, developed with support of the Open edX LMS technology, with the purpose of providing online training course to employees of companies in the agri-food industry in Northern Portugal and Galicia. In the development of the INTERNOVA platform, the target audience has always been taken into account: company employees. Thus, the platform was designed as simple and intuitive as possible, seeking to maximize the platform's usability, which was tested by trainees and trainers whose feedback from them was very positive. Additionally, it should be noted that the INTERNOVA platform can also be used in an educational context. The results obtained suggest that the platform has a potential for good usability, is intuitive and dynamic.

ACKNOWLEDGMENT

This work was supported by INTERREG V-A Espanha-Portugal (POCTEP) 2014-2020 (0437_INTERNOVAMARKET-FOOD_1_E) under the development of the project entitled "INTERNOVAMARKET-FOOD – Programa acelerador para aumentar a competitividade do sector alimentar da Galiza-Norte de Portugal".

REFERENCES

Alheit, P. & Dausien, B., 2006. Lifelong learning and training process. *Educação e Pesquisa*, Vol. 32, Nº 1, pp 177-197.

Balaouras, P., Gatzonis, M., Tsimpanis, K., Apostolidis, H. & Tsiatsos, z., 2018. Towards an online video platform for MOOCs. *Multimedia Tools and Applications,* Vol. 77, pp.12749–12775.

Barros, D. & Neves, C., 2017. ELearning pedagogic identification instrument for the business environment. *RPGE– Revista on line de Política e Gestão Educacional*, Vol. 21, Nº 3, pp. 1517-1549.

Ch. S. & Popuri, S., 2013. Impact of online education: A study on online learning platforms and edX, *IEEE International Conference in MOOC, Innovation and Technology in Education (MITE)*, pp. 366-370.

Field, J., 2000. *Lifelong learning and the new educational order*. Stoke on Trent, UK.

Ice, P., 2013. Advancing Platform Technologies in Online Learning. *eLearning & Software for Education*. No 1, pp. 616-621.

Krug, S., 2006. Don't Make Me Think: A common sense approach to web usability. Second edition, p.135. California: New Riders.

McGill, T. & Klobas, J., 2009. A task–technology fit view of learning management system impact. *Computers & Education*, Vol 52, pp 496-508.

Moreno, J., 2015. O valor económico da informação na sociedade em rede. *Observatório Journal*, Centro de Investigação e Estudos de Sociologia – Instituto Universitário de Lisboa. Vol. 9, Nº 2, pp 001-028.

Nielsen, J., 2012. Usability 101: Introduction to Usability. *Nielsen Norman Group.* Retrieved in May 12, 2020. http://www.nngroup.com/articles/usability-101-introduction-to-usability.

Simões, T., Rodrigues, J. & Torre, I., 2013. Personal Learning Environment Box (PLEBOX): A New Approach to E-Learning Platforms *Computer Applications In Engineering Education*, Vol. 21, No 1, pp. 100-109.

'HEDGING' AND GENDER IN PARTICIPATORY DESIGN

Alice Ashcroft
Lancaster University
School of Computing and Communications, Lancaster University, Lancaster, UK

ABSTRACT

There has been much dispute over the role 'hedging' – equivocation in expressing opinions - plays in group conversation as well as the impact of gender on a range of processes including Participatory Design; (Holmes, 1986, Dixon and Foster, 1997, Stokoe and Smithson, 2001, Stokoe and Weatheral, 2002, Brulé, E. and Spiel, K. (2019),). This paper addresses these issues by analysing gender differences and hedging in an Innovation Participatory Design workshop focused around the creation and combination of ideas for app development. Discussions were transcribed and analysed; 'hedging' terms seemed an interesting theme for analysis, but no statistical significance was found to prove that 'hedging' was gender-biased. This initial, exploratory, short paper reflects on this finding; on the contrast with research that has found gender differences (Holmes, 1986); on the importance of supplementing statistical with contextual forms of analysis; and what effect or implications this may have on the process of Participatory Design, by acknowledging the importance of giving voice and parity, and trying to facilitate group dynamics that properly reflect the views of all participants.

KEYWORDS

Hedging, Participatory Design, Gender

1. INTRODUCTION

Gender has long been considered an important factor in shaping participation in STEM subjects including Design. Consequently, when considering Participatory Design (PD) as an approach to system development it's important to consider the effect that gender might play, especially in a group setting (Rommes, E., 2006; Buchmuller et al., 2011; Bleijenbergh, I. and Van Engen, M., 2015); that gender is one of the "different identities negotiated both through personal interactions and in the materials used and objects created during the participatory design processes" (Brule and Spiel, 2019). An initial analysis of a PD innovation workshop suggested the possibility that gender differences in language use might impact on levels, forms and types of participation. Of particular interest was the possible different use of 'hedging' terms. Hedging refers to the idea of uncertainty, of ''hedging' your bets' with phrases such as "I think", "you know" and "sort of" (Murphy, 2010, Holmes, 1986, Holmes, 1990). Hedging is recognised as a "significant communicative resource" (Hyland, 1996). Some suggest gender plays a role in hedging; Murphy (2010) for example, states that "the use of hedges among females before a key word" is used "to avoid the appearance of playing the expert". Holmes (1986) states that hedging has two purposes, either to express speaker confidence e.g. "you know" or "reflecting uncertainty" e.g. "I think". Research by Dixon and Foster (1996) found that hedging was used the same number of times by both genders, (contradicting Holmes (1986)). They did however find that the results based on the gender of the audience of the speaker had a significant influence on "their use of epistemic *sort of* and confident *you know*." The analysis presented in this short paper focuses on the use of hedging in participatory design, whether and how this varies by gender, and what implications this might have for PD approaches to Design.

What can be defined as 'hedging' is somewhat subjective and retrospective as it is difficult to tell when hedging is used deliberately, for example to seem more approachable, or when it used due to genuine uncertainty. This is supported by Holmes (1986) and Fraser (2010) dissecting how hedging can lead to misinterpretation when used in the incorrect part of a sentence, for example when discussing how intelligent 'John' is, you might say "**sort of**, John is smart" or by placing the hedge in the wrong part of the sentence, the meaning may change entirely accidentally with "John is **sort of** smart." The potential for miscommunication is one that could be investigated in significant detail when observing innovation in a group setting to see if this hinders or helps the process. For example, could misinterpretation generate a stronger idea? Or will it simply frustrate the participants? It is therefore important to reflect upon literature that focuses on hedging and gender and to carry out research on possible gendered uses of hedging. Is it used as frequently but in different ways? Do we notice it more in one gender? Or is there simply no difference? These research questions are the focus of this short paper.

2. METHODOLOGY

PD, has a set structure as a research methodology including; "initial exploration of work", "discovery process" and "prototyping" (Spinuzzi, 2005). In this study, the "initial exploration" took the form of an innovation workshop; a style of focus group, where participants are encouraged to adopt an innovative and creative thinking style. In this instance this included; independent ideation around problem areas, followed by collaborative grouping. The "discovery process" was done through independent ideation of solutions around those problem areas, with the "prototyping" being carried out by the group at large. Ideation, in this instance, refers to the process of noting ideas around a topic on a sticky note. Many innovation workshops are based around this method of ideation; the differences lie in the topics of ideation and how these are derived (Silverstein, Samuel and DeCarlo, 2013).

This research builds on the use of conversation analysis (CA) (Stokoe and Weatheral, 2002), to provide 'the tools to explore in fine detail how issues around gender are occasioned in talk" (Stokoe and Smithson, 2001). This study uses a very rudimentary form of CA to uncover any gender differences in the use of hedging within PD. The study involved seven University students (five identified themselves as female, and two identified themselves as male) in an innovation workshop with the aim of designing digital solutions to help with their academic studies. This was run as part of the IT system service's innovation department at the University. Innovation workshops tie strongly into the journey of PD because participants are innovating and carrying out PD as it relates to their own experience as University students who are also the target audience of the product to be designed. In this instance, this is to be a digital solution to support students in their academic studies. The workshop began with ideation around problems with their academic lives, then participants were asked to present their problems to the group. After categorisation and independent ideation of solutions, they were then asked to combine their solutions. It is these transcribed discussions that this paper considers.

From the transcripts, a list of "hedging" terms were listed, categorised and contextualised for analysis. This was done using existing hedging terms such as "I think", "you know" and "sort of" (Murphy, 2010, Holmes, 1986, Holmes, 1990) and considering the importance of context (Gribanova and Gaidukova, 2019). Analysis was then carried out based on the number of occurrences of hedging based on gender, considering the distribution of gender in the group, as well the context. As well as a basic numerical analysis on which terms were more popular with each gender, the context was then analysed in further detail, since the aim of this paper is to uncover exactly *how* hedging is used differently between genders, not just how frequently.

3. RESULTS AND ANALYSIS

The initial research carried out on the transcripts revealed many examples of hedging. Table 1, below, shows the list of terms classified as "hedging" terms (Murphy, 2010, Holmes, 1986, Holmes, 1990) as well as "kind of" and "maybe" which this study choses to define as hedging terms. They were only recorded in the results when clearly used as hedging, not in discussion. The "context" column refers to how they were used, be it to express uncertainty or to persuade the other participants or the facilitator, adapted from Fraser (2010) and Holmes (1986). The average use per gender columns were calculated by dividing the number of uses by that gender by the number of participants of that gender to account for the uneven distribution (two men and five women).

Table 1. A list of hedging terms and their frequency of use by gender, as well as an average to account for an uneven mix of gender in participants

Term	*Context*	*Uses by men*	*Uses by women*	*Average use of hedge per man*	*Average user of hedge per woman*
"I think"	Expressed uncertainty	3	14	**1.5**	**2.8**
"Kind of" or "kinda"	Expressed uncertainty	1	20	**0.5**	**4**
"Maybe"	Persuasion	5	5	**2.5**	**1**
"Sort of"	Expressed uncertainty	1	2	**0.5**	**0.4**
"You know" or "y'know"	Persuasion	2	4	**1**	**0.8**

Uses of "I think" were discounted when opinions were being discussed in categorisation as this was a use of language and not a case of hedging, as can be seen below in Excerpts 1 and 2. An example of "I think" used as hedging can be seen in Excerpt 2. This was also done with the other terms, and they were only noted as a hedging use if the context supported this. Cases of "um" and "er" have also been discounted as, although they were used frequently, they were used more by participants as a means of delay.

Excerpt 1. An example of "I think" being discounted due to context:

M2: So which do you guys think is the biggest problem?
F7: **I think** the library is probably one of the bigger problems.
M2: Ok
F7: So…
M2: What do you guys **think**?

Excerpt 2. An example of "I think" being used as hedging:

F1: Um... Some lecturers don't use the interactive screen, so, um, so **I think** you want more people to use it... So...

As can be seen in the Table 1, hedges such as "kind of" and "I think" were used more frequently by women to express uncertainty. But this difference is not statistically significant as the p value is 0.472 which is more than our stated p value 0.05, which can be seen in Table 2.

Table 2. A calculation of the statistical difference between the frequency of hedging between men and women

	Average use of hedging by men	*Average use of hedging by women*
Mean	1.2	1.8
Variance	0.7	2.36
P(T<=t) two-tail	**0.472192325**	

It could also have been argued that the use, or category, of hedging varied between gender, however the results for this are also not significant, as can be seen in Table 3 for persuasive hedging and Table 4 for expression of uncertainty, because both 0.463, for persuasive, and 0.299, for uncertainty, are also both more than 0.05 (our stated p value).

Table 3. A calculation of the statistical difference between the frequency of hedging between men and women for terms categorised as 'persuasion'

	Average use of persuasive hedging by men	*Average use of persuasive hedging by women*
Mean	1.75	0.9
Variance	1.125	0.02
P(T<=t) two-tail	**0.463047182**	

Table 4. A calculation of the statistical difference between the frequency of hedging between men and women for terms categorised as 'expressed uncertainty

	Average use of uncertainty hedging by men	*Average use of uncertainty hedging by women*
Mean	0.833333333	2.4
Variance	0.333333333	3.36
P(T<=t) two-tail	**0.293452734**	

All the above results show a similar frequency of hedging used by both male and female participants, and supports the findings by Dixon and Foster (1996), but contradicts the differences found by Holmes (1986). Of course the statistical analysis is impacted by the rather small sample and further workshops might provide further and more conclusive evidence. Clearly too there is a need to research some of the more contextual features of the various 'hedging' utterances through both observation and especially through interviewing – "when you said 'maybe' here, what were you thinking? Why did you use that particular term?"

4. CONCLUSION

While Murphy (2010) states "the use of hedges among females before a key word" is used "to avoid the appearance of playing the expert". our analysis found no statistically significant gender differences in how hedging was used. The data is interesting and perhaps suggestive but, unfortunately, not statistically significant. Sample size has an impact on this but perhaps there is a need for more subtle, more contextual, analysis. Perhaps the issue may be that each occurrence of hedging is being treated as equal, and a more subtle analysis of 'hedging' is required to truly determine if there are any gender differences at play in group interaction in PD. The differences in past research (Holmes, 1986, Dixon and Foster, 1997, Stokoe and Smithson, 2001, Stokoe and Weatheral, 2002) show that this lack of statistically significant results may not be all it appears, in fact it could be suggested that it simply shows the need for a more subtle means of analysis. Perhaps using only two hedging categories was not enough, or perhaps as Murphy (2010) and Fraser (2010) suggest, it is important to consider exactly where in an utterance a 'hedging' term is used. Therefore, this paper concludes that further research and contextual analysis and more detailed transcription is required. With past research showing contradictory findings of any relationship between gender and hedging (Holmes, 1986, Dixon and Foster 1996), this paper has shown that the frequency of hedging (from predefined utterances classified as hedging) is used on average no more frequently or infrequently based on the gender of the participant. This is not to say, however, that there are no differences at all. Further research will be carried out to take into account the contextual features of conversation; to find out if where in an utterance, and in what circumstances, hedging varies by gender, or by gender identity. This extended research may also include how this impacts the artefacts created. Overall, this research suggests that the topic requires further research, not least because of its implications for the process and value of PD, the design of PD workshops and consideration of the role of workshop facilitators in considering and regulating the effects of 'hedging' in design discussions. If workshop facilitators learn to recognise the differential use of 'hedging' terms by participants then they can respond in various ways and hopefully improve the value of workshop discussions, through acknowledging the importance of giving voice and parity, ensuring group dynamics and outcomes that properly reflect the views of all participants.

ACKNOWLEDGEMENT

With thanks to Dr Lynne Blair and Dr Mark Rouncefield for their support and guidance, and to the anonymous reviewers for their advice and feedback.

REFERENCES

Bleijenbergh, I. and Van Engen, M. (2015). Participatory modelling to support gender equality. *Equality, Diversity and Inclusion: An International Journal*.

Brulé, E. and Spiel, K. (2019), June. Negotiating gender and disability identities in participatory design. In *Proceedings of the 9th International Conference on Communities & Technologies-Transforming Communities* (pp. 218-227).

Buchmüller, S., Joost, G., Bessing, N. and Stein, S. (2011). Bridging the gender and generation gap by ICT applying a participatory design process. *Personal and Ubiquitous Computing*, *15*(7), p.743.

Crabtree A., Tolmie P., Rouncefield M. (2013). "How Many Bloody Examples Do You Want?" Fieldwork and Generalisation. Proceedings of the 13th European Conference on Computer Supported Cooperative Work, 21-25 September 2013, Paphos, Cyprus. Springer, London

Dixon, J. and Foster, D. (1997). *Journal of Psycholinguistic Research*, 26(1), pp.89-107.

Fraser, B. (2010). Pragmatic Competence: The Case of Hedging. *New Approaches to Hedging*, pp.15-34.

Gribanova, T. and Gaidukova, T. (2019). Hedging in different types of discourse. *Training Language and Culture*, 3(2), pp.85-99.

Hansen, N., Dindler, C., Halskov, K., Iversen, O., Bossen, C., Basballe, D. and Schouten, B. (2019). How Participatory Design Works. *Proceedings of the 31st Australian Conference on Human-Computer- Interaction*.

Holmes, J. (1986). Functions of You Know in Women's and Men's Speech. *Language in Society*, 15(1), pp.1-21.

Holmes, J. (1990). Hedges and Boosters in Women's and Men's Speech. *Language & Communication*, 10(3), pp.185-205.

Hyland, K. (1996). Writing Without Conviction? Hedging in Science Research Articles. *Applied Linguistics*, 17(4), pp. 433-454.

Murphy, B. (2010). Corpus and sociolinguistics: investigating age and gender in female talk, Amsterdam; Philadelphia: John Benjamins Pub. Co.

Rommes, E. (2006). Gender sensitive design practices. In *Encyclopedia of gender and information technology* (pp. 675-681). IGI Global.

Silverstein, D., Samuel, P. and DeCarlo, N. (2013). *The Innovator's Toolkit*. 2nd ed. Hoboken, N.J.: Wiley.

Spinuzzi, C. (2005). The Methodology of Participatory Design. *Applied Theory,* 52(2), pp.163-174.

Stokoe, E. and Smithson, J. (2001). Making Gender Relevant: Conversation Analysis and Gender Categories in Interaction. *Discourse & Society*, 12(2), pp.217-244.

Stokoe, E. and Weatheral, A. (2002). Gender, language, conversation analysis and feminism. *Discourse & Society*, 13(6), pp.707-713.

EXPLORATORY STUDY EXAMINING THE FEASIBILITY OF A TECHNOLOGY-BASED TOOL TO SUPPORT CREATIVITY IN CHILDREN WITH AUTISM

Aurora Constantin, Cristina Adriana Alexandru, Georgia Fox and Lauren Meikle
University of Edinburgh, School of Informatics
10 Crichton Street
Edinburgh EH89AB, UK

ABSTRACT

Previous research suggests that Participatory Design (PD) is a very promising approach for involving children with Autism Spectrum Conditions (ASC) in generating design solutions, but also in practising essential skills (e.g. collaboration skills). However, because of their difficulties with social communication accompanied by rigidity in thought and behaviour, these children face significant challenges during PD. Specifically, in the idea generation stage of PD, they have difficulties expressing their creativity. Based on user participation, we built a first version of a low fidelity prototype (iGeneration) for a technology-based tool to elicit creativity in children with ASC during idea generation. This article reports on a research study which explored the feasibility of iGeneration to support children with ASC in creating design ideas for an educational game. The results revealed that the participants engaged and enjoyed working with iGeneration. The children created a number of ideas which were diverse, novel and appropriate for the design tasks.

KEYWORDS

Participatory Design, Children, Autism, Feasibility Study, Idea Generation

1. INTRODUCTION

Previous research suggests that PD is a very promising approach for involving individuals with Autism Spectrum Conditions (ASC) in generating technological design solutions (Constantin et al. 2019, Escobedo et al. 2014, Grawemeyer et al. 2012, Keay-Bright. 2007). For children with ASC, PD can not only lead to the design of effective systems, but also be engaging, motivating and inspire them to become design partners (Mazzone et al. 2012). Participation is empowering, giving them confidence to share opinions and ideas with others. In addition, it offers opportunities to develop new skills, such as problem solving, collaboration (Malinverni et al. 2014), design related skills, and a reflective viewpoint towards technology, which are essential in our digital society (Iversen et al. 2017). Particularly, PD is fundamentally intertwined with creativity and could contribute essentially to unlocking it (Makhaeva et al. 2016).

Despite these widely recognized advantages, involving children with ASC in PD is often avoided because of various challenges, including their "communication barriers" (De Leo and Leroy 2008, Keay-Bright 2007) or "time and resource constraints" (Randolph and Eronen 2007). Idea generation, one of the most common PD activities, is particularly challenging as children with autism have difficulties expressing their creativity. Moreover, they require tailored support to be able to generate and communicate their design ideas.

Technology may be a good candidate to support children with ASC during the PD process. Over the last few decades, it has been increasingly designed and employed with children with ASC (Malinverni et al. 2014, Escobedo et al. 2014, Grawemeyer et al. 2012, Frauenberger et al. 2013), particularly due to their affinity toward it, as well as the advantages it brings over traditional methods (e.g. pencil and paper). However, very little has been done to explore how technology can best support children with ASC and designers/researchers during PD. Therefore, the proposed project aims to design the first personalisable technology-based tool (iGeneration) to support creativity during the idea generation stage of PD with children with ASC. We believe that such a tool can act as an interface between designers and children with ASC, making their collaboration easier within a more predictable and controllable environment compared to traditional approaches to PD.

Moreover, technology affordances can support personalisation, making it easier for the designers/researchers to tailor their PD methods to the individual needs of the involved children.

In this paper, we describe a first low-fidelity version of the iGeneration prototype which was focused on individual interaction to generate design ideas. In the feasibility study reported, we explored whether children with ASC engage, enjoy working with the prototype, and are able to produce design ideas as supported by it and the designer only (collaboration between children will be considered in the next prototype version). To this end, we decided to use paper-based prototype screens and a researcher playing the role of the computer, instead of a technological solution. This may be seen as a limitation, but had a strong motivation given by the need to provide something tangible and concrete enough for the autistic children, to get their views on feasibility, before delving into detailed design. In particular, as they may have difficulties interpreting abstractions (Ropar and Peebles 2007) which are inevitably used in technological tools, we considered it essential to understand whether this would be an issue with our prototype. This way, we can ensure that what is being developed gets the autistic children's 'seal of approval' by respecting their needs.

This study contributed to answer the following three research questions: 1. Could a low-fidelity prototype for technology-based tool support engagement in children with ASC during the idea generation stage of a PD process? 2. Do children with ASC enjoy using the prototype? 3. Are children with ASC able to generate design ideas using the prototype? Additionally, we were interested in collecting ideas to improve the tool.

2. STUDIES TO INFORM THE DESIGN OF IGENERATION

The version of the iGeneration low-fidelity prototype presented here was iteratively designed by involving various stakeholders (N=15): practitioners (e.g. teachers), carers, and researchers. A description of the studies is available in (Constantin and Hourcade 2018). Once the prototype was ready, we evaluated its usability and suitability with five neurotypical (NT) children aged 7 to 11. The study revealed that the NT children engaged and enjoyed using the prototype and that the designed activities/tasks were suitable. They also perceived the tool as being useful to support them in creating design ideas. Some usability problems were identified (e.g. visibility of some buttons and use of error prevention messages), which we addressed.

3. THE IGENERATION PROTOTYPE

The prototype opening page (Figure 1) welcomes the user via a customisable virtual character (VC). The child is asked to type their name, then selects a project to work on and the VC introduces them to the design problem through a fictional story (as in Fails et al. 2013) (Figure 2). The child can read the story or choose the VC to read the story for them. After that, the VC presents the first task, encouraging the child to generate as many design ideas as possible. It tells the child to add an idea on a digital sticky note which can be displayed when pressing the button "Add note" in the bottom left corner of the screen (Figure 3). When the sticky note is displayed, the VC guides the child to introduce ideas by typing, drawing, adding an image from the gallery or through voice recording. These were chosen to encourage the children's creativity and offer freedom to express themselves in their preferred way. When the child is stuck, the VC prompts them to ask for help by pressing a button, which displays hints (Figure 4). The VC rewards the child for each achievement (after adding a new idea like in Figure 5, completing a task or completing the entire project). The reward is incremental, reflecting the child's progress, as recommended by (Constantin et al. 2017) based on their research with autistic children. The designer can offer additional support during the interaction, and is meant to analyse the text, drawings, images, recordings of the child's ideas.

Figure 1. iGeneration: Screenshot of the opening page

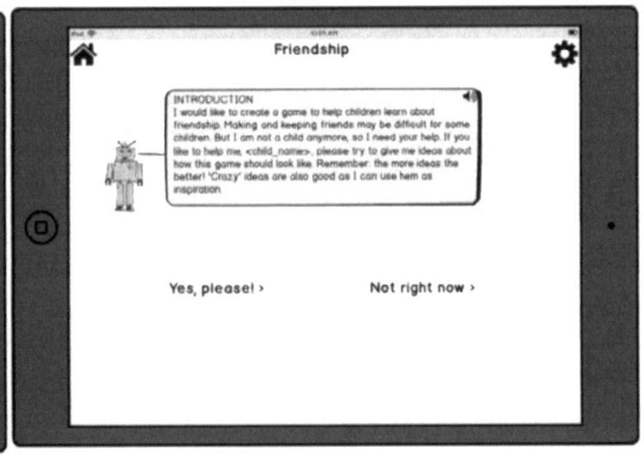

Figure 2. iGeneration: Screenshot with a story

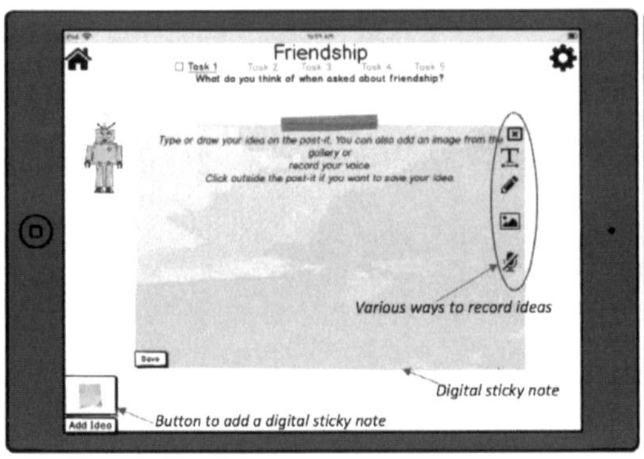

Figure 3. iGeneration: Screenshot with a sticky note

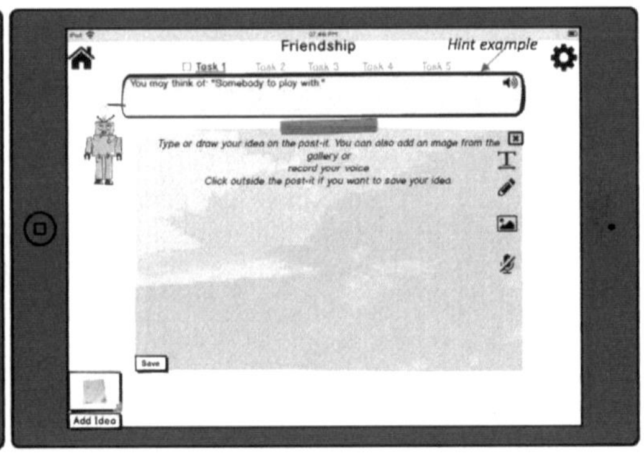

Figure 4. iGeneration: Screenshot with a hint suggested

4. DESIGN OF THE FEASIBILITY STUDY

The feasibility study aimed to explore whether children with ASC can interact with the prototype and are able to produce design ideas. It was carried out during a visit to a holiday-time event for autistic children organised in the Connolly School Campus in Blackburn, UK by the Lothian Autistic Society, with the researchers being offered by the organisation 4 hours to finalise it. The study was approved by the University of Edinburgh School of Education Ethics Committee. Well in advance of the day of the study, information sheets and consent forms were sent to parents. We set up the study after we received the signed consent forms. Five children (3 male, 2 female) with a previous ASC diagnosis (all at level 2 according to DSM-5 (APA, 2013)), aged 10-14 ((Mean = 12.2; SD = 1.64) and no reported comorbidities (including no intellectual disability), all verbal, participated in the study. Before beginning a session, each child provided informed assent for participation. Three children participated one-by-one, while two preferred to interact with the prototype simultaneously, yet still individually. Each child was accompanied by a parent or carer who were asked to intervene only if needed, to help explain or support the child. Three researchers were present, playing the roles of facilitator, computer to change the paper screens for the child, and video recorder of the session. A session lasted for about 40 minutes.

After a brief introduction, the children were asked to use the prototype without training and create design ideas for an educational game focused on friendship (characterising friends and the activities they would enjoy together). The game was structured around five tasks. The first four were designed to gather ideas of game features (e.g. characters and activities) while the last collected ideas of rewards (possibly different to the ones already received) children preferred when they came up with an idea, completed a task or the entire game. Finally, a short questionnaire gathered the children's perceived experience with the prototype.

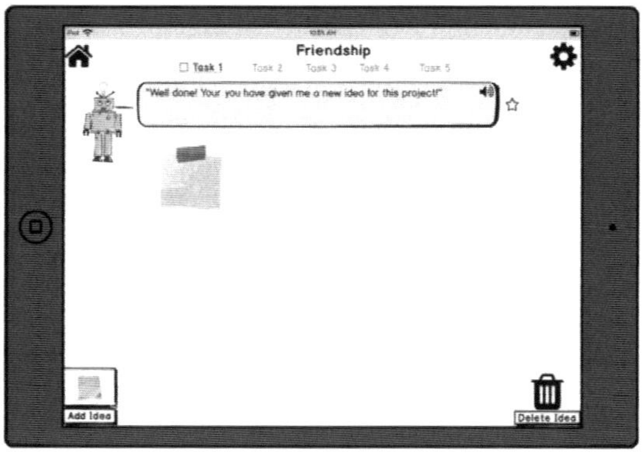

Figure 5. iGeneration: Rewards

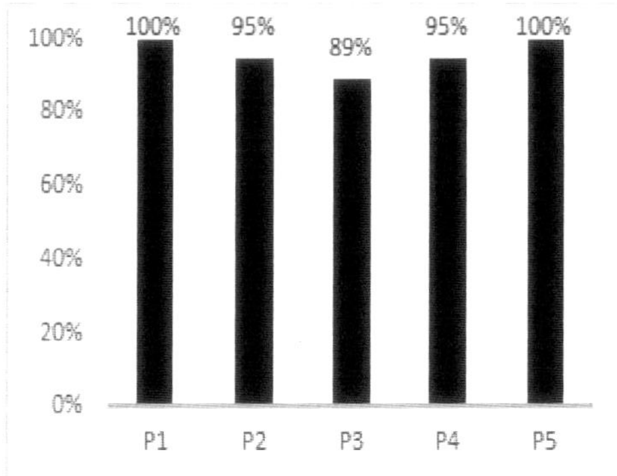

Figure 6. Levels of engagement

5. DATA COLLECTION AND ANALYSIS

The video recordings (N=4, T=212 minutes) of the sessions were transcribed (including noting non-verbal communication and pauses) two at a time by two researchers, after which they were swapped and proofread. Analysis was then performed following a top-down thematic analysis (Braun and Clarke 2006). Similarly, the researchers analysed transcripts two at a time, and swapped. Discrepancies were discussed with the team.

Similar to previous work (e.g. (Xie et al. 2008)) the level of engagement was measured by percentage of on-task time per child. The level of enjoyment during prototype use was also analysed, using three measures: 1) positive and negative verbal and non-verbal behaviours from the video recordings (Xie et al. 2008); 2) general level of child enjoyment, on a 5-point smileyometer, a Likert scale with emoticons ranging from very unhappy to very happy (Read and MacFarlane 2006; Frauenberger et al. 2013); 3) level of enjoyment with the VC, the ways that ideas can be entered (text, drawings, images and voice recording) and the received rewards; these were also ranked using a smileyometer. To answer the third research question, all ideas generated by children were counted and analysed in terms of appropriateness (i.e. relevance to the design task), diversity/uniqueness (i.e. not being mentioned before), and novelty (not being facilitated by a hint).

6. RESULTS

Level of engagement. The time spent by the children on-task was 96% of the total time across the four sessions, and is represented for each child in percentages in Figure 6. Breaks were not requested. Moreover, three children were asked to move to the next task after generating a number of ideas, due to our time limit.

Level of enjoyment. On the general opinion smileyometer, three children selected an emoticon for 'very happy', one for 'happy' and one for 'neither happy nor unhappy'. In addition, the analysis of verbal and non-verbal behaviour revealed a number of instances when children enjoyed working with the prototype, and no frustration with it (Figure 7). All children reported they liked the virtual character (2 selected 'very happy' and 3 'happy'). Most of them liked the ways of recording ideas and the rewards, with no answer lower than 'neither happy nor unhappy' but some variability (especially for the ways of recording ideas).

Ideas Generated. Children generated 39 ideas, with at least one per task per child (Figure 8). The maximum number of ideas generated by a child across tasks was 10. However, the children did not exhaust their ideas since a time limit was imposed. Only two employed all ways of introducing their ideas. Out of the 39 ideas generated, 34 were appropriate for the tasks, 27 were diverse (unique) and 30 were novel.

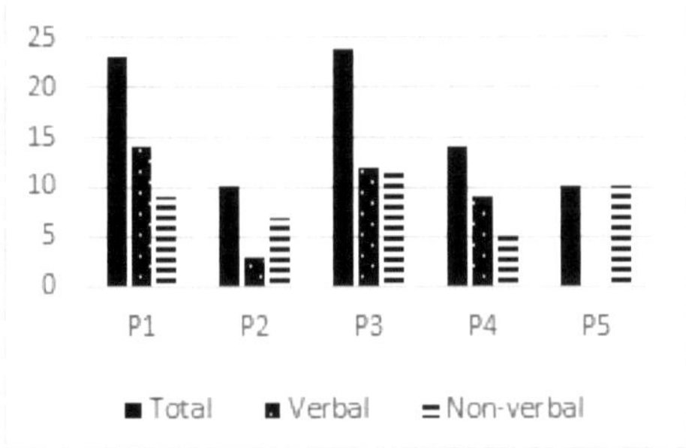

Figure 7. Instances of enjoyment with the prototype

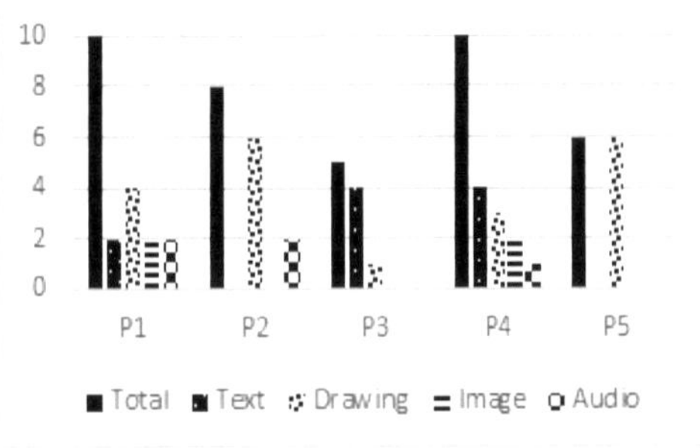

Figure 8. Numbers of ideas per child

7. DISCUSSION

We investigated the feasibility of a future technology-based tool (iGeneration), specifically designed to support autistic children to engage and contribute their ideas during PD's idea generation, as individually in this initial version. We employed a low fidelity prototype which had been iteratively designed and improved based on a series of studies involving 20 stakeholders. Our main aims were to find out whether children with autism would engage with the prototype, enjoy working with it and be capable of generating design ideas.

The fact that all participants completed the tasks without asking for a break and spent on average a very high percentage (96%), and a minimum of 89%, of session time on them indicates that the tool is promising for engaging children with autism during the idea generation stage of PD. Both the results from questionnaires and behaviour observations (verbal and non-verbal) clearly indicate that the children enjoyed using the prototype. The child who selected the emoticon 'neither happy nor unhappy', when asked for a reason for her answer, explained that she would like the prototype to be on a tablet. This suggests that she would enjoy more using a more finished product, rather than not liking the prototype at all. The small variability of opinions on ways of recording design ideas may be related to each child's abilities, and it would be interesting to further investigate how these features could be made more useful and attractive to children. Children were all able to generate ideas (at least one per task) and four out of the five generated more than one idea for at least one task. With few exceptions, the ideas were appropriate to the task. Sometimes the children were distracted, e.g. one of them (P3) was interested in Microsoft products and spent a long time describing them, and another (P2) appeared to sometimes be more interested in drawing than relating the idea to the task. Designing features to redirect child attention to the task as well as taking advantage of their interests to facilitate idea generation should be considered at the next stage of the tool design. In addition, most of the ideas generated were quite diverse (not repetitive) and novel (with no hint needed before).

Although our findings are promising, there are a few limitations which should be considered in the future. Firstly, our sample size was small, therefore the reported findings should be interpreted with caution. Actually, most studies with children with ASC include small sample sizes, mainly due to a general difficulty in recruiting participants (Bozgeyikli et al. 2018). However, in spite of the small sample, this study has contributed to our understanding of how a new technology-based tool can support children with ASC to contribute their ideas during a PD process. Moreover, children's suggestions will help us further improve the design of the tool. Secondly, our study had a time limit which was imposed by the autistic organisation's holiday campus activities. After developing the high-fidelity prototype, we intend to conduct a within-subject design study with children with ASC to compare engagement, enjoyment and ideas generated (both in quantity and quality) when working with it (condition A) and without (condition B). In addition, we are interested to look at the impact of the tool on children's behaviour and abilities (e.g. anxiety, self-efficacy).

Despite the limitations of this study, the results support a positive answer for the research questions, and constitute a strong basis for us to continue designing and developing iGeneration. In version two of iGeneration, we will focus on including collaborative idea generation (i.e. children working together to generate design ideas) and automatic personalised hints to support autistic children. For the latter, an idea reported in (Constantin et al. 2019) is to use crowdsourcing with a team of selected online workers (experts and practitioners in autism) as a way of generating hints and rating them in terms of appropriateness and usefulness for a child. Machine learning could remove noise and redundancy before the most frequent, appropriate and useful hint is provided. This approach has ethical challenges which will need to be addressed. We will also consider personalising other features for autistic children (e.g. the VC, the rewards).

REFERENCES

American Psychiatry Association (APA). 2013. Diagnostic and Statistical Manual of Mental Disorders Fifth Edition DSM-V. *Washington, DC.*

Braun, V. and Clarke, V., 2006. Using thematic analysis in psychology. *Qualitative research in psychology*, 3(2): 77-101.

Constantin, A., Alexandru, C.A. and Dragomir, M., 2019. Using crowdsourcing to foster creativity in children with autism during Idea Generation. *CHI'19 Extended Abstracts*.

Constantin, A. and Hourcade, J.P., 2018, October. Toward a technology-based tool to support Idea Generation during Participatory Design with children with Autism Spectrum Disorders. In *Proceedings of the 20th International ACM SIGACCESS Conference on Computers and Accessibility,* 385-387.

Constantin, A., Johnson, H., Smith, E., Lengyel, D., & Brosnan, M., 2017. Designing computer-based rewards with and for children with Autism Spectrum Disorder and/or Intellectual Disability. *Computers in Human Behav.*, 75: 404-414.

Constantin, A., Korte, J., Fails, J.A., Good, J., Alexandru, C.A., Dragomir, M., Pain, H., Hourcade, J.P., Eriksson, E., Waller, A. and Garzotto, F., 2019, June. Pushing the boundaries of participatory design with children with special needs. In *Proceedings of the 18th ACM International Conference on Interaction Design and Children*, 697-705.

De Leo, G. and Leroy, G., 2008, June. Smartphones to facilitate communication and improve social skills of children with severe autism spectrum disorder: special education teachers as proxies. In *Proceedings of the 7th international conference on Interaction design and children*, 45-48.

Druin, A., 2002. The role of children in the design of new technology. *Behaviour and information technology*, *21*(1):1-25.

Escobedo, L., Tentori, M., Quintana, E., Favela, J. and Garcia-Rosas, D., 2014. Using augmented reality to help children with autism stay focused. *IEEE Pervasive Computing*, 13(1):38-46.

Fails, J.A., Guha, M.L. and Druin, A., 2013. Methods and techniques for involving children in the design of new technology for children. *Foundations and Trends in Human-Computer Interaction*, 6(2):85-166.

Frauenberger, C., Good, J., Alcorn, A. and Pain, H., 2013. Conversing through and about technologies: Design critique as an opportunity to engage children with autism and broaden research (er) perspectives. *IJCCI*, 1(2):38-49.

Grawemeyer, B., Johnson, H., Brosnan, M., Ashwin, E. and Benton, L., 2012, June. Developing an embodied pedagogical agent with and for young people with autism spectrum disorder. In International Conference on Intelligent Tutoring Systems, 262-267. Springer, Berlin, Heidelberg.

Iversen, O.S., Smith, R.C. and Dindler, C., 2017, June. Child as protagonist: Expanding the role of children in participatory design. In *Proceedings of the 2017 Conference on Interaction Design and Children*, 27-37.

Keay-Bright, W., 2007. The reactive colours project: demonstrating participatory and collaborative design methods for the creation of software for autistic children. *Design Principles and Practices: an International Journal*, 1(2): 7-15.

Malinverni, L., Mora-Guiard, J., Padillo, V., Mairena, M., Hervás, A. and Pares, N., 2014, June. Participatory design strategies to enhance the creative contribution of children with special needs. In *Proceedings of the 2014 conference on Interaction design and children*, 85-94.

Mazzone, L., Ruta, L. and Reale, L., 2012. Psychiatric comorbidities in asperger syndrome and high functioning autism: diagnostic challenges. *Annals of general psychiatry*, 11(1):16.

Randolph, J.J. and Eronen, P.J., 2007. Developing the Learning Door: A case study in youth participatory program planning. *Evaluation and Program Planning*, 30(1):55-65.

Read, J.C. and MacFarlane, S., 2006, June. Using the fun toolkit and other survey methods to gather opinions in child computer interaction. In *Proceedings of the 2006 conference on Interaction design and children*, 81-88.

Ropar, D. and Peebles, D., 2007. Sorting preference in children with autism: the dominance of concrete features. *Journal of autism and developmental disorders*, *37*(2), 270-280.

Xie, L., Antle, A.N. and Motamedi, N., 2008, February. Are tangibles more fun? Comparing children's enjoyment and engagement using physical, graphical and tangible user interfaces. In *Proceedings of the 2nd international conference on Tangible and embedded interaction*, 191-198.

MOTIVATEME!: AN ALEXA SKILL TO SUPPORT HIGHER EDUCATION STUDENTS WITH AUTISM

Ami Bakhai, Aurora Constantin and Cristina Adriana Alexandru
University of Edinburgh, School of Informatics
10 Crichton Street
Edinburgh EH89AB, UK

ABSTRACT

The rate of successful completion of studies for students with Autism Spectrum Disorders (ASD) in Higher Education (HE) is only 40%, which is lower than that for many other students with disabilities. This is caused by a series of challenges encountered by this population in HE. This paper reports on research studies which identified the top challenges faced by HE students with ASD and explored how a Skill (a custom application) for Amazon Alexa Echo Show (AAES) can be designed to support them in overcoming these challenges. A Skill named MotivateMe! was implemented in two iterations for the AAES. During the evaluation study of MotivateMe!, the Skill was perceived by students and experts as being appropriate for students with ASD to deal with distractions and to motivate them to study (which were identified as being the top challenges).

KEYWORDS

Higher Education, Intelligent Virtual Assistants, Autism, User-Centred Design

1. INTRODUCTION

In the UK, the number of students with Autism Spectrum Disorders (ASD) at university is increasing (Gurbuz et al. 2019). However less than 40% of them complete their qualification, which is the lowest rate of success among the other groups of students with disabilities (Gurbuz et al. 2019). Moreover, they often underachieve academically and face a decreased satisfaction of their experience in Higher Education (HE) (Drake 2014). All of these are mainly consequences of a series of difficulties that students with ASD face, such as the change of environment or unstructured teaching (Friedman et al.2013, Howlin & Moss 2012). Two main categories of challenges have been identified: social and academic (Gurbuz et al. 2019). Social problems include those with relationships and peer-to-peer conversations. On the academic side, problems lie in managing time, creating a routine and being motivated to study (Gurbuz et al. 2019, Jansen et al. 2018, White et al. 2016).

Recently, attention has been increasingly directed toward the benefits of using technology to support autistic people to deal with their difficulties. Some examples of technological solutions developed to help students with ASD in their studies are smartphone applications (Ayres et al. 2013, Bereznak et al. 2012) and wearable technology (Sahin et al. 2018) which targeted understanding social interactions, as well as a Personal Digital Assistant intended to help with multitasking independently (Mechling et al. 2009).

However, literature is scarce on designing Intelligent Virtual Assistants (IVAs), such as Amazon Alexa, to help students in HE overcome their challenges. Available on the market only since five years ago, Amazon Alexa is the most sold and grossing IVA to date (Gartner, 2017). It allows users to interact with it through speech at a level of quality which feels like talking to a human (Gao et al. 2018). A very recent product, Amazon Alexa Echo Show (AAES), is a voice activated assistant with a visual screen which potentially/presumably makes it more useful for ASD students, since most of them are visual learners (Kokina and Kern 2010). The study by (Lopatovska et al. 2019) discusses the interest in AAES for all individuals, including individuals with disabilities such as ASD. (Yu et al. 2018) highlighted the need of looking into the potential of AAES to support students in general, and students with ASD in particular.

This paper reports on a project which focused on identifying the top challenges faced by HE students with ASD and exploring how a Skill (a custom application for Amazon Alexa) has to be designed to support them overcome these challenges. The following research questions guided our research: *RQ1: What are the top challenges that HE students encounter in their studies? RQ2: How can an AAES Skill be best designed to support HE students with ASD in coping with these challenges? RQ3:To what extent does the new technology help HE students with ASD cope with their challenges?*

2. METHODOLOGY OVERVIEW

The methodology followed four main stages. First, the research literature was reviewed to identify common challenges faced by HE students with ASD, various technology-based applications to support HE students, and guidelines to design technology for the ASD population. The following guidelines were identified to guide the design: G1. predictability (which evokes the feeling of sameness characteristic in autism and reduces anxiety which is a common problem for this population (Baron-Cohen et al. 2007); G2. visuals (due to the fact that most of the autistic individuals are visual learners (Kokina and Kern 2010); G3. customisation (as individuals with autism form a very heterogeneous population and hence tailoring the Skills to meet particular individual needs is essential (Baron-Cohen et al. 2007). Second, the top challenges faced by HE students with ASD were identified and a set of requirements for the AAES Skill were devised (section 3). The third stage, Implementation, involved the technical development of two iterations of the Skill and the first iteration's formative evaluation (section 4). The final stage, Evaluation (section 5), investigated the potential of the new Skill to help ASD students in HE to deal with distractions and be motivated to study (which were identified as being the top challenges).

A User-Centered Design (UCD) framework was adopted, in which users were involved at every stage of the design process (Norman et al. 1986). However, despite HE students with autism being the end users of the new Skill, their vulnerability means that involving them in empirical studies can cause distress (as supported by (Constantin et al. 2019, Boyd-Graber et al. 2006) and also advised by Disability Student Office in the researchers' university), and is moreover very time and resource consuming. Instead, the researchers involved neurotypical (NT) students, following prior study examples with other ASD population groups (e.g. Frauenberger et al. 2012). That ensured that the age-related expertise was brought into the initial design of the technology. Also, HCI experts with experience in usability and ASD were involved to advise what is appropriate to help students with ASD cope with their challenges.

3. INFORMING THE DESIGN

This stage included two studies. During the first, semi-structured interviews were conducted with six NT students between the ages of 18 and 24 and four experts in HCI, ASD and Education. The main aims of interviews were to: 1. understand better the problems faced by students in their daily lives in HE (RQ1), and 2. gather requirements for the Skill (RQ2). The interviews were transcribed and the data was analysed using thematic analysis (Leavy 2014). The most important resulting requirements were mainly related to usability (ease of use, efficiency, predictability, error prevention), and interaction, outlining the need for positive and encouraging interactions which are adapted to the user (G3). The main problems identified by students were the ease of getting distracted and lack of motivation when studying, not being able to start studying or working, and difficulty in remembering content. The second study consisted of a focus group and design workshop with seven NT students aged 21 to 24, with the aims of 1) prioritising the problems faced by students which had been identified in the interviews (RQ1) and 2) gathering more requirements (RQ2). For the latter, two examples of existing Amazon Alexa Skills were shown to the students for inspiration: wikiHow, a knowledge-based Skill which is very popular on AAES, and mathMania, an audio-only very popular educational Skill which proposes mathematical challenges to the users and assesses their answers. The ease of getting distracted and the lack of motivation when studying were identified as the students' top priority problem. The students were asked to design a Skill for this problem, as guided by some questions. The data was analysed using the same methods and in the first study. Most of the requirements from the first study were confirmed, and more requirements were added, the most important of them being the following:

- On the user interface design: providing visuals which are familiar to the users to show the status of the Skill, as well as textual instructions; both of these matching the audio output; being positive and customised to the user; using a virtual character (VC) to foster emotional attachment to the Skill.
- On the decision elements of the design: the need for creating a routine through fun with a customisable VC, while also monitoring and blocking other websites/apps that may distract the user.
- On use by autistic students: the need for simple, robust and flexible controls fostering independent use without support, with clear and consistent instructions and feedback.

4. THE MOTIVATEME! SKILL

The Skill was built using Amazon's proprietary Alexa Skills Kit (ASK) (Amazon 2020). In its **first iteration**, it allowed users to verbally register to the Skill (if new to it), then set up a new task (e.g. studying for a certain course) with its expected duration, or open an existing task. Each action was supported by on-screen instructions (e.g. Figure 1) and feedback when the action was completed. For each newly created task, the user was able to pair a VC (a tree or a cat, Figure 2) with their task. The more the user worked on their task in proportion to its expected duration, the more the paired VC would grow on the screen. If the user did not work on the task for a while, the chosen VC would get ill and be unhappy. The user was expected to complete each task in one go. After the first iteration was completed, a formative evaluation with 22 participants (20 NT students and two HCI and Education experts) was carried out. The participants were asked to try the Skill and complete a questionnaire consisting of the System Usability Scale (SUS) (Brooke 1996) as well as three open ended questions. The SUS was intended to assess the Skill's usability, while the open ended questions were meant to elicit suggestions for improving the Skill. A calculation of the SUS score according to (Brooke 1996) and (Sauro 2011) revealed a letter grade of B in usability (mean score of 76). The open ended questions were analysed using open coding (Saldana 2015) and thematic analysis (Leavy 2014) and revealed as main suggestions adding a 'stop' command to stop a task rather than using a timer of the user's expected time, using simpler commands to activate an action and adding the ability to add notes to the task as reminders to e.g. revisit something in the course. The feedback helped to refine the Skill through **a second iteration**. In this second iteration, the user has been given more independence by being allowed to set up tasks without starting them, and being able to keep working on the same task by stopping and restarting it verbally. The timer was removed, and progress towards the task's total expected duration is calculated based on the difference between the time when the task was stopped and when it was started. While working on the task, the user can ask for statistics which will indicate progress and how much more work is needed to get the VC to grow further. Moreover, as suggested by the participants, notes can now be added to the task and the user can request to see the full list of notes on the screen. A diagram showcasing the actions that are available to the user, in order, in the second iteration of the Skill is available in Figure 3.

5. EVALUATION

The final evaluation stage involved a task-based evaluation method followed by a questionnaire with seven NT students (new to this study) and two experts (ASD and HCI, Education). It was conducted online due to the COVID-19 pandemic, which led to the smaller number of participants. The questionnaires included SUS (Brooke 1996) for gathering the participants' views on the task's usability, but also open questions aimed to determine the general user experience with the Skill, the Skill's appropriateness and potential to motivate students with autism (the experts' questionnaire only), and open questions collecting suggestions for the Skill's future development. The data was analysed similarly to the formative evaluation. The results of the SUS indicated a grade of B in usability (mean SUS score of 71.66). Both of the expert participants considered the Skill appropriate and potentially motivational for students with autism: *"I would encourage a student with ASD to give it a try [..], this could motivate them to study"*. They would recommend the Skill both for ASD and NT students. Moreover, all the NT students enjoyed the Skill and predicted that it would be useful for them as well, to help them with their motivation and concentrating on studies. They all mentioned being willing to recommend the Skill to a fellow student: *"I would recommend it to some friends who I think would be motivated by caring for a virtual animal/plant"*.

The following were the three most important suggestions:

- Reducing the complexity of verbal interactions (all NT students and experts): A student participant mentioned *"Maybe how many words they [the students] are required to say in the interaction and when the device wouldn't understand them, it could be frustrating"*.
- Increasing the level of customisation and personalisation to facilitate engagement and encourage motivation (all NT students and experts), through a more varied choice of VCs or a narrative around the VC which is personalised to the student.
- Improving the transparency of the Skill status (3/7 students, 2/2 experts) and available actions (5/7 students, 2/2 experts) by including a menu screen or an indication of the different actions possible from the present screen.

Figure 1. First screen of MotivateMe! and setting up username

Figure 2. Confirmation of setting up a task and request for pairing it up with a virtual character on MotivateMe!

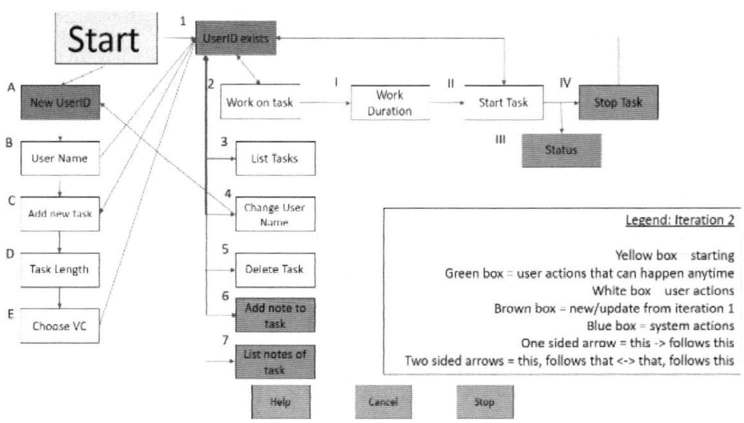

Figure 3. Action Diagram for the second iteration of MotivateMe!

6. CONCLUSION

The project focused on researching the best intervention for HE students with ASD through an AAES Skill. The main problems were getting distracted and the lack of motivation to study, and requirements to address them by a Skill were gathered. The AAES Skill MotivateMe! was developed through two iterations, each followed by evaluation with NT students and experts in ASD, HCI and Education. The final evaluation showed a general positive response towards MotivateMe! and demonstrated that the Skill is appropriate for HE students and it also has the potential in supporting HE students with ASD. However, to understand the extent of the potential for students with autism, more research with such students is necessary. The next part of the project includes a larger sample size of participants and participation of autistic students and ASD practitioners. Future work could also involve integration with calendar systems and with course websites such that deadlines (e.g. for coursework) are automatically considered, adding reminders to study, and network monitoring such that distracting websites or apps can be automatically blocked (this could not be implemented in the first iterations of the Skill).

REFERENCES

Ayres, K.M., Mechling, L. and Sansosti, F.J., 2013. The use of mobile technologies to assist with life skills/independence of students with moderate/severe intellectual disability and/or autism spectrum disorders: Considerations for the future of school psychology. Psychology in the Schools, 50(3):259-271.

Baron-Cohen, S., Golan, O., Chapman, E., and Granader, Y. (2007). Transported to a world of emotion. The Psychologist, 20(2):76-77.

Bereznak, S., Ayres, K.M., Mechling, L.C. and Alexander, J.L., 2012. Video self-prompting and mobile technology to increase daily living and vocational independence for students with autism spectrum disorders. Journal of Developmental and Physical Disabilities, 24(3):269-285.

Boyd-Graber, J.L., Nikolova, S.S., Moffatt, K.A., Kin, K.C., Lee, J.Y., Mackey, L.W., Tremaine, M.M. and Klawe, M.M., 2006, April. Participatory design with proxies: developing a desktop-PDA system to support people with aphasia. In Proceedings of the SIGCHI Conference on Human Factors in Computing Systems, 151-160.

Brooke, J., 1996. SUS-A quick and dirty usability scale. Usability evaluation in industry, 189(194):4-7.

Constantin, A., Georgiou, N., Alexandru, C.A. and Korte, J., 2019, September. S2C2: Toward an App to Support Social Story™ Comprehension Checking in Children with ASD. In IFIP Conference on HCI, 153-160. Springer, Cham.

Drake, S., 2014. College experience of academically successful students with autism. Journal of Autism, 1(1), p.5.

Friedman, N.D., Warfield, M.E. and Parish, S.L., 2013. Transition to adulthood for individuals with autism spectrum disorder: current issues and future perspectives. Neuropsychiatry, 3(2):181.

Gao, Y., Pan, Z., Wang, H. and Chen, G., 2018, October. Alexa, my love: Analyzing reviews of amazon echo. In 2018 IEEE SmartWorld, Ubiquitous Intelligence & Computing, Advanced & Trusted Computing, Scalable Computing & Communications, Cloud & Big Data Computing, Internet of People and Smart City Innovation (SmartWorld/SCALCOM/UIC/ATC/CBDCom/IOP/SCI),372-380. IEEE.

Gurbuz, E., Hanley, M. and Riby, D.M., 2019. University students with autism: The social and academic experiences of university in the UK. Journal of autism and developmental disorders, 49(2):617-631.

Howlin, P. and Moss, P., 2012. Adults with autism spectrum disorders. The Canadian J. of Psychiatry, 57(5):275-283

Jansen, D., Emmers, E., Petry, K., Mattys, L., Noens, I. and Baeyens, D., 2018. Functioning and participation of young adults with ASD in higher education according to the ICF framework. Journal of Further and HE, 42(2):.259-275.

Kokina, A. and Kern, L., 2010. Social Story™ interventions for students with autism spectrum disorders: A meta-analysis. Journal of autism and developmental disorders, 40(7):812-826.

Leavy, P. ed., 2014. The Oxford handbook of qualitative research. Oxford University Press, USA.

Lopatovska, I., Rink, K., Knight, I., Raines, K., Cosenza, K., Williams, H., Sorsche, P., Hirsch, D., Li, Q. and Martinez, A., 2019. Talk to me: Exploring user interactions with the Amazon Alexa. Journal of Librarianship and Information Science, 51(4):984-997.

Mechling, L.C., Gast, D.L. and Seid, N.H., 2009. Using a personal digital assistant to increase independent task completion by students with autism spectrum disorder. J. of Autism and developmental disorders, 39(10):1420-1434.

Sahin, N.T., Abdus-Sabur, R., Keshav, N.U., Liu, R., Salisbury, J.P. and Vahabzadeh, A., 2018, September. Case Study of a Digital Augmented Reality Intervention for Autism in School Classrooms: Associated With Improved Social Communication, Cognition, and Motivation via Educator and Parent Assessment. In Frontiers in Education, 3:57.

Saldaña, J., 2015. The coding manual for qualitative researchers. Sage Publications Ltd.

Sauro, J., 2011. Measuring usability with the system usability scale (SUS). [online] Available at https://measuringu.com/sus/ [Accessed 10 Jul 2020]

White, S.W., Elias, R., Salinas, C.E., Capriola, N., Conner, C.M., Asselin, S.B., Miyazaki, Y., Mazefsky, C.A., Howlin, P. and Getzel, E.E., 2016. Students with autism spectrum disorder in college: Results from a preliminary mixed methods needs analysis. Research in Developmental Disabilities, 56, pp.29-40.

Yu, C., Shane, H., Schlosser, R.W., O'Brien, A., Allen, A., Abramson, J. and Flynn, S., 2018. An exploratory study of speech-language pathologists using the Echo Show™ to deliver visual supports. Advances in Neurodevelopmental Disorders, 2(3):286-292.

A CASE STUDY ABOUT FACEBOOK USAGE FOR VISUALLY IMPAIRED USING THE ANDROID PLATFORMS

Arda Uslu[1] and Pinar Sarisaray-Boluk[2]
[1]*Bahcesehir University, Computer Engineering*
[2]*Bahcesehir University, Software Engineering*
Istanbul, Turkey

ABSTRACT

The use of social media plays an important role in our lives. It is crucial that visually impaired (**VI**) can likewise take part in various social media platforms. In this paper, we tried to discover the problems and interactions faced by VI on Facebook with the help of tasks that are prepared beforehand. We, researchers helped the participant to pass the steps required to complete these predetermined tasks if the participant encountered a problem. According to the first factor, the results are displayed in terms of points attributed to the steps. Secondly, the time required to complete the task is checked. The third factor is if the participant had already known it before or not. As a result, findings in terms of usability and accessibility are discussed. Hence, we tried to find out what can be done to address these issues.

KEYWORDS

Visually Impaired, Accessibility, Usability, Facebook

1. INTRODUCTION

Social Network Sites (SNS) are the most visited websites in the world. As of October 2018, the social networks by number of monthly active users are; Facebook (2.234 billion), YouTube (1.9 billion), WhatsApp (1.500 billion), Facebook Messenger (1.300 billion), Instagram (1 billion) (Global social media ranking 2019. (n.d.)). These numbers are expected to grow even further especially with the robust growth of the population in developing countries. Faster internet access and a boost in mobile phone sales with economic development will inevitably consolidate this trend. Naturally, these numbers also include users with special needs. In today's modern world it is an obligation to integrate them from all perspectives. In an increasingly equal and just society, VI deserves to be treated as equal as possible in comparison to people who do not have special needs. Accessibility of disabled users began to be a major issue in the last decade. To overcome these challenges, Facebook (**FB**) founded its Accessibility Team in July of 2011.

In this paper, research is carried out with the help of a VI person on FB. Prior research shows that visually impaired people have difficulty in accessing it (Barbara Leporini et al., 2012; Bavani Ramayah et al., 2013; Berglind Smaradottir et al., 2017; Brian M. Celusnak, 2016; Cynthia L. Bennett et al., 2018; Haley MacLeod et al., 2017; Rakesh Babu & Rahul Singh, 2013; Rakesh Babu, 2014; Ramayah, B. et al., 2012). There is a lot of research regarding this phenomenon. Wu and Adamic (2014) had an extensive study about FB usage that benefits from huge chunk of FB data. They utilize big data techniques to gain information about VI behaviors on FB. However, it's only on iOS devices. Most of the research about visually challenged people's use of social media are on iOS devices (Barbara Leporini et al., 2012; Berglind Smaradottir et al., 2017; Brian M. Celusnak, 2016; Cynthia L. Bennett et al., 2018; Haley MacLeod et al., 2017; Joao Guerreiro & Daniel Gonçalves, 2013; Shaomei Wu et al., 2017; Shaomei Wu & Lada A. Adamic., 2014; Shi Qiu et al., 2015; Violeta Voykinska et al., 2016). Android devices are so rare (Aditya Vashistha et al., 2015; Andre Rodrigues et al., 2015; Cynthia L. Bennett et al., 2018). From those, Vashistha et al., (2015) made a detailed study about the usage of social media in rural and peri-rural parts of India. In it, the only thing about Android is just the brief mention of Talkback screen reader. André Rodrigues et al. (2015) mentioned the smartphone adoption process and general functions of smartphones with no comment about social media practices (Andre Rodrigues et al., 2015). Cynthia L. Bennett et al., (2018) made a research about the photo-taking habits of VI by using audio and video recordings just like our study. Roughly half of the participants in that study are Android users. There is a lack of research in Android devices although they are widely used throughout the world as well. We are trying to fill in this gap. In this paper, we aim to test the usability of FB functions with the help of a visually impaired person in an Android platform. There are 6 specific tasks (Change Language, Change Profile, Edit Username, Ignore Message, Unignore Message, Activate Status) given to test her on Facebook Messenger.

The rest of the paper is organized as follows: Section II gives our methodology. Section III presents the results and discussion. The paper concludes in Section IV concerning future work.

2. METHODOLOGY

Before the interview and the scenario section that followed, we had already prepared a document that includes necessary steps to complete certain functions on FB. Those functions were determined beforehand. Unlike, the works (Brian Wentz & Jonathan Lazar, (2011); Shi Qiu et al., (2015)) that have more basic operations such as read and post, check-in, create an account, log in to an account we tested operations like ignore/unignore message, change the language settings. Think aloud observation method in Rakesh Babu & Rahul Singh, (2013) was not chosen for this method. It was thought to lengthen the natural time the participant would otherwise spend using that method. The online survey used by Meredith Ringel Morris et al. (2016) on Twitter was not an option because of the lack of suitable participants.

This work is examined and confirmed by the Ethical Committee of the Bahcesehir University for ethical standards. This is realized for any kind of experiments that require human interaction in any discipline. The questionnaires and the detailed explanation of the project have been added to the authorization form. All the participants accepted to be part of the project. They accepted that they will not take any kind of benefits as a result of this study. They also have the right to give up whenever they want. We read the conditions each time before we started our interviews and we started as soon as they accepted it. Their acceptance speeches are kept in my voice recorder device (Sony IC Recorder ICD-P110) with the other parts of the interviews. Sometimes we took a video to see which buttons they pressed. Few of them asked questions to clarify the things they wanted to know. We did not disclose their identity and we signed a paper that conditions us to obey the rules determined by the University Ethical Committee. We searched lots of candidates in a Visually Impaired Association Headquarters. However, it was not possible to find long-term FB users. Some of them were not using it for a long time. Their stay was also not permanent. That's why we found another participant from the disabled unit of the university.

Figure 1. While the participant of the experiment was trying to perform the duties according to the scenario

Our participant is a female of 22 years old. She studies English Language Teaching (ELT) in the university that we conducted this research. She was prematurely born of 5.5 months. That made her visually impaired. She has a %20 vision in one eye. Her other eye is slightly worse even though she cannot remember the exact value. She has no difficulty in detecting light, colors, etc. She uses Facebook for almost 10 years in both English and Turkish. She does not recall using computer web browsers to access FB since 2016. She also uses Instagram. She never used Twitter. When she registered on for Facebook the first time, she does not remember that she had a problem with the CAPTCHA (Completely Automated Public Turing test to tell Computers and

Humans Apart) that existed in those days. She said she could see when she opens her eyes wide. However, she needs to come near a little bit like the VI person who takes photos (Cynthia L. Bennett et al., 2018).

To make a usability analysis of FB functions for an impaired person, we used 6 different tasks which include Change Language, Change Profile, Edit Username, Ignore Message, Unignore Message, Activate Status. All of the tasks are firstly divided into main steps and assigned a success percentage value for each step. After identifying these steps, the participant tried to finish her tasks, which was shown in Figure 1.

Change Language

Add the language if it is not on the list. (5*10=%50)
Settings -> General Management -> Language and input -> Language ->Add Language.
If it is already on the list.
i. Click Edit. (%15)
ii. Click arrows to move it at the top of the list. (%15)
iii. Check Facebook for change. (%20)
Social->Facebook

Change Profile

How to change profile picture (DP) in the Facebook messenger app.
1. Click on "Add to your story" with the + icon. (%20)
2. Take a photo or go to the Gallery. (%20 for Gallery)
3. Select the picture you want to add. (%20)
4. Press "->" icon. (Your story icon) (%20)
5. In the send to screen check the box to make it easy to share. (%20)

Edit Username

How to edit username in Facebook Messenger
1. In the Chats, click on my Facebook profile picture. (%25)
2. Click on Username under the Profile section. (%25)
3. Click on "Edit username". (%25)
4. In the Username section, you can rewrite the already existing username. (%25)

Ignore Message

How to ignore messages from someone (in messenger)
1. In the Chats screen, click on a recent conversation to reach someone's (either a friend or not) profile. (%40)
2. Click on "i" (for info) icon at the top right. (%10)
3. Close to the bottom click on "ignore messages" (%40)
4. Press "Ignore". (%10)

Unignore Message

How to unignore messages from someone
1. Click on People. (%25)
2. On People section, press the "Add Contacts" icon at the top right corner. (%25)
3. In Add controls, click on "Requests" with icon just below Add Contacts (one of the four icons right next to each other) (%25)
4. In Message Requests, click "See all" to see filtered messages. (%25)

Activate Status

How to activate Status.
1. In Chats, click on your profile picture. (%25)
2. In Me section, click on "Activate Status" under Profile. (%25)
3. In Activate Status, turn off Activate Status. (%25)
4. Click on "Turn off" in the message box. (%25)

3. RESULTS AND DISCUSSION

Table 1 has given the successful performance of our participant on FB messenger in terms of total success point, time by indicating the knowledge of participant and, the number of steps for each function. If a participant knows how to do the task, the value is YES. As shown in Table 1, depending on the knowledge of VI, the duration time to complete tasks varied. Additionally, the successes of the tasks were dependent on the general behavior of the VI on SNS. In the Change Language task, the participant mixed the change language settings with the options for translating posts. That led her to waste considerable time. She achieved 100 points in change language task while spending the highest amount of time. The timing can be attributed to the highest number of total steps in this experiment. In the Change Profile Picture Task, there was no problem despite she did not want to do it. She did not want her friends to see her with a different picture. This change would easily be recognized by her friends as an update. She changed the picture back to normal as soon as she achieved it. Change Profile Picture was the second fastest after Activate Status and she received full points. Edit Username was the most problematic with 0 points and the longest time. That was mainly because no message showed the username was changed. She had already done in 1 minute 51 seconds. However, at that time, she could not understand that she made it. That was also because of the username she chose to change.

Table 1. Facebook Tasks' Performance in Terms of Points, Time, Knowledge, and Steps

Function to Perform	Points	Time	Know-How to Do	Total Number of Steps
Change Language	100	3 minutes 15 seconds	Yes	9
Change Profile Picture	100	47 seconds	Yes	5
Edit Username	0	4 minutes	No	4
Ignore Message	0	1 minute 29 seconds	No	4
Unignore Message	25	2 minutes	No	4
Activate Status	100	25 seconds	Yes	4

Normally (by default), the username is in the form of **name.surname.number** . However, she chose to make it in the form of **namesurname.number** . She could not understand it because of her lack of vision and message. Even for a sighted person, it might be difficult to do for the first time. She did not know about the operation so I told her how to do it. She was not familiar with either ignore or unignore message. I had to explain step by step. The problem about ignore was mainly because she confused it with block operation. She also could not understand why that operation is used. She received 0 points although she gave up the earliest in the ones that she had not known. For unignore operation, she correctly guessed that it is about the people menu but 4 icons on the request made her confused. Unignore message is related to the ignore message so she could get 25 points in 2 minutes. Activate Status was the easiest for her because that's the one she knew before. Moreover, she said that she used it regularly. Activate Status is the one with the best performance in terms of time (25 seconds) and one of the best for points (100 points).

4. CONCLUSION

In this paper, we make a VI usability analysis on Facebook in the Android platform. Six different Facebook functions are used to test the usability performance of VI on this site. Our results show that the knowledge of the VI about the task played a positive role in the task completion time. The best times are achieved when-knowledge about that specific function is concomitant with the high frequency of usage in the past. When a function includes lots of controls like unignore message, task completion time increases even it may not be completed by VI. If there is a similar function she remembered like in Language Settings, this might also be a problem. The most visible usability problem is the lack of a message in the edit username. A message like "Your username is changed" will make it much easier to understand. It will significantly reduce the time required to complete the task. As future work, we want to find more participants. Heuristic approaches may also be added to crosscheck the efficiency of the study.

ACKNOWLEDGMENT

I would like to thank the Disability Unit of Bahcesehir University and Visually Impaired Association for their kind assistance.

REFERENCES

Aditya Vashistha, Edward Cutrell, Nicola Dell, et al. 2015. Social Media Platforms for Low-Income Blind People in India. *In Proceedings of the 17th International ACM SIGACCESS Conference on Computers & Accessibility.* (pp. 259-272). New York, NY: ACM. Doi:10.1145/2700648.280985

Andre Rodrigues, Kyle Montague, Hugo Nicolau, et al. 2015. Getting Smartphones to Talkback: Understanding the Smartphone Adoption Process of Blind Users. *In Proceedings of The 17th International ACM SIGACCESS Conference on Computers and Accessibility (ASSETS'15).* October 26-28, 2015, Lisbon-Portugal. (pp.23-32).ACM. DOI: http://dx.doi.org/10.1145/2700648.2809842

Barbara Leporini, Maria Claudia Buzzi, and Marina Buzzi. 2012. Interacting with mobile devices via VoiceOver: Usability and accessibility issues. *OZCHI'12,* 1-10.

Bavani Ramayah, Azizah Jaafar, and Noor Faezah Mohd. Yatim. 2013. Visually Impaired User's Navigation Experiences in Facebook. *IVIC 2013,* LNCS 8237, 788-796.http://dx.doi.org/10.1007/978-3-319-02958-0_71

Berglind Smaradottir, Jarie Haland, Santiago Martinez. 2017. Accessibility of Mobile Devices for Visually Impaired Users: An Evaluation of The Screen-Reader VoiceOver. *MEDINFO 2017: Precision Healthcare through Informatics.* Doi:10.3233/978-1-61499-830-3-1381 p.1381

Brian M. Celusnak. September-October 2016. Teaching the iPhone with VoiceOver Accessibility to People with Visual Impairments. *Journal of Visual Impairment & Blindness.* p.369-372

Brian Wentz and Jonathan Lazar. 2011. Are separate interfaces inherently unequal?: an evaluation with blind users of the usability of two interfaces for a social networking platform. *In Proc iConference'11,* 91-97.

Cynthia L. Bennett, Jane E, Martez E. Mott, et al. 2018. How Teens with Visual Impairments Take, Edit, and Share Photos on Social Media. *In Proceedings of the SIGCHI Conference on Human Factors in Computing System (CHI'2018),* Montreal, QC, Canada (p.1-11), https://doi.org/10.1145/3173574.3173650

Global social media ranking 2019. (n.d.). Retrieved June 19, 2019, from https://www.statista.com/statistics/272014/global-social-networks-ranked-by-number-of-users/

Haley MacLeod, Cynthia L. Bennett, Meredith Ringel Morris, et al. 2017. Understanding Blind People's Experiences with Computer Generated Captions of Social Media Images. *In Proceedings of the SIGCHI Conference on Human Factors in Computing Systems (CHI' 2017),* Denver, CO, USA, DOI: https://dx.doi.org/10.1145/3025453.3025814

Joao Guerreiro, Daniel Gonçalves. 2013. Blind People Interacting with Mobile Social Applications: Open Challenges. *3rd Workshop on Mobile Accessibility at the ACM SIGCHI Conference on Human Factors in Computing Systems.*

Meredith Ringel Morris, Annuska Zolyomi, Catherine Yao, et al. 2016. "With Most of It Being Pictures Now, I Rarely Use It": Understanding Twitter's Evolving Accessibility to Blind Users. *In Proceedings of the 2016 CHI Conference on Human Factors in Computing Systems (CHI '16),* 5506-5516, https://doi.org/10.1145/2858116

Rakesh Babu, Rahul Singh. 2013. Accessibility and Usability of Social Media: Convergence between Blind Users and Design Standards. *In Proceedings of the Nineteenth Americas Conference on Information Systems,* Chicago, Illinois, August 15-17, 2013. p.1-9.

Rakesh Babu. 2014. Can Blind People Use Social Media Effectively? A Qualitative Field Study of Facebook Usability.*American Journal of Information Systems,* Vol. 2, 33-41.doi: 10.12691/ajis-2-2-2

Ramayah, B., Jaafar, A., N.F.M.: Accessibility Issues of Social Networking Sites to Blind Users in Malaysia. *In: Visual Informatics International Seminar 2012 (VIIS 2012)*(2012)

Shaomei Wu, Jeffrey Wieland, Omid Farivar, et al. 2017. Automatic Alt-text: Computer-generated Image Descriptions for Blind Users on a Social Network Service. *In Proceedings of the 20th ACM Conference on Computer Supported Cooperative Work and Social Computing,* https://doi.org/10.1145/2998181.2998364

Shaomei Wu, Lada A. Adamic. 2014. Visually Impaired Users on an Online Social Network. *In Proceedings of the SIGCHI Conference on Human Factors in Computing Systems(CHI '14),*3133-3142. New York, NY: ACM. https://doi.org/10.1145/2556288.2557415

Shi Qiu, Jun Hu, and Matthias Rauterberg. 2015. Mobile Social Media for the Blind: Preliminary Conference on Enabling Access for Persons with Visual Impairment *(ICEAPVI),* pp. 152-156.

Violeta Voykinska, Shiri Azenkot, Shaomei Wu, et al. 2016. How Blind People Interact with Visual Content on Social Networking Services. *In Proceedings of the 19th ACM Conference on Computer-Supported Cooperative Work & Social Computing (CSCW'16),*1584-1595. https://doi.org/10.1145/2818048.2820013

INTERACTIVE VISUALIZATION OF COMPLEX THREE-DIMENSIONAL MODELS: CASE STUDY IN ZEBRAFISH

Feibo Duan, Kristian F. D. Rietveld and Fons J. Verbeek
Leiden Institute of Advanced Computer Science (LIACS), Leiden University,
Niels Bohrweg 1, 2333 CA Leiden, The Netherlands

ABSTRACT

Modern microscope imaging techniques can generate three-dimensional (3D) images in high numbers. Understanding of the content of such images requires visualization and some form of interaction with the content. In this paper a generic processing pipeline from two-dimensional (2D) microscopy data to interactive visualization of complex 3D models is presented. This pipeline supports 3D images reconstructed from different microscopy modalities and interactive visualization using various display devices and interaction methods. Using an annotated zebrafish model containing 188 substructures as a case study, we illustrate the importance of developing suitable visualization and interaction methods to empower researchers better understand and analyze the problem at hand.

KEYWORDS

Interactive Visualization, 3D Models, 3D Visualization, Bioimages

1. INTRODUCTION

Modern microscope imaging techniques are capable of rapidly acquiring and generating three-dimensional (3D) imagery and it is expected that with current developments there will be a further decrease in acquisition time. Data acquisition methods in optical microscopy that are used to this end are confocal laser scanning microscopy (CLSM), optical projection tomography (OPT) and serial sectioning. In all above three cases two-dimensional (2D) images are acquired from which a 3D volumetric image is reconstructed.

Zebrafish model system is widely used in biomedical research. George Streisinger at the University of Oregon first used zebrafish as a model system in the late 1960s, biologists thereafter are increasingly using zebrafish in their research (Grunwald & Eisen, 2002). Zebrafish offer many advantages in biomedical research such as high fecundity, small size, short generation time, external fertilization, and numerous transparent specimens.

Sophisticated 3D visualization of zebrafish is in high demand. This has led to more general availability of 3D images. During the data analysis process, researchers have a need to get more detailed information such as organ detail, a system detail, entire object, spatial relationship of different parts of whole object and so on. To support this, substructures in 3D images can be segmented and annotated by hand or in an automatic fashion (Tang, 2020). These developments call for improved visualization and interaction methods to help researchers better understand and analyze the problem at hand. To this end, a visualization system is required that is flexible in the selection of parts that are visualized, in contrast to conventional visualization methods that only show the whole model or single specific parts. To facilitate the study of these more complex and more detailed 3D models, multiple interaction methods should be provided, as a regular desktop monitor and mouse used by conventional systems are often not well suited.

To solve these problems, we propose a generic processing pipeline from 2D raw data to interactive visualization of complex 3D models, which supports 3D models generated using different microscopy modalities and allows interactive visualization of 3D models on various display systems.

2. OVERVIEW OF THE PIPELINE

Our focus is on the visualization of 3D models that are obtained from 3D reconstructions of 2D microscopy data. Our intention is supporting 3D models acquired through different modalities and visualization with various interaction methods. To achieve this, we propose a generic processing pipeline from 2D raw data to visualization of a complex 3D model. This pipeline, depicted in Figure 1, consists of three main components: 3D volumetric image acquisition, surface model generation ("mesh"), and interactive visualization.

In this paper, we use zebrafish model system as a case study. With our OPT system, 400 2D images acquired from the specimen are reconstructed to a 3D volumetric image through cropping, background subtraction, center of rotation correction and 3D reconstruction (Tang et al., 2017). Note that 3D data generated using other modalities will also work in our processing pipeline, as indicated in Figure 1. Subsequently, an optional segmentation step generates and labels all substructures of a model, to support visualization of and interaction with substructures. As the next step a surface model is generated from the 3D volumetric image using contour extraction and surface reconstruction which uses the Boissonnat method (Boissonnat & Geiger, 1993). Finally, this surface model is visualized by an interactive visualization application that works on different display devices employing different interaction methods.

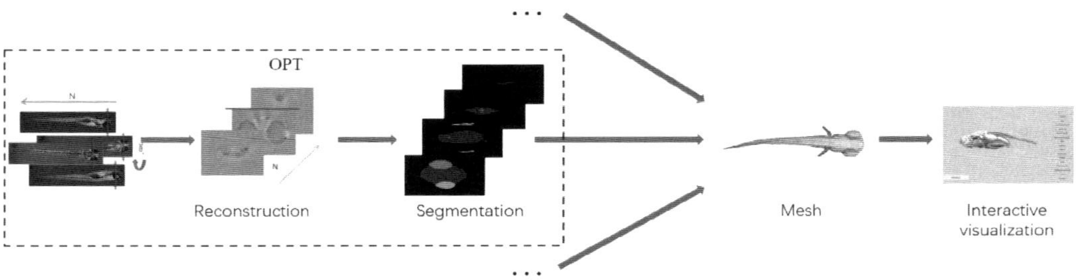

Figure 1. The generic processing pipeline from 2D raw data to interactive visualization of a complex 3D model

3. GENERATION OF SURFACE MODELS

The 3D models that are the result of the reconstruction processing pipeline are volume models. Such models are not very suited for rapid 3D rendering, in which case surface models are typically used. Therefore, our processing pipeline applies contour extraction followed by the Boissonnat method to generate surface models. However, this might lead to the situation where the surface of the 3D object is incomplete, as shown in Figure 2(a). This is caused by the fact that some face normals are inverted. When the direction in which light is emitted is the same as the direction of the face normal, then, in the computational sense, light does not reflect in the user's eye. To alleviate this problem there are two possibilities: either all face normals are adjusted to the correct direction, or a rendering method is chosen that renders both sides of the surface. To consider inclusiveness of different surface models, double-sided rendering is used in our case. The result is shown in Figure 2(b), which is clearly an improvement.

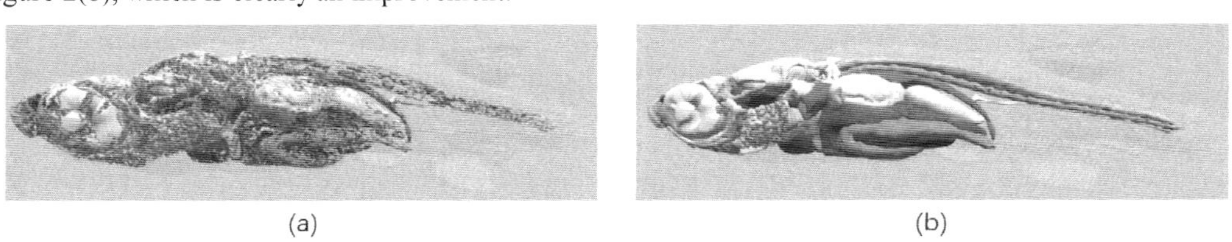

Figure 2. Display results: (a) standard rendering and (b) double-sided rendering

4. INTERACTION VISUALIZATION ON DIFFERENT DEVICES

To design and implement an interactive visualization application of complex 3D models that can run on different display devices and support different interaction methods, Unity 3D is used as a development platform. The application that we have developed is generic in nature and has two main features: 1) It can show substructures, i.e. organ systems with respect to the entire structure, so that a user can observe position relationships of several organs or parts without occlusion. 2) It allows a user to select a part of the object and interact with it. To enable manipulation of substructures, separate surface reconstructions of annotated parts of a complex 3D model are loaded into the Unity project.

As can be seen in Figure 3, the interactive visualization application that we have developed supports various display devices: i.e. regular computer monitor, HD video wall, Virtual Reality (VR) system, hologram system and smartphone. The available interaction methods differ per display device; a mouse is used with a regular computer monitor, VR systems use specific input methods and smartphones employ touch screens. Some display devices, such as a video wall, support multiple input methods. Whereas a mouse is used with a regular computer monitor, a mouse is not suitable for interaction with a model displayed on a video wall. To improve interaction with the video wall, we are experimenting with the WiiMote, Leap Motion and Kinect controllers. The generic implementation of the visualization pipeline described in this paper allows us to evaluate all of these different interaction methods with ease.

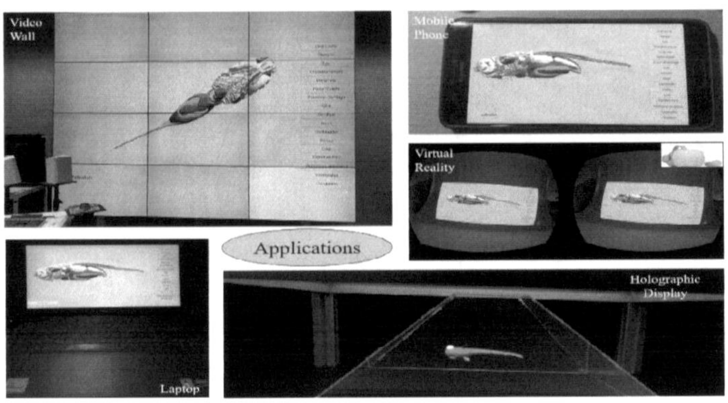

Figure 3. Interactive visualization on different platforms

5. PRELIMINARY RESULTS

To illustrate the generic processing pipeline that has been developed, we present the interactive visualization of 3D zebrafish as a case study. Our complex 3D model of juvenile zebrafish contains 188 annotated structures that are displayed separately in the interface. The large amount of structures is organized in an ontology so that they can also be manipulated as groups. This makes the visualization very versatile. Figure 4(a) shows an entire zebrafish model with substructure options (the zebrafish skin is rendered transparent). In Figure 4(b), the eyes substructure has been selected. Users can observe the spatial information of eye parts whereas the other parts of the zebrafish are now rendered semi-transparent. As is shown in Figure 4(c), it is also possible to select one particular substructure and hide the other parts of the model. Finally, Figure 4(d) shows that users can also obtain an exploded view that provides all substructures and their annotation. In all of these different modes, the user can interact with the displayed objects through rotation, zooming and translation using a controller suitable for the display device at hand.

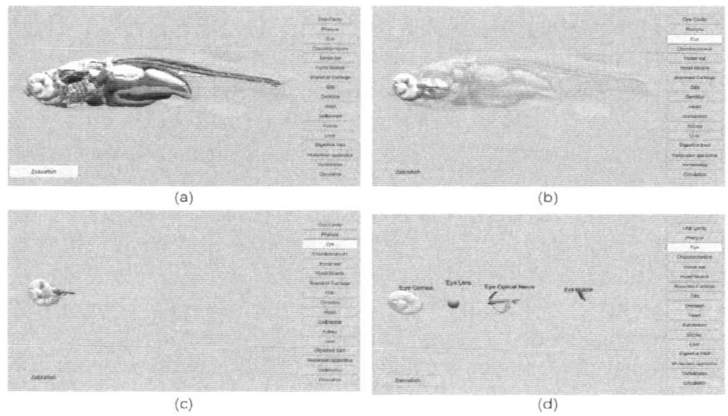

Figure 4. Interactive visualization of a 3D zebrafish model using different display modes

6. CONCLUSIONS

In this paper we have described a generic processing pipeline starting from coherent 2D microscopy raw data to interactive visualizations of complex 3D models. The intention of the processing pipeline is to separate the device dependent from the generic. To that end, we distinguish imaging device dependences, display device dependences and interaction device dependences. The preparation of the 3D model is considered generic. Subsequently, specific applications can be generated for each visualization platform. Using an annotated zebrafish model as a case study, we have developed an application that runs on different platforms employing different interaction methods. In our future work, we will further experiment with different interaction devices as well as supporting 3D reconstructions that have been created with other imaging modalities. Moreover, the surface reconstruction method will be further improved to enhance image quality, for instance by getting an optimized surface mesh from a point cloud (Cao & Verbeek, 2013) which is derived from the initial surface mesh.

ACKNOWLEDGEMENT

This research was partially supported by the China Scholarship Council (CSC). We thank Robin Megens for his work on the annotation of a juvenile Zebrafish.

REFERENCES

Boissonnat J., Geiger B., 1993. Three dimensional reconstruction of complex shapes based on the Delaunay triangulation. *Proc. SPIE 1905, Biomedical Image Processing and Biomedical Visualization*, San Jose, CA, United States, pp. 964-975.

Cao L., Verbeek F.J., 2013. Analytical evaluation of algorithms for point cloud surface reconstruction using shape features, *J. Electron. Imaging*, Vol. 22, Issue. 4, 043008.

Grunwald D. J., Eisen J. S., 2002. Headwaters of the zebrafish -- emergence of a new model vertebrate, *Nat Rev Genet*, Vol. 3, Issue. 9, pp. 717- 724.

Tang X. *et al*, 2017. Fast Post-Processing Pipeline for Optical Projection Tomography, *IEEE transactions on nanobioscience*, Vol. 16, Issue. 5, pp. 367-374.

Tang X., 2020. Computational optimisation of optical projection tomography for 3D image analysis, PhD thesis, Leiden University, Leiden.

E-OWL: A FIRST USABILITY STUDY OF A NEW E-LEARNING PLATFORM FOR DIGITAL NATIVE STUDENTS

Isabel Araújo, Pedro Miguel Faria and João Nuno Azevedo
Instituto Politécnico de Viana do Castelo, Viana do Castelo, Portugal

ABSTRACT

In today's society, whose higher education students are digital natives, the availability of information and communication technologies is a reality. It is pertinent the development of virtual learning environments, which are extremely useful in periods such as of those of a pandemic situation, which force the confinement of people. This article highlights the importance of the use of ICT in educational contexts, in particular, the use of e-learning platforms, in higher education, as support to the teaching/learning process. A literature review was carried out, in order to demonstrate some advantages for the teaching/learning process, both for students and teachers. Thus, the general structure of an e-learning platform, designated E-OWL, to support an area of mathematics at higher education level is described. Also, the opinion of students after having used the platform in an educational context is presented, through an usability study carried out using the SUS method. The results obtained show great satisfaction among students who used the platform, which is naturally a contribution to the improvement of learning and a useful tool in an educational context. This study encourages the use of technologies as a support to the teaching/learning process, promoting more interactive learning environments closer to the students.

KEYWORDS

E-learning Platform, LMS, Virtual Learning Environments, Higher Education, Mathematics Education

1. INTRODUCTION

In a modern society, education is one of the key sectors for an advanced and well-organized community. Distance education, as e-learning is called in is reaching wider audiences, making it become the next evolutionary step regarding education (Zhang & Bao, 2010). The concept of e-learning has been growing and spreading throughout the last years. Since its first appearance in the early 90's, it has been getting more efficient and advanced aiming towards a student-centered design as the technologies keep evolving (Rodríguez-Sevillano et al, 2016). Based on information technology (Boneu, 2007), e-learning brings plenty of advantages into the education field, encouraging greater interactivity in teaching and learning processes (Daniela, Strods, & Daiga, 2019). With a good and well supported e-learning platform, the students benefit from a quicker and easier content update, they determine their own pace of learning and their own study schedule (Araújo, 2014; Kizim *et al*, 2016). Combining those factors to a logistics cost reduction due to less travelling the students also develop their self-study and self-learning skills. From a teacher perspective is also advantageous using this methodology. For most of the e-learning platforms it is possible to monitor student's participation on the subject as well as having a larger amount of people learning at the same time. However, there are also a lot of criticisms towards e-learning pointing out some disadvantages that this modern learning system might bring. Factors such as lack of human contact, possible technical difficulties like internet failures that would make the access to the service impossible and technophobia that is still present in part of the population are the main cons against this technology (Boneu, 2007). It is noticeable that the teenagers use e-learning platforms more frequently than older people. It is explained in (Danesh, 2010) that the reason behind this is the fact that the older people are used to traditional methods, however, this age group agrees that the e-learning is more efficient. Both claim that is a way of learning that requires less effort and saves a lot of time when doing research for any content. Another point of convergence in their perspectives is that the future of education will tend to a gradual increase of this e-learning methodology, thus replacing the current, traditional lecturing. According to the study of Lin & Fang (2008), where the objective was to explore students' thoughts and concerns as well as their experience when using e-learning platforms, there are three key aspects that support a well-functioning system. The teacher, being the first actor on the process, is a very relevant factor in the equation who directly affects the results of the e-learning experience, should take primary care of the instructional content has and properly plan it before the course starts to improve the system function and quality. The second care to be taken carefully for a better student experience is the way the instructional resources are arranged. A well-organized content design is achieved by planning ahead the steps that the student is going to go through the learning material. And, finally, when it comes to the platform itself, it is also advised that the system has the automatism to determine whether the student's answers are correct or not and provide the learning profile of the students from statistics obtained through the students' interactions with the platform. Several studies have been carried out reinforcing the relevance of the use of technologies in an educational context (Al-Rahmi *et al* 2018; Al-Samarraie, 2018; Araújo, 2019).

2. THE E-OWL PLATFORM

The E-OWL platform is a mathematical content platform supported on the Open edX technology. This LMS supports various multimedia contents, enabling the student to participate in personalized learning experiences. Team learning development is possible through the Project-based learning methodology, aimed at company employees or students, through the use of collaborative tools such as discussion forums, chat groups or file sharing. The Open edX LMS provides a backend for teachers and a frontend for students. The teachers may publish course contents, promote discussion forums, manage teams, publish assessment results and communicate with students. The students can access their profile, check the status of their enrollment and search for subjects they wish to enroll, in in order to carry out their planned activities. It was necessary to adapt the LMS, in order the E-OWL platform (Figure 1) would correspond to the identified needs. Thus, several changes were made to the original LMS code.

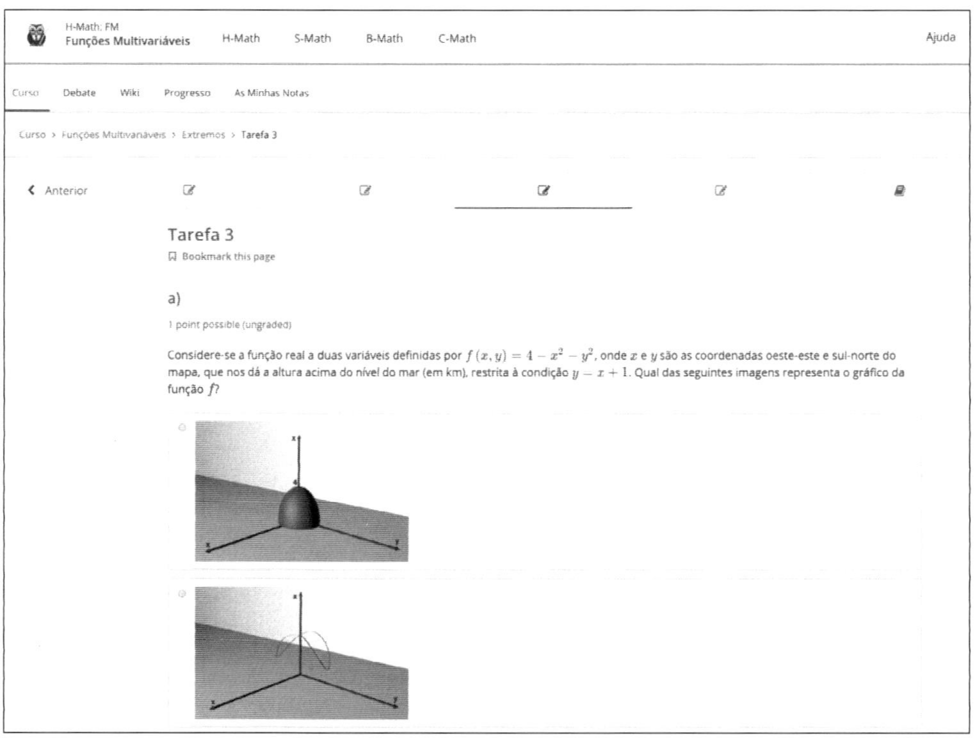

Figure 1. E-OWL interface

Some mathematical contents were selected to be available in the E-OWL platform. Thus, several images, graphics, animations, videos, 2D and 3D contents were produced. Every 2D graphic was created using the Adobe Illustrator and some of these graphics were animated or had animated text, trying to be more eye catching and appellative to the students. The animated part was made with a mix of illustrations, several cuts and some light animations using the Adobe Premiere Pro. Other 3D representations and animations were made using Cinema 4D.

3. METHODOLOGY OF THE STUDY

In the context of the E-OWL platform it was decided to do a first study about the usability of it and if the students consider that the platform helps to learn about the contents of the mathematic course. Thus, a questionnaire was applied consisting on 10 questions related to usability. Thus, the System Usability Scale survey (SUS) (Bangor, Kortum & Miller, 2008; Brooke, 1986) was used, because is considered to be one of the most accepted by its reliability and validity. It contains a simple scale of ten items related to usability, enabling evaluation of subjective perceptions. It uses the Likert scale with values ranging from 1 (strongly disagree) to 5 (strongly agree), where 3 means neutral. To calculate the SUS scores, the contributions of each score item are added together. For items 1, 3, 5, 7 and 9, the score contribution is the scale position minus 1. For the items 4, 6, 8 and 10, the contribution is 5 minus the scale position. To obtain the total amount of system usability is necessary to sum the counts of the totals obtained for the 10 questions, multiplied by 2.5. The SUS scores have a range from 0 to 100, and less than 51 is considered Bad, greater than 68 is Good, greater than 86 is Excellent and 91 is the Best Achievable (Bangor, Kortum, & Miller, 2009). Additionally, a SUS analysis was carried out, which encompasses five quality components: ease of learning, efficiency, ease of memorization, minimization of errors and satisfaction (Nielsen, 2012) followed by a descriptive statistical analysis. The study was applied for two months (March and April of 2020) to 1st year students of the Computer Graphics and Multimedia Engineering course, of a higher education institution in the North of Portugal, in a Mathematics Course. The students were asked to use the E-OWL platform, performing tasks contained in the platform, either in the classroom or in extra-classes period, regarding the programmatic contents of the 1st module of Mathematics, Integrals. It must be noted that due to the pandemic period of Covid 19, half of the classes were face-to-face, and the rest were carried out virtually, using the Zoom and Moodle platforms.

4. DATA ANALYSIS AND RESULTS

The questionnaire was applied to thirty-five students aged between 18 (17.1%) and 30 (2.9%), of which 75% are up to 23 years old and 45.7% had already attended this course. From the SUS analysis we obtained a score of 76.3, classified as B, which corresponds to an evaluation of Good (Figure 2). Specifically, considering the quality components indicated by Nielsen (2012) the following values were obtained:

- Learning easiness - the average result of questions 3, 4, 7 and 10 from SUS is 80.0;
- Efficiency of the system - the average result of questions 5, 6 and 8 of SUS is 76.2;
- Ease of memorization - result of question 2 whose score is 76.4;
- System inconsistency - result of question 6 whose score is 72.1;
- Satisfaction - the average result of questions 1, 4 and 9 of SUS is 73.6.

On a scale from 1 - Totally Disagree to 5 – Totally Agree, regarding the ease of use of the E-OWL platform 89% indicated 4 (66%) or 5 (23%) that the platform is easy to use, with 89% agreeing 1 (54%) and 2 (34%) that the E-OWL platform was complicated to use (Figure 3). The majority 77% disagreed that they needed to learn many new things before they could use the E-OWL platform, with 57% totally disagreeing. Also, 82% disagreed (51% totally disagreed) that they would need help from a person with technical knowledge to use the platform. Furthermore, 80% refer that many people would learn to use the platform very quickly. Furthermore, in this context, 80% rated the E-OWL platform between 1 (29%) and 2 (51%) as unnecessarily complex. Concerning the consistency of the platform, 74% indicated between 1 (17%) and 2 (57%) that the E-OWL platform presents a lot of inconsistency, with the majority (71%) indicating 4 (54%) or 5 (17%) that the various features of the E-OWL platform are very well integrated.

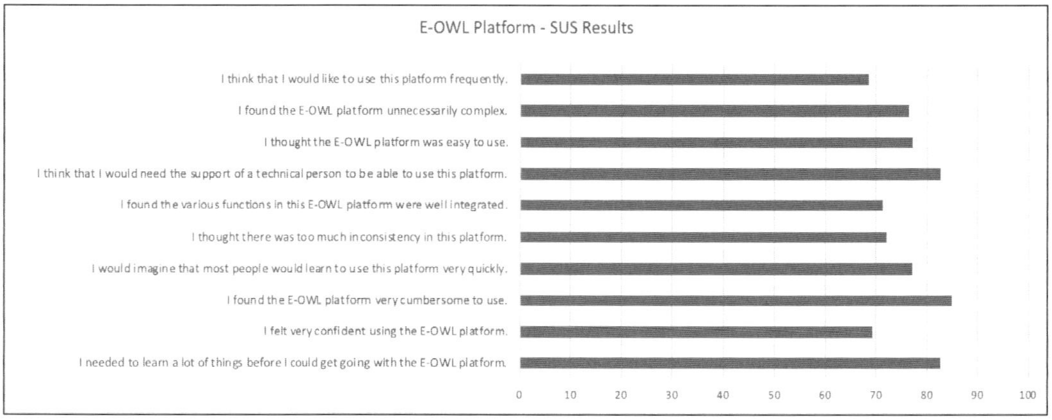

Figure 2. SUS results of E-OWL platform survey

Finally, with regard to the considerable confidence in using the platform, the responses varied between 3 (40%), 4 (43%) and 5 (17%). Among the respondents, only 6% indicated disagreement (by ticking option 2) with the use of the E-OWL platform frequently. The remaining respondents ranked between 3 (29%), 4 (51%) and 5 (14%).

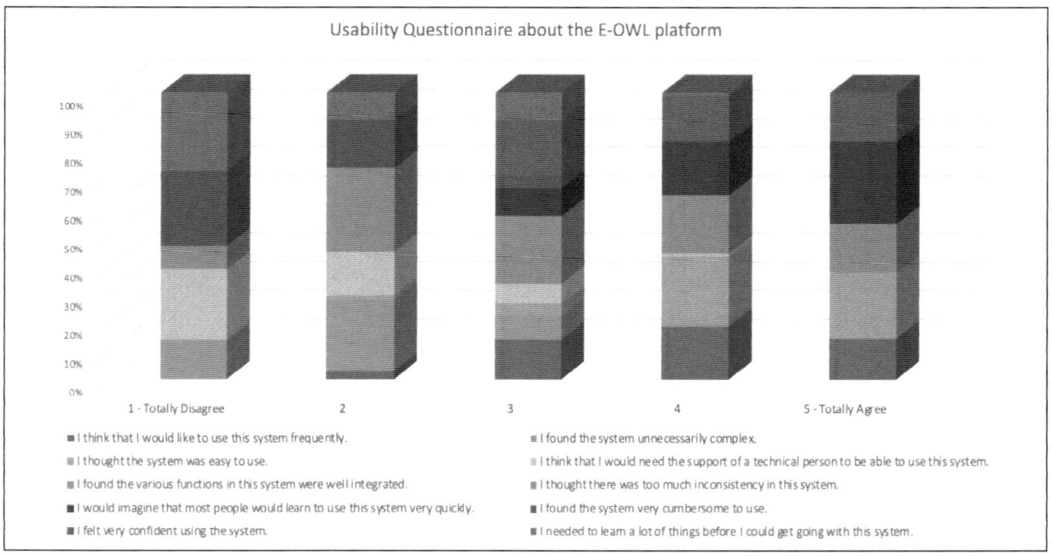

Figure 3. Usability Questionnaire about the E-OWL platform

From the usability study carried out, it appears that the majority of the respondents totally disagreed that it is necessary to learn a lot before using the E-OWL platform, the platform is difficult to use and that it requires help from a person with technical knowledge to use the platform, thus, can be considered that the E-OWL platform is accessible, i.e. easy to use. A vast majority of the surveyed students (over 95%) indicated that they like to use this platform frequently, feel very confident in using it and the different features of the platform are well integrated. Furthermore, the users found the E-OWL platform to be easy to learn and easy to remember, and an efficient system.

5. CONCLUSION

The choice of Open edX technology to support the creation of the E-OWL platform proved to be very appropriate. The versatility of this technology has allowed the creation of an e-Learning platform, capable of supporting a wide variety of media content, which greatly contributes to good acceptance by the students who use it. Teachers have access to a backend structured in 3 components that facilitate the management of content and access, as well as obtaining statistical information on the use of the platform by students. A first usability study of the E-OWL platform was carried out for higher education students, after having used it in an educational context. From the results obtained it can be seen that the platform has good usability. Moreover, considering the quality components indicated by Nielsen (2012), it is possible to verify a great satisfaction of the students for the use of the platform, which naturally is a contribution to the improvement of learning. In this sense, it is intended to contribute to the development of the platform for other areas of knowledge and to increase active learning more focused on students.

REFERENCES

Al-Samarraie, H., Teng, B., Alzahrani,A. & Alalwan, N., 2018. E-learning continuance satisfaction in higher education: a unified perspective from instructors and students. *Studies in Higher Education*, Vol 43, Nº 11, pp 2003-2019.

Al-Rahmi, W., Alias, N., Othman, M., Alzahrani, A., Alfarraj, O., Saged, A. *& Rahman, N.* (2018) Use of E-Learning by University Students in Malaysian Higher Educational Institutions: A Case in Universiti Teknologi Malaysia. *IEEE Access*, Vol. 6, pp. 14268-14276.

Araújo, I., Cabrita, I. (2014). Construction and Application of Mathematical Knowledge with Autonomy. Revista Investigação Qualitativa em Educação, Vol. 1 (2014), pp. 361-367.

Araújo, I. & Faria, P. M., 2019. Potentialities of Using an Online Platform to Learn Mathematics in Engineering. *In Proceedings of International Symposium on Project Approaches in Engineering Education: Preparing Teachers and Students for Challenging Times in Engineering Education / 16th Active Learning in Engineering Education Workshop - PAEE/ALE'2019*, pp 268-275.

Bangor, A., Kortum P. & Miller, J., 2008. An empirical evaluation of the system usability scale. *International J Hum Computer Interaction*, 24(6): 574–594.

Bangor, A; Kortum, P. & Miller, J., 2009. Determining what individual SUS scores mean: Adding an adjective ratingscale. *J Usability Studies*, 4(3): 114–23

Boneu, J. M., 2007. Plataformas abiertas de e-learning para el soporte de contenidos educativos abiertos. *Revista de Universidad y Sociedad del Conocimiento, 4*(1), 36-47

Brooke, J., 1986. SUS: a "quick and dirty" usability scale. In P. W. Jordan, B. Thomas, B. A. Weerdmeester, & A. L. McClelland. Usability Evaluation in Industry, London, *Taylor and Francis*.

Danesh, M., 2010. Comparing the Satisfaction of the E-learning Between Teenagers and People with More than 45 Years Old in Cyberjaya. *2010 International Conference on e-Education, e-Business, e-Management and e-Learning*, pp. 432-435.

Daniela, L., Strods, R. & Kalniņa, D., 2019. Technology-Enhanced Learning (TEL) in Higher Education: Where Are We Now? In M. Lytras, L. Daniela, A. Visvizi (Eds.), *Knowledge-Intensive Economies and Opportunities for Social, Organizational, and Technological Growth*, pp 12-24.

Kizim, A., Matokhina, A., Vayngolts, I. & Shcherbakov, M., 2016. Intelligent platform of monitoring, diagnosis and modernization of technical systems at various stages of life cycle. *2016 International Conference System Modeling & Advancement in Research Trends (SMART)*, pp. 145-150.

Lin, S. & Fang, K., 2008. Success factors of E-learning system based on students' perspectives. *2008 IEEE International Conference on Industrial Engineering and Engineering Management*, Singapore, pp. 1451-1455.

Nielsen, J., 2012. *Usability 101: Introduction to usability*. Disponível em https://www.nngroup.com/articles/usability-101-introduction-to-usability/

Rodríguez-Sevillano, A., Barcala-Montejano, M., Tovar-Caro, E. & López-Gallego, P., 2016. Evolution of teaching tools and the learning process: From traditional teaching to edX courses. *2016 13th International Conference on Remote Engineering and Virtual Instrumentation (REV)*, pp. 48-55.

Zhang, N. & Bao, H., 2010. Research on E-Learning with Digital Technology in Distance Education. *The 2010 International Conference on E-Education, E-Business, E-Management and E-Learnin,*. 299-302

"BN ANATOMY" AN INTERACTIVE AUGMENTED REALITY SYSTEM FOR LEARNING BONE ANATOMY

João Vitor de S. Chagas, Phellipe C. Santiago, Cristina A. P. Fontes and Aura Conci
Universidade Federal Fluminense (UFF), Brazil

ABSTRACT

The study of bone anatomy has a great impact on the courses of health courses and brings a series of challenges, since books and other 2D materials cannot present all the details of these organs. In this paper, an interactive augmented reality system for teaching this field of science is presented. The system's usability was tested by a group of volunteers, containing students and health professionals, indicating the system's ability to motivate students to learn bone anatomy.

KEYWORDS

Augmented Reality, Bone Anatomy, Gamification, Gesture Analysis, Health Games

1. INTRODUCTION

Health professionals are subjected to physical and psychological pressure in workplace or in academy. In this context, gamification is increasingly used as a complement to traditional teaching strategies in medical education, to increase student engagement and motivation to learning. Thinking about it, several technologies have emerged with the purpose of making the teaching process, from the most diverse branches of health, more pleasant, motivating and immersive. Applications involving augmented reality (AR) or virtual reality (VR) have a special ability to generate greater immersion in learning.

AR presents a vision of the real world that incorporates information from the virtual world to broaden the perspective of the real world (Singh and Singh, 2013). The information incorporated has a broad meaning, it can be any type of data (video, image, audio), although, in most part, this information represents images, which may be consistent or not with the real environment. To interact with the AR environment, the use of markers or gestural analyzes may be necessary. AR systems, in general, have the properties (Azuma et al., 2001) of (1) combine the real world with virtual objects within the real environment; (2) promote real-time interactivity; and (3) align real and virtual objects together.

The AR faces in its usability challenges similar to those of traditional interfaces, such as excessive information presented to the user and problems to determine the focus of the user's attention. When focused on the educational aspect, this technology comes up against the problem of content creation, since this type of project demands a great effort, with the need for computational knowledge, which creates a barrier for educators in fields other than computing to develop solutions in AR. Just as there is also a need for knowledge on the topic addressed and pedagogical, which brings obstacles for computer professionals to develop this type of solution alone that is, projects involving AR need a multidisciplinary team (Martins, 2012). In addition, it is always a challenge to combine new teaching technologies, which escape the conventional methodology, with evaluation processes that can effectively indicate the student's progress.

This article presents BN Anatomy: an application that uses AR technology for learning bone anatomy through game concepts such as: rewards, progress feedback and competition. The prototype was designed to be accessible and inexpensive since its only requirement is to install the software on a common smartphone (provided it has a rear camera and a system version superior to Android 7.0), in order to bring the experience of the bone anatomy classroom, even without the existence of real skeletons in the environment. BN Anatomy presents a great immersion for presenting a 360° view of the skeleton and all its interactions happen through 3D gestural analyzes in real time, provided from the smartphone camera.

2. RELATED WORK

The study of human anatomy plays an important role in doctors and nurses training. However, the practical knowledge of this area is subject to some obstacles, since in the conventional format these classes need laboratories that have dissected bodies and human skeletons to happen. Solutions involving the use of AR have already been proposed to support this study. Ferrer-Torregrosa et al. (2016) investigate didactic strategies for distance learning, based on an inverted classroom concept. This study presented an experiment with 171 students from medicine, physiotherapy and podiatry courses, divided into 3 groups. Each group received a distinct material to anatomy studies: annotations with images; videos and; an AR book. The AR group obtained a significantly higher average score and lesser dispersion on the exams than the others. Despite the promising results, the study does not address the issue of gamification, as this work does.

Andayani et al. (2019) proposed a 3D visualization system with AR for interactive medical learning of pulmonary anatomy. In this research, the authors used the Blender software for object modeling and image targeting techniques for displaying 3D objects from markers, but they did not present results regarding the usability and performance of the students, being restricted to tests of functioning of such markers.

Kurniawan et al. (2018) point out the students' difficulty in learning about anatomy of the human body through books, since 2D images cannot accurately represent the 3D body anatomy. To overcome this difficulty, researchers developed a mobile application allowing visualization of different parts of body using AR and markers. The project presents positive feedbacks; however, it only displays objects and their information, do not challenging the students in order to further increase their motivation on the topic.

Stefan et al. (2014) work is most related to this here proposed. It is a medical education and entertainment system with AR for learning bone anatomy. It is considered as an "AR bone puzzle", where Kinect is used to assemble a skeleton on users own body from the bones that are being randomly drawn, among 16 possible parts, working as a puzzle. This solution, like ours, uses gesture-based interaction, but differently of ours has a higher cost, since a Kinect is necessary (our project is based only on the use of smartphones).

3. PROPOSED METHODOLOGY

This section presents the purposed system based on the use of AR, gesture analysis and gamification activities to challenges and rewards students, designed to be accessible and to retain the student's attention.

3.1 Developed Prototype

In this prototype the APIs (Application Programming Interface) ARFoundation and ARCore were used, they provide architecture to work using AR, where it is possible to simulate the 3D model of a human skeleton in a real environment, maintaining its proportions and characteristics of virtual world. For prototype development, the Unity game development engine (version 2019.3.19f1) is also used, together with the SDK (Software Development Kit) and Devkit Manomotion that provides a structure for real-time 3D gesture analysis, requiring only a minimal computer power and a smartphone camera from for real time uses.

3.1.1 Details Related to Bones

We are currently working on 12 bones of the human body for interaction; these bones are represented in Figure 1. The choice of implemented bones followed the criteria of relevance to the matter, according to direct research with professionals in the area, and diversity of regions. However, more bones are being added in new versions in order to have an interactive representation of all the bones of a complete human skeleton at the end of the work.

The student should point out in the 3D model which bone is indicated in the question. Each bone has a flag that will be compared with the flag of the question drawn, so if the user hits the bone of the question another one will be drawn for a new question. The execution of the prototype can be seen in the Figure 2.

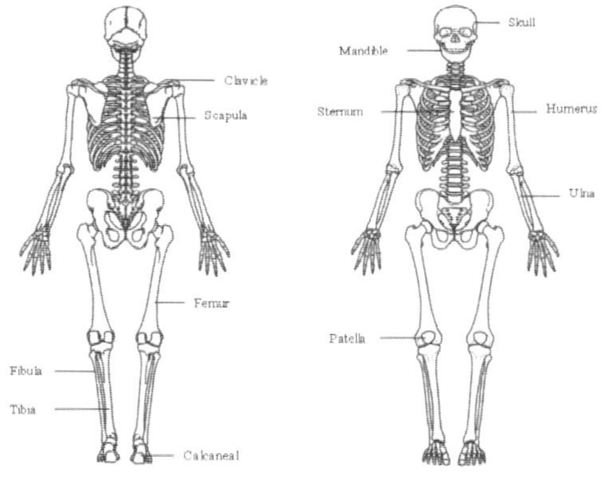

Figure 1. Skeleton images representing the interactive bones in the prototype

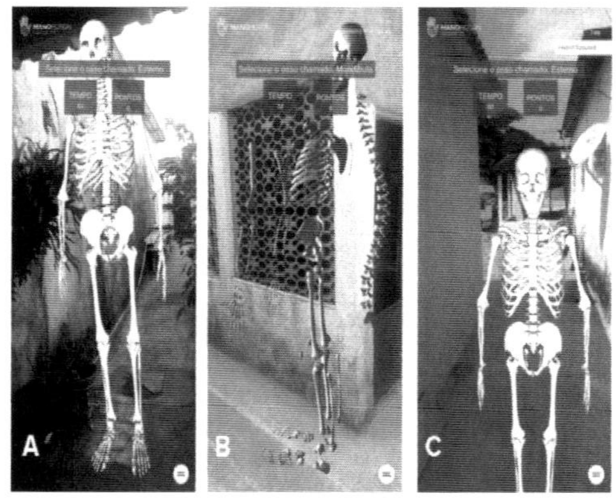

Figure 2. Virtual Skeleton projected (a) in a wooded environment (b) in a garage (c) on the street

3.1.2 Gamification

Quiz, scoring and time are used to improve self-learning. The player must correctly select the bone presented in questions: he receives points for hitting the bone and her points are reduced when he misses. In the punctuation system used, the skeleton was divided into 4 regions (head, chest, lower and upper limbs) the player loss more point when the answer is a bone belonging to a region other than the one presented. This system also makes use of combos, where the player gains more points for certain bones in a row. There is a time challenge of 1 minute for the user to get the highest score possible. In addition, a visualization tool allows the user to group, separates and rotates skeleton bones. These details and others can be seen well in this play: https://www.youtube.com/playlist?list=PLt-HAUhESHxVvzcVBzgt9uiTMsBkF7fT8

3.1.3 How Augmented Reality Works in BNAnatomy and Was Tested

Figure 3 presents a flowchart of augmented reality operation in the project. The application starts if the device meets the minimum requirements for operation, otherwise it is closed. Right after its initialization, the camera captures the environment and then detects a flat area to use as a reference when the virtual object is instantiated in the real world. If the flat area is valid, the application will calculate the position of the virtual object using the flat region of the physical world detected as a reference and the last step is to render the virtual object in the correct position within the flat region of the physical world.

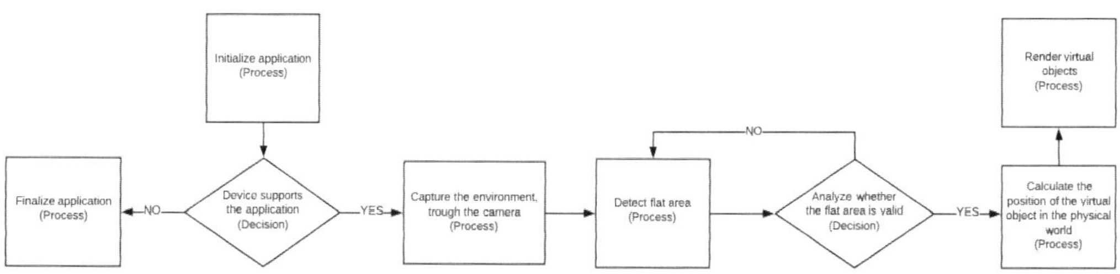

Figure 3. Flow chart of the functioning of augmented reality in BNAnatomy

The prototype was subjected to tests that allowed us to reach conclusions about aspects of its usability. Six participants, male and female, all students or professionals in health-related areas, answered a total of 15 questions, all of them subjective, divided into two questionnaires. They answered the questions with values from 1 to 5, with grade 1 being defined as the lowest level of approval and grade 5 as the highest level of approval possible.

The first questionnaire included a total of 9 questions, all related to aspects of system interaction and interface. The systematic review by Martins et al. (2015) served as a starting point for formulating these questions. These are the questions from the first questionnaire: q0) is the object easy to handle? ; q1) is gestural control compatible with movement? ; q2) was the text provided in this system clear? ; q3) was the audio feedback clear?; q4) is the application response / latency time appropriate? ; q5) is it possible to notice that the objects are in 3D? ; q6) is it difficult to make mistakes in the application? ; q7) does the application report your progress? ; q8) is the application easy to start? .

The second questionnaire had 6 questions regarding the learning aspects. The following questions were covered in this: q0) were you satisfied with the application? ; q1) do you believe that the application is relevant to the field of knowledge? ; q2) did you find the application fun? ; q3) does the application provide a learning facility superior to conventional teaching methodologies? ; q4) does application bring a greater motivation for learning than conventional teaching methodologies? ; q5) would you recommend it to a friend (student or professional) in the health field? .

4. RESULTS AND DISCUSSION

4.1 Results of the Questionnaire about the System and Interface

The results show that the system is easy to be manipulated, intuitive, with clear commands and with acceptable latency, but users have shown a lack of information about their progress. Table 1 shows the average of user ratings for the questions in the first questionnaire.

Table 1. Average of the evaluations obtained on the questions related to the first questionnaire

Question	Average
Q0) Is the object easy to handle?	4.17
Q1) Is gestural control compatible with movement?	4.83
Q2) Was the text provided in this system clear?	4.50
Q3) Was the audio feedback clear?	4.83
Q4) Is the application response / latency time appropriate ?	4.00
Q5) Is it possible to notice that the objects are in 3D?	5.00
Q6) Is it difficult to make mistakes in the application ?	4.00
Q7) Does the application report your progress?	3.67
Q8) Is the application easy to start?	4.83

4.2 Results of the Questionnaire on the Learning Aspects

Regarding the learning aspects, the answers were very satisfactory, showing a great degree of enthusiasm from the volunteers with the approach that we propose for teaching bone anatomy. Table 2 shows the average user ratings for the questions in the second questionnaire.

Table 2. Average of the evaluations obtained on the questions related to the second questionnaire

Question	Average
Q0) Were you satisfied with the application?	4.83
Q1) Do you believe that the application is relevant to the field of knowledge?	5.00
Q2) Did you find the application fun?	4.67
Q3)Does the application provide a learning facility superior to conventional teaching methodologies?	5.00
Q4) Does application bring a greater motivation for learning than conventional teaching methodologies?	5.00
Q5) Would you recommend it to a friend (student or professional) in the health field?	4.83

5. CONCLUSION

Despite the research being in its initial state, the results obtained with the tests were encouraging. We found evidence of a considerable relevance of the solution presented in this paper for the study of bone anatomy.

Regarding aspects that involve learning, the evaluations collected reveal a satisfaction with the application by the volunteers. In addition, almost all users claim that the experience stands out from conventional teaching methodologies, such as textbooks and atlas of human anatomy. We believe that this results from both the augmented reality experience and the proposed gamification.

The opinions about the interface and system were also positive; all users were able to use the application intuitively, without monitoring or guidance from third parties. However, part of the volunteers reported not being able to accurately understand their progress within the proposed experience in the system.

Although the application limits its operation only to cell phones with the Android operating system above version 7.0, it remains more accessible and cheaper than other similar solutions. Finally, we believe in the potential of the solution presented to add value to the teaching of bone anatomy. However, we see the need to add more bone models to the experiment and the reproduction of the experiment in a larger sample.

ACKNOWLEDGMENT

The authors are thankful to the volunteers that answered the questionnaires. A. C. thanks to INCT-MACC and CNPq, Universal 402988/2016-7 and PQ 305416/2018-9 Projects.

REFERENCES

Andayani, U., Siregar, B., Hernina Pulungan, S., Syahputra, M.F., Muchtar, M.A., Arisandi, D., 2019. A Visualisation of 3D Lung Anatomy with Augmented Reality as Interactive Medical Learning. J. Phys.: Conf. Ser. 1235, 012095. https://doi.org/10.1088/1742-6596/1235/1/012095

Azuma, R., Baillot, Y., Behringer, R., Feiner, S., Julier, S., MacIntyre, B., 2001. Recent advances in augmented reality. IEEE Comput. Grap. Appl. 21, 34–47. https://doi.org/10.1109/38.963459

Ferrer-Torregrosa, J., Jiménez-Rodríguez, M.Á., Torralba-Estelles, J., Garzón-Farinós, F., Pérez-Bermejo, M., Fernández-Ehrling, N., 2016. Distance learning ects and flipped classroom in the anatomy learning: comparative study of the use of augmented reality, video and notes. BMC Med Educ 16, 230. https://doi.org/10.1186/s12909-016-0757-3

Kuhn, C.M., Flanagan, E.M., 2017. Self-care as a professional imperative: physician burnout, depression, and suicide. Can J Anesth/J Can Anesth 64, 158–168. https://doi.org/10.1007/s12630-016-0781-0

Kurniawan, M.H., Suharjito, Diana, Witjaksono, G., 2018. Human Anatomy Learning Systems Using Augmented Reality on Mobile Application. Procedia Computer Science 135, 80–88. https://doi.org/10.1016/j.procs.2018.08.152

Martins, V.F., 2012. Desafios para o uso de Realidade Virtual e Aumentada de maneira efetiva no ensino 10.

Martins, V.F., Kirner, T.G., Kirner, C., 2015. Subjective Usability Evaluation Criteria of Augmented Reality Applications, in: Shumaker, R., Lackey, S. (Eds.), Virtual, Augmented and Mixed Reality, Lecture Notes in Computer Science. Springer International Publishing, Cham, pp. 39–48. https://doi.org/10.1007/978-3-319-21067-4_5

Singh, M., Singh, M.P., 2013. Augmented Reality Interfaces. IEEE Internet Comput. 17, 66–70. https://doi.org/10.1109/MIC.2013.107

Stefan, P., Wucherer, P., Oyamada, Y., Ma, M., Schoch, A., Kanegae, M., Shimizu, N., Kodera, T., Cahier, S., Weigl, M., Sugimoto, M., Fallavollita, P., Saito, H., Navab, N., 2014. An AR edutainment system supporting bone anatomy learning, in: 2014 IEEE Virtual Reality (VR). Presented at the 2014 IEEE Virtual Reality (VR), IEEE, Minneapolis, MN, USA, pp. 113–114. https://doi.org/10.1109/VR.2014.6802077

THE IDEAL FAIRYTALE: DIY CINDERELLA

Saeryn Ryu, Jun Hyung Lee and Hyun Bin Cho
Sogang University
Seoul, South Korea

ABSTRACT

Programming was once considered as a high-level technique that only experts can handle, however, now the range of programmers has expanded to the general public, as coding is becoming a basic and popular skill. It can now work as a fundamental tool for everyone to express their creativity. Starting from a single program such as a smartphone app, a lot of small businesses have now developed their economic scales to the level of big conglomerates that influence the society as a whole. Besides the economic success that this technology can bring, it also has the potential to contribute to an educational aspect, which means it can have a great impact on how young children might be able to think in the future.
In this article, we suggest a program, or it can also be referred as a 'game,' that goes against the contents of conventional educational materials that has been used and is still being used by the society to educate young children. As three university undergraduates who were born and raised in South Korea, we developed a program that challenges the fixed contents and the fixed method of the previous educational material that we had been taught as children. We used Python to create the program and the name of the program is <DIY Cinderella>, an acronym for "Do it Yourself Cinderella." Through making this program, we expect that children's education and entertainment can be made into more diverse content and forms.

KEYWORDS

Gender, Stereotype, Python, Fairytale, Game, Education

1. INTRODUCTION

In recent years there has been rising controversy regarding the issue of portrayal of gender within the media. For example, there have been criticism regarding the lack of diverse characters, or the questionable depictions of the way characters act according to gender. These are indeed serious issues, and of these various media and genres, fairy tales must receive proper attention because they are especially problematic. This is because, "fairy tales not only influence a child's moral development but also their ideas of appropriate gender conduct. These childhood texts 'represent 'internalized' formulas for social and by extension, gender behavior' (Haase and Primeau, 1993). Impressionable children absorb these lessons and begin to shape their own life around them" (Steinzeig, 2012). Considering the influence that can be implicated by such fairy tales, we came up with the question of: In what ways are fairy tales problematic in the portrayal of gender and how can we solve the issues they implicate?

After some research, we came to conclusion that fairy tales are problematic in the representation of gender and sexual orientation and the construction of gender roles. First, characters in fairy tales are overwhelmingly heterosexual, the reason for which, we found in the history of the genre. The earliest publications of collections of folk tales were by Charles Perrault or, Brothers Grimm, who were all from European countries that were Christian at the time, which explains the heterosexuality in the stories. Yet this is outdated and is detrimental in their effects on construction of views regarding sexual orientation and gender. Also, they reinforce several gender roles, shown in how, "the hero is generally characterised by his activity," while, "the heroine is usually pictured as more helpless" (Toomeos-Orglaan, 2013). These portrayals of the characters are influential in the development of children's perspectives regarding gender, and thus are in dire need of resolution.

The first idea we had was to choose a fairy tale, analyze their various problems and by fixing them, create the perfect fairy tale. However, while brainstorming stories to change and how to change them, we ran into a major obstacle. Can an ideal fairy tale truly exist? For example, with princess stories, we wanted to change the personality of the characters, so they would not be as helpless. We soon realized however, that though we intended to solve the problem of stereotyping women as weak, this in turn reinforced the notion that they should be strong. Instead of eradicating the gender role, it simply created a new, different one in its place. We therefore concluded that a correct answer does not exist and thus, neither does an ideal fairy tale.

Thus, we decided to focus on the concept of there being no correct answer. With no singular correct answer, only diversity is left. We realized that it was the idea of there being an ideal answer that was the cause of gender roles, when in reality, all outcomes have meaning. To build upon this idea we resolved to create a program of sorts, a kind of game, in which people could recreate fairy tales. This would not be an ideal fairy tale, but one that is distinct, and their own. Through this program, we aimed to help the participant realize that fairy tales could, without losing their original color, be changed to embody both contemporary and individual values in diverse ways. With this diversity, it would be possible to realize just how trapped we are within gender roles imposed on us by fairy tales we came to love when we were children and break free of them.

2. WHY CINDERELLA?

The fairy tale we decided to focus on was the Disney Cinderella. This was because the story itself embodies the aforementioned common issues of fairy tales in gender and is one of the most iconic fairy tales there are. The story of Cinderella has been criticized that "she is a sorry excuse for a heroine, pitiable and useless. She cannot perform even a simple action to save herself, though she is warned by her friends, the mice. She does not hear them because she is 'off in a world of dreams'" (Yolen, 1977), and thus "suggests that a girl does not have to fight for the justice and she can let others hurt her feelings and treat her in a bad and inferior role. Everything a girl has to be is good and kind in any case" (Veselá, 2014). There are problems in the portrayal of men as well, in the, "emphasis on the hero´s financial provision as even little girls are already guided to find a rich husband who will render them the necessary comfort that will secure their contentment" (Veselá, 2014). Considering these serious problems in the story, we thought it would be especially meaningful to handle the Disney Cinderella because of how iconic she is.

3. THE FIXED AND VARIABLE ELEMENTS OF DIY CINDERELLA

Table 1. Fixed elements and Variable elements of <DIY Cinderella>

Fixed elements	Variable elements
Name of the main character 'Cinderella'	Gender and Sexual Orientation
Stepfamily being jealous of Cinderella	Course of events
Leaving behind a possession & returning home before midnight	Details
Existence of Cinderella's potential partner	

Determining what elements to fix or make variable was essential before creating our program and we have concluded as it shows in Table 1. Since there are many versions of Cinderella, we decided to keep fixed the common characteristics, so that that the recreation could be recognizable as a Cinderella story. "The structure seen in the stories based on Cinderella's topic can be divided as (…) the prosecuted heroine, magic help, meeting the prince, proof of identity, marriage of the prince" (Veselá, 2014). We fixed the elements of the persecuted heroine, magic help, proof of identity, and meeting the prince, although as the gender and sexual orientation of all characters were made variable, the terms 'heroine' or 'prince' are inappropriate. The last element of marriage was made variable because we did not want marriage to be the only means of "living happily ever after". In addition, characters' behavior and personality were also made variable so that the participants could change the passive Cinderella of the original story. Moreover, objective features of appearance (height and skin color rather than 'pretty' or 'ugly') were added as variable elements. This is because we wanted to include the visual factors, since our program's story was based on the Disney version of Cinderella, iconized by the animation.

4. WHY PYTHON?

Figure 1. The Python Script of <DIY Cinderella>

As you can see in Figure 1, we utilized Python in order to make this program. Google and Naver surveys are the most common methods of gathering information when it comes to Korean University students' projects. However, we wanted people (children) to make the most individual and original version of Cinderella that suits their sexuality and sexual orientation. This led to a thought that we have to utilize programming system as our format in order to realize our intention of the whole project. Since Python was the only tool we were all familiar with, we chose to use Python as the platform for our program, despite its lack of accessibility in that the process of downloading Python program to participate in our program was relatively complicated.

5. BRIEF MANUAL OF HOW <DIY CINDERELLA> WORKS

First, in order to use our program, you will have to install the Python program. After the install, the first screen you will get after clicking our program is the first page of our program, shown in Figure 2. The story will begin with the cliché fairytale opening of "Once upon a time…" and the user will be ready to fill in the blanks right away.

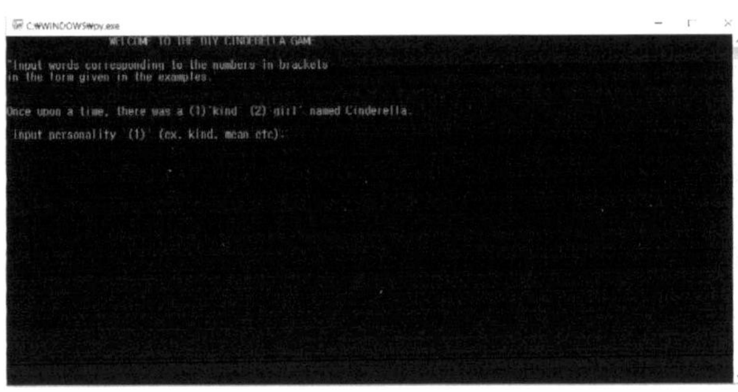

Figure 2. How the program appears when you first run it

Now you start to create and construct your own Cinderella story using different adjectives, pronouns, nouns, etc. Next, see Figure 3, which the red circles refer to the input of the user and the red underlines are how the user input is reflected to the storyline.

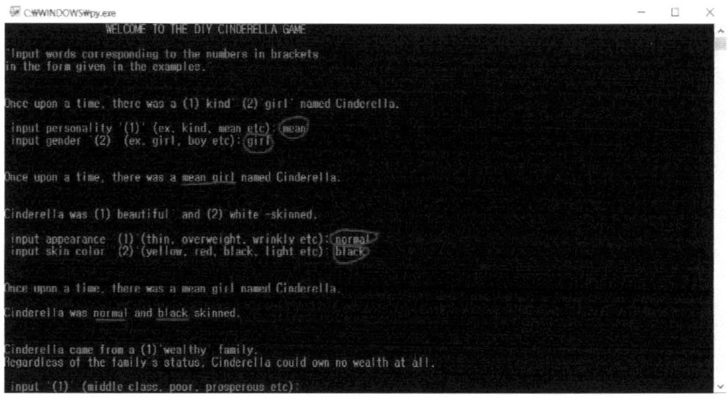

Figure 3. Process of running the program

If you input 'mean' instead of 'kind' the story reflects your input and starts to create the story with the words that you chose. Same way, in the next part, because the user inputted 'normal' and 'black' instead of the original words 'beautiful' and 'white,' the story changed from "Cinderella was beautiful and white-skinned" to "Cinderella was normal and black-skinned." This goes on with more than 20 inputs.

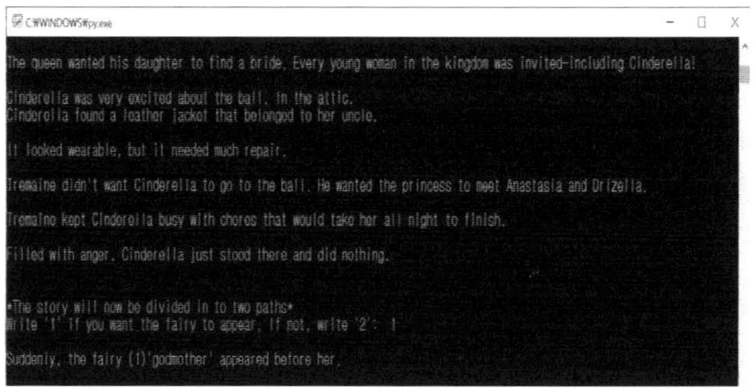

Figure 4. Part where the user can choose the path of the storyline

Not only the words, but we tried to make the program reflect more of the users' personality. In Figure 4, the program makes the user to choose whether the fairy should appear or not, which is the part where the fairy godmother appears in the original story. Since the fairy godmother basically does everything in the original story, Cinderella is criticized of being passive and submissive. Therefore, we included the fairy godmother scene as a variable element though it was first considered one of the most important fixed elements that symbolized the original Cinderella story. In other words, if you want your Cinderella to be more active and confident, you don't need to make the fairy appear in the story at all. This path-choosing scene appears once more in the last part of our program, which is the part where Cinderella loses one of her possessions (glass slipper in the original story). In the original one as everyone knows, Prince Charming make his servants find Cinderella. This part also shows how passive Cinderella is and how male characters tend to appear as the hero in all fairytales. We wanted to break the stereotype, so we made the users to choose whether they want their Cinderellas to be found or their Cinderellas finding their possessions by themselves.

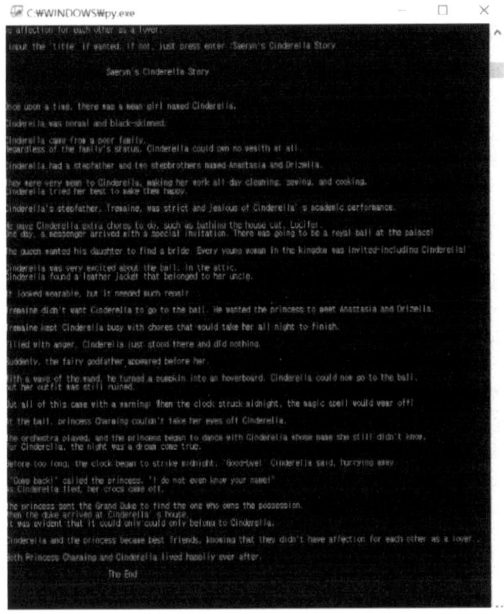

Figure 5. A completed version of <DIY Cinderella>

The happily-ever-after ending is also a very common stereotypical ending of most fairytales. We felt that there should be no obligation for young children to feel that every relationship has to end happily and getting married, so we made the users to create their own ending. For example, in Figure 5, instead of Cinderella getting married to the Prince/Princess Charming, the story ends by saying "They became best friends, knowing that they didn't have affection for each other as a lover." Any kind of endings are possible, such as getting married but getting divorced shortly after.

6. SHARING SESSION

We uploaded mainly three things on the Facebook page Sogang Univ. and other several KakaoTalk chat rooms (National chatting app in South Korea). The DIY Cinderella game itself, the manual for the program and the Python download file. These are the materials required to play the game. Moreover, we also uploaded the link to an "Anonymous DIY Cinderella Chat Room", where people could share their own DIY Cinderella stories and exchange feedback on both the stories and the project itself. The chat room was created so that people could enjoy the game further and learn what other diverse choices people made. We created the DIY Cinderella Chat Room as we wanted something more to our project than just simply making and sharing the program.

Members in the chat room could largely be divided into "Readers" and "Writers. "Readers" were those who only read and responded to the stories of others, while "Writers" were those who not only read other's stories but also shared their own. We found that the participants seemed to enjoy playing the game along with reading others' stories even more than we anticipated. "Writers" showed the tendency of uploading multiple stories, proving their interest through repeated participation in the program.

The variety of stories uploaded constituted an incredibly wide spectrum. The variable words for describing Cinderella's gender were much more diverse in participants' stories than we originally imagined. "Girl", "boy", "guy", "bisexual", "MTFtransgender", are some examples of the wide spectrum of terms that were used. As expected, the binary gender terms were most often used. However, many people attempted to facilitate the usage of non-binary gender terms, which eventually became natural in the story room. Nobody questioned or found it strange that Cinderella was bisexual or gay in others' stories, embracing terms naturally as they should be.

Surprisingly, there were lots of stories that focused only on entertainment rather than on gender itself. "The father wanted his bird to find a cookie. Every puppies in the kingdom was invited including Cinderella!" This display of random placement of words caused much laughter in the chat room. This aspect of entertainment allowed the "Readers" to also enjoy the project. More importantly, it induced the participants' reading of others' stories in general, allowing them to think about the diversity of choices that others made in DIY Cinderella, especially gender roles.

Participants also participated more actively by giving feedback on others' stories. People tended to react more to the funnier ones, like Cinderella getting divorced with the prince. But for stories where Cinderella was MTF Transgender, gay, bisexual, etc., people tended not to react as much. Most comments were simply about how that particular characterization of Cinderella was "creative" or "interesting". From the lack of reactions, we could find that people were not familiar with the various gender terms and feared giving the wrong impression regarding the sensitive matter. This exemplified the concept of sexual stigma, in which, "members of society know that homosexual behaviors and attractions are devalued relative to heterosexuality" (Herek et al, 2009). Moreover, we could witness some of the stereotypes people had within the chat room, although most people enthusiastically contributed to expanding the diversity of stories and breaking such stereotypes.

7. CONCLUSION & LIMITATIONS

Although we were satisfied with the project and its results overall, we felt there were some limitations. The first were the constraints imposed by the format of the program itself. Through restricting the extent to which the participant can change the story, and the examples provided to assist in showing what kind of words (nouns, descriptions of characters, etc.) should be inserted, our own values were inevitably connoted which could have lessened how creative the participants could be in their recreations. Plus, there was the problem of accessibility due to the program being in the form of Python and also English, which was difficult for some Koreans. Also, we were regretful that we could not handle more inequalities or problems that the story of Cinderella does not encompass. Yet, we are certain that through our program, we were able to create a method through which people could realize and change their views on gender roles with the concept of diversity.

REFERENCES

Haase, D. and Primeau, M., 1993. *The Reception Of Grimms' Fairy Tales*. pp.120~121.

Herek, G., et al, 2009. *Internalized stigma among sexual minority adults: Insights from a social psychological perspective*. Journal of Counseling Psychology, 56(1), p.2.

Steinzeig, Aleah E., 2012. *Waiting for Prince Charming: Gender Expectations in the European Fairy Tale*. Humanities Capstone Projects. 12.

Toomeos-Orglaan, K., 2013. Gender Stereotypes in Cinderella (ATU 510A) and The Princess on the Glass Mountain (ATU 530). *Journal of Ethnology And Folkloristics*, 7(2), pp. 49-64.

Veselá, A., 2014. *Gender Stereotypes In Fairy Tales*. Masaryk University, Faculty of Education.

Yolen, J., 1977. America's Cinderella. *Children's Literature in Education*, 8(1), pp.302-303.

A PROPOSED TECHNOLOGY SOLUTION FOR ENHANCING ORDER PICKING IN WAREHOUSES AND DISTRIBUTION CENTERS BASED ON A GAMIFIED AUGMENTED REALITY APPLICATION

George Plakas, Eleni Aretoulaki, Stavros T. Ponis, Konstantinos Agalianos
and Theodoros Nikolaos Maroutas
School of Mechanical Engineering, National Technical University Athens
Heroon Polytechniou 9, Zografos 15780, Athens, Greece

ABSTRACT

Industry 4.0, since the first introduction of the term back in 2011, has gained significant traction and nowadays it is -almost unanimously- considered as the main technology driver, leading supply chain in the new era of faster, flexible and more intelligent processes and reduced operational, planning and management costs. One of the most prominent technologies in the Industry 4.0's arsenal is Augmented Reality (AR), which utilizes the capabilities of computer-generated display, sound, text and effects to enhance the user's real-world experience, through wearable equipment. In logistics environments, the use of AR to support workers in their everyday order picking tasks is currently a business reality with growing number of applications and significant scaling potential. However, in this new business reality, despite the efforts made to support workers, order picking still stands out as the most labor intensive, prone to error and expensive process in the modern warehouse. These characteristics indisputably put significant strain to pickers creating both fatigue, feelings of monotony and dissatisfaction usually leading to employee underperformance and demotivation. This paper proposes a technology solution that introduces AR in the picking process to efficiently support pickers in their everyday tasks, while at the same time evaluates the potential of enhancing AR with gamification elements as a tool for increasing motivation, positively influence job satisfaction and behavior and subsequently increase performance and productivity.

KEYWORDS

Augmented Reality, Gamification, Order Picking, Warehouses, Smart Glasses, Logistics 4.0

1. INTRODUCTION

Logistics state-of-the-art has evolved in recent years, since warehouses and distribution centers are facing challenges, such as the need of faster and more efficient operations and reduced inventory maintenance. Major factor for these challenges is the global development of e-commerce and upward demand for personalized products. The most labor intensive task in warehousing and supply chain management is the order picking process (De Koster, 2007). It is estimated that 75% of the tasks in a warehouse are conducted by warehouse workers and more than 50% (Elbert and Sarnow, 2019) of the operating cost of the warehouse derives from order picking procedures. While this process is necessary, its traditional approach is expensive, prone to errors and with high labor intensity. The most important measurable efficiency indicators of order picking are time and accuracy (Reif and Günthner, 2009; Reif et al., 2010). Time determines the productivity of the warehouse's workforce and affects the efficiency of the entire supply chain. Lack or accuracy and errors on the other hand, have a severe impact on the warehousing quality, as they can lead to significant financial consequences. The three most common errors in order picking are: a) wrong item collection, b) collection of items in the wrong quantity and c) omission of items.

One of the Industry 4.0 technologies, that are tested to improve the intralogistics performance, is Augmented Reality (AR), which refers to the addition of computer-generated visualizations, to the real environment and is mainly displayed through smart wearable systems. The AR purpose is adding objects to a real environment, but also hiding objects from it, in real time (Azuma et al., 2001). In the near future, warehouse workers will use their smartphones, wearables and other AR and VR devices to join the IoT environment and increase human-to-machine interaction (Efthymiou and Ponis, 2019). As a matter of fact, AR is able to support warehousing, providing the possibility of an interactive work with fewer errors (Cirulis and Ginters, 2013) and as result rendering pickers' daily tasks simpler, enjoyable and less stressful. Visual content provided by a wearable system in picker's field of view is able to reduce the time between information's perception and action (Wang and Dunston, 2006). Thus, in the specific case of order picking, labor effort and mental fatigue may be reduced and efficiency subsequently increased. Moreover, a wearable system sets both picker's hands free, facilitating the productive part of his/her work (picking). Evidently, the most important task that can be improved by an AR system is the navigation. According to Schwerdtfeger et al. (2011), order picking involves two phases of navigation. In the first phase (course navigation), the picker has to walk to the right aisle and rack. In the second phase (fine navigation), the picker stands in front of the right rack and has to locate the correct shelf, bin or box, to complete the collection. The second phase is deemed the most critical, especially for distribution centers providing an extensive variety of small items. With the utilization of an AR navigation system, it is possible to present the employee with visual navigation aids, displaying the exact position of the targeted item to pick. As a result, the time for finding and collecting products will be substantially reduced and potential errors may be prevented, leading to a more productive order picking process.

The technique of using AR as an aid-providing subsystem of the order picking process has been named Pick-by-Vision. The first appearance of this term in modern literature is by Reif and Walch (2008). A search in the literature brought to the foreground some existing studies focusing on improving the way navigation of a picker through the warehouse's aisles is carried out and searching for the optimal way to improve fine navigation. Despite the fact that the efforts of AR researchers in this field are still young, there are already commercial AR systems for order picking (Guo et al., 2014) and systems used by high-profile players in the supply chain industry (DHL Logistics, 2019).

Nevertheless, in spite of its indisputable merits, AR technology is unable to countermand the fact that order picking is an inherently intensive and repetitive manual process, leading to fatigue, demotivation (Hense et al., 2013) and consequently, decreased performance in the long run, increasing operational costs for the supply chain overall (De Koster et al., 2007). So, it goes without saying that the enhancement of motivation is a primary factor in ameliorating the performance of order picking (van den Berg, 2017). Gamification, i.e. "the use of game design elements in non-game contexts" (Deterding, 2011) has proved to be able to effectively serve this purpose, by using game elements to meet various psychological needs , such competence, autonomy and social relatedness, with the aim of motivating workers, influencing their behavior and as a result, improving their productivity. The proposed solution presented in this paper appraises the potential of introducing AR and game elements into the order picking process of modern distribution centers, with a view to assisting pickers' daily tasks, increasing their motivation and hence, their performance.

2. THE PROPOSED SOLUTION

The proposed technology solution involves the development of a system aspiring to support man-to-goods order picking within warehouses and distribution centers. The solution aims to combine the functionalities of Augmented Reality and the techniques of Gamification and its final product will be able to be fully integrated into any existing Warehouse Management System (WMS). The development of the system consists of a set of two integrated modules (i.e. AR picking module and Gamification module) which are connected through appropriate APIs to the existing WMS utilized by the warehouse. The existing WMS is a key component of the final product, as it transfers data to both modules and receives data from the AR Picking module. The design and development of a comprehensive solution that can be configured to meet all possible needs and address various scenarios that may occur during the order picking process, within any warehousing establishment, is of great importance for the authors.

The AR Picking module is responsible for providing the picker in his/her eye level with the necessary information for collecting the item (ID, position, quantity) and subsequently navigating him/her through an imaging feature, able to solve any course and fine navigation issues, utilizing three-dimensional arrows and shapes to highlight the right isle or self, according to the data provided by the WMS. During standard AR-enhanced collection, the picker will be able to complete his/her assignment by a) understanding the order received from WMS b) following the route provided by the imaging feature, c) collecting the item from the right shelf and d) informing the WMS about the finalized collection, through one of the smart glasses' functionalities (buttons, microphone, camera etc.). The process will be repeated until the list is over and it is significant that the picker's hands are both free during this process, thanks to the wearable equipment.

Evidently, the smart wearable system is the most important part of the AR Picking module and the choice of the appropriate visualization device would affect the successful implementation of the entire solution. The basic challenge for the smart glasses is the fact that the employees are required to wear them throughout their shift, so they should be lightweight and ergonomically designed. Also, the smart glasses' screen should not interfere with picker's field of view towards the real warehouse environment, for safety reasons. At the same time, the operating time of the battery has to be sufficient and need no recharging until the end the picker's shift. The authors believe that all of these are covered sufficiently by an industrial product, VUZIX M300XL (Vuzix, 2020).

On the other hand, the Gamification module will be responsible for providing a new working experience, by enabling managers to create a gaming environment (scenarios) for the employees to compete in. The gamification mechanism will operate around this set of work-related competition scenarios among the pickers and the WMS will feed data into the Process Center of the Gamification module to enable the attainment of goals. The authors believe that the best way to enhance the order picking process is to create scenarios based on the most important measurable efficiency indicators of order picking as they were mentioned in the introduction, which are time and accuracy. Taking this into account, every correct collection will add points to picker's gamification profile and every error (collection of wrong item or wrong quantity of an item collected) will have negative impact to the profile, subtracting multiple points. Last but not least, a quick collection will be rewarded by offering bonus points to the picker. The warehouse managers can take advantage of these basic elements to build different scenarios, either based on personal goals for each one of their employees or based on weekly or monthly leaderboards to reward exclusively the best-performing pickers in a period of time. Leaderboards and rankings announcing performance-related information will be displayed to warehouse managers, supervisors and pickers, by the Report Center of the Gamification module, through a web reporting tool, which could be also displayed via a public screen within the warehouse. The authors believe that a gamified approach is a solution that can potentially boost pickers' productivity and performance and combined with the game-related interface offered by the AR Application, the system is expected to meet high acceptance levels. The entire system has to be exploited as a whole, in order to upgrade the work experience within the warehouse to a flexible, smart and playful process for the benefit of the entire supply chain. A schematic of the proposed solution is presented in Figure 1.

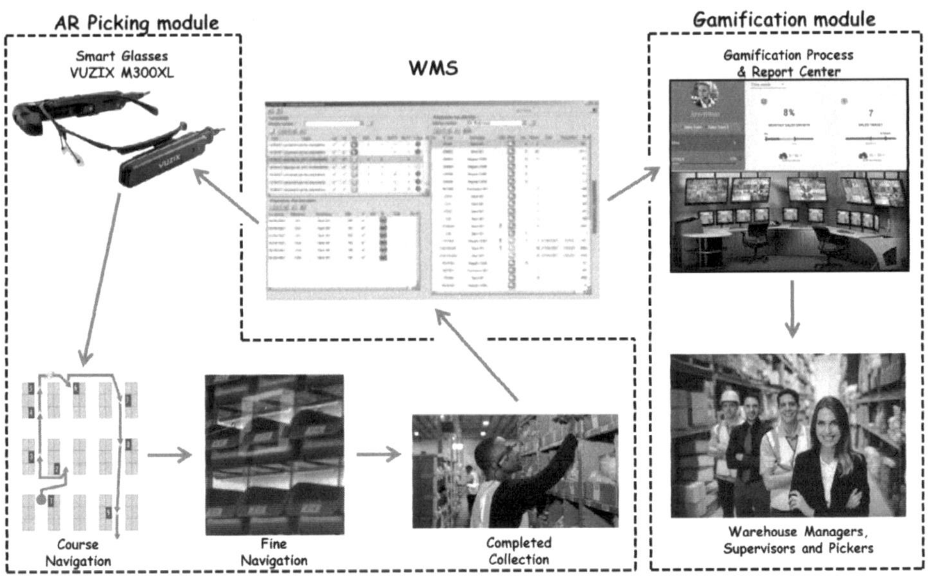

Figure 1. The proposed technology solution

The authors are currently in the phase of assessing the technical components and the overall viability of the system, while at the same time identifying possible ways for design improvements. Their future objective is to produce a small-scale pilot-tested Proof of Concept (POC), including:

- An ergonomic coupling of the system's hardware components (VUZIX M300XL, battery, warehouse helmet).
- A generic and fully customizable man-to-goods AR order picking application, integrated in the VUZIX M300XL android software.
- A gamification application for setting all the competition scenarios between pickers and calculating results according the WMS-provided data.
- A fully integrated web reporting tool informing the stakeholders of the system (warehouse managers, supervisors and pickers) about the results of the competitions.
- APIs for connection with the existing WMS (one API for each module).

3. CONCLUSION

The proposed solution will provide warehouse managers with innovative software and its final product will be seamlessly integrated with existing warehouse management systems in a WMS close to agnostic fashion, in order to effectively support the order picking process. Hardware and software capabilities of all AR applications still require improvements, but the technology has already demonstrated its potential and left many promises for the future, as a new way of supporting the intralogistics workforce. Through the AR Picking module, the authors focus on making the order picking process faster, with fewer errors and more ergonomic for the employees. Providing information on pickers' and items' real-time position is able to present the former with navigation instructions, drastically reducing time, both on course and fine navigation. Furthermore, through the Gamification module, the authors try to achieve greater employee engagement and offer incentives to increase productivity, which combined with AR's ability to dispense pickers from needing to use their hands, will transform their daily tasks into an enjoyable routine. All in all, research on the implementation of AR and Gamification in order picking is still in progress and the authors plan to further explore its potential in the future, by examining the possibility of adding live Gamification statistics to the glasses' screen, while taking into account that such a decision could be conducive to stress and countermanding the benefits of Gamification.

ACKNOWLEDGEMENT

The present work is co-funded by the European Union and Greek national funds through the Operational Program "Competitiveness, Entrepreneurship and Innovation" (EPAnEK), under the call "RESEARCH-CREATE-INNOVATE" (project code: T1EDK-01168 & acronym: SMARTFLEX Warehouse).

REFERENCES

Azuma R. et al, 2001. Recent advances in augmented reality. *IEEE computer graphics and applications*, 21(6), pp.34-47.

Cirulis A. and Ginters E., 2013. Augmented reality in logistics. *Procedia Computer Science*, 26(11), pp.14-20.

De Koster R. et al., 2007. Design and control of warehouse order picking: A literature review. *European journal of operational research*, 182(2), pp.481-501.

Deterding S. et al., 2011, September. From game design elements to gamefulness: defining" gamification". *In Proceedings of the 15th international academic MindTrek conference: Envisioning future media environments* (pp. 9-15).

DHL Logistics, 2019. *DHL SUPPLY CHAIN DEPLOYS LATEST VERSION OF SMART GLASSES WORLDWIDE.* Available at: <https://www.dhl.com/global-en/home/press/press-archive/2019/dhl-supply-chain-deploys-latest-version-of-smart-glasses-worldwide.html> [Accessed 10 June 2020].

Efthymiou, O.K. and Ponis, S.T., 2019. Current Status of Industry 4.0 in Material Handling Automation and In-house Logistics. *International Journal of Industrial and Manufacturing Engineering*, 13(10), pp.1370-1374.

Elbert R. and Sarnow T., 2019, February. Augmented Reality in Order Picking—Boon and Bane of Information (Over-) Availability. *In International Conference on Intelligent Human Systems Integration* (pp. 400-406). Springer, Cham.

Guo A. et al., 2014, September. A comparison of order picking assisted by head-up display (HUD), cart-mounted display (CMD), light, and paper pick list. *In Proceedings of the 2014 ACM International Symposium on Wearable Computers* (pp. 71-78).

Hense J. et al., 2013, June. Using gamification to enhance staff motivation in logistics. *In International Simulation and Gaming Association Conference* (pp. 206-213). Springer, Cham.

Reif R. and Walch D., 2008. Augmented & Virtual Reality applications in the field of logistics. *The Visual Computer*, 24(11), pp.987-994.

Reif R. et al., 2010, March. Evaluation of an augmented reality supported picking system under practical conditions. *In Computer Graphics Forum* (Vol. 29, No. 1, pp. 2-12). Oxford, UK: Blackwell Publishing Ltd.

Reif, R. and Günthner, W.A., 2009. Pick-by-vision: augmented reality supported order picking. *The Visual Computer*, 25(5-7), pp.461-467.

Schwerdtfeger B. Et al., 2011. Pick-by-vision: there is something to pick at the end of the augmented tunnel. *Virtual reality*, 15(2-3), pp.213-223.

van den Berg, T., 2017. Gamification to enhance motivation in a real world order picking environment of an online grocer: A case study at Picnic.

Vuzix, 2020. *Vuzix M300XL | Industry AR Solutions*. [online] Available at: <https://www.vuzix.com/products/m300xl-smart-glasses> [Accessed 7 June 2020].

Wang X. and Dunston P.S., 2006. Compatibility issues in Augmented Reality systems for AEC: An experimental prototype study. *Automation in construction*, 15(3), pp.314-326.

ON THE DESIGN OF INTELLIGENT PUBLIC INFORMATION FACILITIES — TAKE THE PUBLIC SERVICE ROBOT AS AN EXAMPLE

Huiping Dai
Shanghai Sanda University, Room 504, No. 12, Lane 792, Fahuazhen Road, Changning District, Shanghai, China 200052

ABSTRACT

In the construction of the smart city, intelligent public facilities are indispensable. As a type of intelligent public facilities, public service robot has some problems in the current application process. For example, technical problems, communication difficulties, lack of guidance and other aspects of the problem, and in view of these problems, in this paper, put forward the corresponding design strategy, hoping to optimize the overall design of the public service robot, improve its comprehensive level, so as to become a booster to improve the public service level of the smart city.

KEYWORDS

Interactive Design, Intelligence, Public Information Facility, Public Service Robot

1. INTRODUCTION

In the city, public facilities such as signboards and information inquiry machines can be seen everywhere. These facilities bring a lot of convenience to people's life. With the progress and development of science and technology, the intelligent level of the facilities will gradually improve, bringing people's life with efficiency and convenience that never existed before.

2. INTELLIGENT PUBLIC INFORMATION FACILITY AND PUBLIC SERVICE ROBOT

Public information facility is a kind of urban public facilities. Its main function is to provide people with direction guidance, instruction, information, public affairs, etc. With the rapid development of modern science and technology, many changes have taken place in the public information facility. Therefore, a variety of intelligent information facilities have emerged, such as electronic rolling screens, interactive touch screens, public service robots, etc. And a public service robot is a new form of intelligent public information facility, which integrates core technologies such as visual recognition, speech recognition, intelligent interaction, network technology, real-time system, sensor detection, control technology, and system integration. It will become a representative form of intelligent public facilities in the future.

3. FEATURES OF PUBLIC SERVICE ROBOT

A public service robot is a kind of intelligent system terminal, which is shaped like a human, has greeting etiquette and navigation services, can speak, sing, interact with people in natural language, has simple actions and facial expressions, can provide public information, guide navigation, realize temperature detection, fire alarm, air quality detection, and other functions. Its main features are as follows: First, a public service robot is a combination of public information facilities and artificial intelligence. The robot combines a variety of intelligent interaction technologies. Through intelligent sensing, information processing, and other technologies, the robot can collect various behavior data of people, and then upload it to the intelligent management system. Second, as an intelligent system terminal, after accessing the Internet of things, it can also control the public facilities (such as lighting, access control, etc.) in an area. Third, public service robot integrates various interaction modes. With the continuous development of intelligent interaction technology, people can experience more natural and rich interaction.

4. THE CURRENT SITUATION OF PUBLIC SERVICE ROBOT

Nowadays, public service robots can be seen in many public places, such as banks, hospitals, libraries, and other public places. For the interaction experience with the public service robot, the author has conducted random interviews. Some people said that "voice input has problems and can't be accurately recognized," some people said "don't know how to use it, it's better to ask the staff directly," some said that "you can chat a few sentences, but it's basically not very meaningful," and there are many problems. In summary, the main problems are as follows:

4.1 Problems of Intelligent Identification Technology

Although speech recognition, face recognition, and other technologies are developing rapidly, as far as robots are concerned, speech recognition and other technologies cannot reach the level of natural communication. People often use voice to communicate with the public service robot. When there are errors in speech recognition, it will lead to communication obstacles. Finally, they need to turn to the real waiter. Therefore, at present, **the intelligent identification technology of public service robots is not mature and stable**, and it cannot recognize the surrounding world as people do, which directly affects the effectiveness of public service robot interaction design.

4.2 Matching the Environment

A public service robot provides services for people in public places. The usual place is basically the entrance or hall of the place, such as the outpatient Hall of the hospital, the railway station hall, etc., while the public place is characterized by open space and dense personnel, and the environment is generally noisy, so **it is questionable whether the public service robot based on voice interaction is suitable for use in such an environment**. Under the current technology, public service robot does not have very mature speech recognition function, which increases the difficulty of recognition in a noisy environment. In addition, the complexity of people in public places, people from different places, have different dialects, voice, and intonation, which makes recognition more difficult.

4.3 Problems with User Interaction

In the beginning, people were curious about the public service robot. However, after the initial contact, many people did not use it again, which shows that the public service robot is not perfect in terms of humanization. Although the public service robot has the functions of singing, chatting and telling jokes, its expression mode is still very stylized, which brings a kind of rigid and cold feeling to people, while the live receptionist has rich emotional expression and more temperature, which is the **key difference** between the public service robot and the real person.

4.4 Lack of Effective Operation Guidance

In the face of new things, people will be curious and confused. Even though new devices are easier to use and more efficient than old ones, people still have **psychological barriers to new devices** before they learn how to use them. Although the public service robot is considered to be able to talk freely with people, due to the current technical limitations, the interaction between robots and people cannot be as flexible as that between people. After a simple attempt to talk, people find that the public service robot does not achieve the desired interaction effect, so they are reluctant to try again, which leads to the public service The robot is idle after a period of time.

5. THE DESIGN STRATEGY OF INTELLIGENT PUBLIC INFORMATION FACILITY

5.1 Improve Technical Level

Human robot interaction (HRI) involves many disciplines. It has gradually developed into an independent research field. Just how to make robots understand the real world like people is a challenging topic. Therefore, the natural interaction between robot and human will not be easy to achieve, but it can be predicted that with the continuous development of technology, researchers will be able to solve all the key problems, improve the effectiveness of human-robot interaction, so that robot can communicate with people normally, and become an indispensable partner in people's life.

5.2 Interactive Design Matching with the Environment

In the public environment, the interaction between public service robots and human is affected by the environment to some extent, so the product design should consider matching with the environment. On the one hand, because the public environment is generally noisy, the voice interaction between public service robots and users is not good. In this regard, other interaction methods can be adopted, such as increasing the size of the screen, mainly touch-screen interaction, supplemented by voice interaction, or at the same time of voice interaction, the screen displays the corresponding visual form information such as subtitles, so that the subtitles can be seen even if the voice cannot be heard clearly. On the other hand, the appearance of the robot, as a part of the interface, should conform to the environmental style. For example, the public service robot in the bank lobby needs to highlight the characteristics of simplicity, lightness, and atmosphere. The public service in the hospital clinic lobby should reflect its fresh, clean and comfortable characteristics.

5.3 Enhance Emotional Experience Design

An important element of human-robot interaction is Emotionalization. Public service robot brings good emotional experience to people, which will make them warmer. For example, when receiving children, we can design some interesting games to play with them, so as to arouse a happy atmosphere. In a hospital, when people have a long waiting time, the public service robot will come forward to interact with people, and its attitude should be warm and full of care, so as to alleviate the anxiety of waiting, and also help patients to prepare for treatment. When encountering the elderly, the public service robot can go forward and ask carefully and provide rest, drinking water, walking assistance, and other physical help.

5.4 Add Operation Instruction

When a new product appears, users need to learn how to use it, so they need to provide necessary operation instruction information, such as what functions a robot has, what public information it can provide to people, how people get the information they need, and what specific operation steps are. For different users, their cognitive level and knowledge reserve are different, so the way of guidance can also be changed accordingly. Young and middle-aged people are familiar with the operation of electronic equipment. They also know some principles of robots in different degrees, so they can use words, pictures, or short videos to convey the operation instructions to them. But for the older people, because they are not familiar with electronic products, and even some will reject them psychologically, so they can let the professional staff guide them by hand, and they need to pay some patience. In this way, users can better use the public service robot, and this kind of intelligent public information facility can play its role to the maximum extent.

5.5 Give Full Play to the Advantages of Multi-Sensory Interaction and Serve the Vulnerable Groups

In addition to people with physical and mental health, there are also vulnerable groups such as the elderly and the disabled. Therefore, public facilities should not only ensure the normal use of people but also facilitate the use of vulnerable groups, so as to become barrier-free public facilities serving the whole society. As for the public service robot loaded with various intelligent technologies, it can be more friendly to vulnerable groups. It can provide personalized communication methods for different people's perception and operation capabilities. For example, the blind people take touch and hearing as the main sensing channels, and the robot will interact with them in voice or Braille and other ways accordingly. It is worth noting that in addition to providing physiological help to vulnerable groups and reducing barriers in communication, we should also pay attention to psychological care for vulnerable groups, improve the sense of pleasure in the use process, so that they can feel calm and comfortable in the process, and get equal and harmonious communication experience with society, environment, and other people.

6. CONCLUSION

A public service robot is a new type of public information facility, which will also be one of the trends of intelligent facilities in the future. However, the current technology level cannot fully meet the needs of people, and there are some defects in the overall design. Public service robot cannot completely replace people, and cannot complete all the work of public service personnel. With the continuous efforts to improve the technical level and strengthen the human-robot interaction design, the development of public service robot will change with each passing day, and gradually become a booster to improve the public service level of the smart city.

REFERENCES

Weiss. Astrid. et al, 2014. Designing a service robot for public space: an "action and experiences" – Approach. *ACM/IEEE International Conference on Human-robot Interaction*, pp. 318-319.

Zhang Mang-mang, 2016. Research of Barrier-free Design under the Background of Building Smarter Cities. *Disability Research,* vol. 1, pp. 39-44.

RAPIDLY GRASPING LEARNERS' MATHEMATICAL PERFORMANCE FROM BRAIN ACTIVITY

Kodai Suzuki, Satoshi Yazawa, Reiko Matsunaka, Toru Iwasawa and Kazuo Hiraki
Graduate School of Art and Science, University of Tokyo
3-8-1, Komaba, Meguro-ku, Tokyo, Japan

ABSTRACT

For most people, it takes a lot of time to acquire mathematical skills. Mathematical problems are complex because they consist of many steps. Therefore, it is not easy to grasp the learners' performance. It is ideal to know the level of learners in a reasonably short time. In this experiment, we aimed to grasp the learners' performance from short time solving time estimation for the mathematical problems. Participants performed the task of estimating the solving time of mathematical problems. Time frequency analysis was conducted from Electroencephalogram (EEG) recordings. As a result, people with well mathematical performance had higher theta activity than those with poor performance. In conclusion, the present research suggests that brain activity measurement during solving time estimation can be effective in grasping the learners' level in a short time.

KEYWORDS

Mathematical Education, Passive BCI, Problem Solving, Educational Technology, EEG, Time Frequency Analysis

1. INTRODUCTION

Many people spend so long time to improve their mathematical skills. Because the cognitive processes involved in mathematical problem solving are very complex, it is very difficult to find an efficient learning method. It is important to be able to diagnose learners' performance rapidly for the efficient improvement of mathematical skills. Passive brain computer interface (passive BCI), which captures the mental state of healthy users (Zander & Kothe, 2011), is a technology of interest and could be effective in achieving this end.

In this experiment, in order to measure brain activity, we used Electroencephalogram (EEG). EEG has superb temporal resolution (Martinez et al., 2004). Using EEG, we can examine brain activity by isolating the epochs during solving time estimation for the mathematical problem from other brain activities. Theta activity has been linked to long-term memory, leading to faster problem solving (Lin et al., 2012). Resolving the problem from the fact retrieval showed higher theta activity than based on insights (Grabner & De Smedt, 2011). However, previous studies have dealt with simple problems such as arithmetic operations, so there was a challenge that multiple processes such as making plans and implementation could not be separated.

In the present research, our goal is to grasp the learners' performance in a short time when the learners are performing meta-cognition, focusing on understanding and planning. In the present research, participants performed a sort of meta-cognition task to estimate their solving time. We examined whether brain activity, especially theta power, was related to learning performance.

2. METHOD

2.1 Participants

Fourteen high school students participated in this experiment (range: 15-16, 12 males and 2 females). Every participant is paid 2000 yen equally. We have obtained the consent of the participants and their parents. We conducted this experiment with the consent of the Ethics Review Committee of university of Tokyo. Each participant submitted a written consent.

2.2 Procedure

2.2.1 Two Phase: Estimating the Problem and Implementing the Problem

The experiment consists of two parts. These two parts were performed on the same day. The experimental stimulus was created using E-Prime, a software for EEG experiments. In the first phase, we used 40 mathematical problems from a high school textbook. The mathematical problem is presented for ten seconds on the display in front of the participant. Participants are required to think about how to solve the presented problems. After the problem was presented, participants answer two questions. First, they give the solving time estimation. Second, they give the degree of certainty (confidence) that they can solve the problem. Participants answer each of the two questions within three seconds. The problems are presented in random order.

In the phase of implementing the problem, we used five mathematical problems. Participants entered their answers in the iPad answer recording app with an Apple pencil. Problems are presented one by one, and participants take a break after solving each problem. The time limit for solving the problem is five minutes. If the participant can solve the problem, the problem solving can be terminated by key input. After completing the problem solving, the participant answers the confidence within three seconds. Five problems are extracted from those presented in the previous phase. Each participant solves the same problems. Problems are presented in random order.

2.2.2 EEG Recording and EEG Analysis

EEG measurement provides a method to non-invasively determine the voltage at the electrode site and investigate the brain activity. We used 128-channel HCGSN v.1.0 (Geodesics, 2007). The sampling rate was 250 Hz. The ground electrode was placed at the position of Cz. Reference electrodes was placed at the right and left ears. The impedance was maintained below 100 kΩ throughout the recordings.

In the analysis, we excluded one participant from the EEG analysis due to a failure of the experiment. One epoch is eleven seconds, one second fixation and ten seconds problem presentation in the phase of estimating the problem. The raw EEG signal was filtered using a bandpass filter with a 1-40 Hz passband. We analyzed the right parietal region, using four electrodes. In time frequency analysis, we apply the fast Fourier transform with a 0.5 second Hanning window. The baseline is the one second fixation interval before the stimulus is presented.

Based on the performance in the phase of implementing the problems, participants were divided into two groups. One point was given for solving one problem, and participants who got 0-1points are classified as the poor group (seven people), and participants who got 2-4 points are classified as the well group (six people). Based on the results of the Smirnov-Grubbs test, one participant of the poor group was excluded.

3. RESULT

We obtained the time frequency pattern of participants during solving time estimation

Figure 1.A shows the average time frequency patterns of those with well performance and those with poor performance in the phase of estimating the problem. Theta band (5Hz) of the participant with the well performance showed higher activity. In particular, a significant difference was observed during the time period of 3.6-3.8s after the stimulus presentation (paired t-test, $p<0.05$). Moreover, figure 1.B shows that participants with well performance showed higher theta activity over the head.

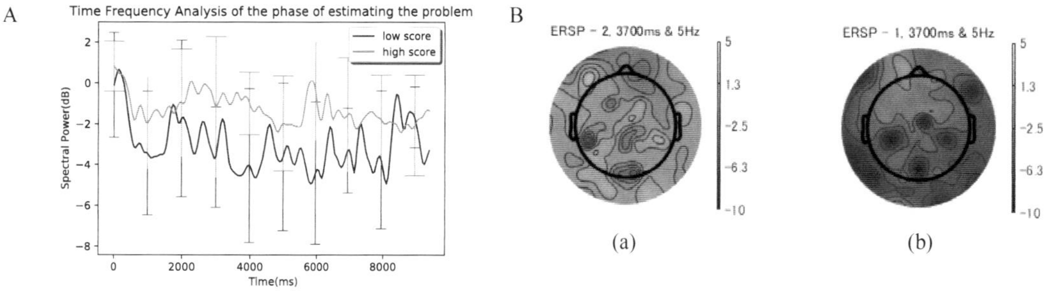

Figure 1. A: This shows the average time frequency patterns (5Hz; theta wave) of those with well performance and those with poor performance in the phase of estimating the solving time. B: (a) is a topography of theta wave of a person with well performance, and (b) is a topography of theta wave of a person with poor performance

4. DISCUSSION

People with well mathematical performance had more theta activity than those with poor performance. Theta activity are associated with the retrieval of facts (Grabner & De Smedt, 2011). People with well mathematical performance are expected to have more mathematical knowledge. Based on the visualization of the topography, theta activity occurs across multiple sites. This result was consistent with the finding that memory and learning act as a whole rather than working separately (Başar, 2005). The results obtained here provide important insights in constructing passive BCI for education.

5. CONCLUSION

The present research focused on the brain activity and meta-cognition on the complex mathematical problems. Participants with well mathematical performance showed higher theta activity. This result suggests that it is possible to predict the learners' performance in a short time from the brain activity during solving time estimation for the complex problems. Since the estimation for the solving time may differ depending on the type and content of the problem, it is important to conduct experiments that control the type of mathematical problems in the future.

ACKNOWLEDGEMENT

This work was supported by CREST, JST and SIP, Japan.

REFERENCES

Başar, E., 2005. Memory as the "whole brain work": a large-scale model based on "oscillations in supersynergy". International Journal of Psychophysiology, 58(2-3), pp.199-226.

Geodesics, E., 2007. Geodesic Sensor Net Technical Manual. *Eugene: Electrical geodesics.*

Grabner, R.H. and De Smedt, B., 2011. Neurophysiological evidence for the validity of verbal strategy reports in mental arithmetic. *Biological psychology*, *87*(1), pp.128-136.

Lin, C.L. et al, 2012, August. Brain dynamics of mathematical problem solving. In *2012 Annual International Conference of the IEEE Engineering in Medicine and Biology Society* (pp. 4768-4771). IEEE.

Martınez-Montes, E. et al, 2004. Concurrent EEG/fMRI analysis by multiway partial least squares. *NeuroImage*, *22*(3), pp.1023-1034.

Zander, T. O. and Kothe, C., 2011. Towards passive brain–computer interfaces: applying brain–computer interface technology to human–machine systems in general. *Journal of neural engineering*, *8*(2), 025005.

AUTHOR INDEX

International Association for Development of the Information Society (IADIS)
Rua Sao Sebastiao Da Pedreira
No. 100, 30, 1050-209
Lisbon, Portugal

ISBN 978-1-7138-2277-6
9 781713 822776

CURRAN ASSOCIATES INC.
proceedings.com

17th International Conference Information Systems 2024

Held at MCCSIS 2024

Porto, Portugal
9-11 March 2024

iadis